NOISE CONTROL

NOISE
CONTROL

The Law and its Enforcement

THIRD EDITION

Christopher N. Penn, M.C.I.E.H.
*Former Director of Environmental Health and Consumer
Services, Walsall Metropolitan Borough Council*

Shaw & Sons

Published by
Shaw & Sons Limited
Shaway House
21 Bourne Park
Bourne Road
Crayford
Kent DA1 4BZ

www.shaws.co.uk

© Shaw & Sons Limited 2002

First Edition .... April 1979
Second Edition .... February 1995
Third Edition .... November 2002

ISBN 0 7219 0832 2

A CIP catalogue record for this book is available from the
British Library

Printed in Great Britain by
Bell & Bain Limited, Glasgow

CONTENTS

LIST OF ILLUSTRATIONS

Tables

ACKNOWLEDGEMENTS

The pace of change in the law on noise appears to be accelerating. I have found it necessary to consult even more people than ever to update this book, which is now in its 23rd year. I have tried to make it as up to date and relevant as possible to the many individuals and organisations who share my concern about the need to control the noisy environment in which we live. If I have managed to achieve my aim of updating the law and practice on noise control in a clear and comprehensive way, it says much for the ongoing encouragement and patience of my wife Sandra; my lack of computer literacy has been made good by the sterling efforts of Beverley who has achieved all of my unreasonable requests for specific information from the dozens of website addresses I have given her; and many extraordinarily helpful individuals in a variety of government departments and other organisations have responded willingly to my requests for information. They are too numerous to mention individually, but I am grateful to them all and their respective government departments and other organisations, which include the Department for Environment, Food and Rural Affairs; Department for Local Government, Transport and the Regions; Department for Culture, Media and Sport; Home Office; Civil Aviation Authority; British Airports Authority; Health and Safety Executive; National Society for Clean Air & Environmental Protection, and the Chartered Institute of Environmental Health.

I mention particularly the following individuals as they have not only provided valuable information and advice, but also offered valuable comment on the areas of text relating to their particular expertise. I remain personally responsible for any errors or omissions.

Peter Havelock	Head of Environmental Research and Consultancy Department, Civil Aviation Authority
Tim Johnson	Chief Executive, Aviation Environment Federation
Bob King	Director of Health, Safety and Environmental Training and Consultancy, Coventry Management Training Centre

Peter Kinsey   Principal Advisor, Emissions and Pollution
                   Group, Highways Agency

Richard Norman   Flight Evaluation Manager, British Airports
                   Authority

Lorraine Powell   Pollution Prevention and Control Policy
                   Advisor, Environment Agency

Lesley Ormerod   Policy Adviser (Noise), Environment Agency

James Russell   Head of Planning and Transportation,
                   Coventry City Council

I have attempted to state the law as it existed up to 1st August 2002.

C.N.P.

TABLE OF STATUTES

TABLE OF STATUTORY INSTRUMENTS

TABLE OF CASES

Table of cases

INTRODUCTION

The first edition of this book was published in 1979. Despite continuing changes in the law on environmental and occupational noise, and technical developments in noise control, noise is still the subject of increasing complaint and public concern. There is little doubt that those increased concerns are also a consequence of greater public expectation for a quieter environment. The number of deaths and injuries associated with noise – through heart attacks, suicide, manslaughter and murder – continues to rise. Neighbour noise remains the prime culprit in these cases.

In 1993, the Institute of Environmental Health Officers[1] reported a 230% increase in complaints about industrial and commercial noise over the preceding ten years, and a 320% increase in neighbour noise complaints. Complaints about noisy neighbours rose ten-fold in the five years to 1993. Since then, statistics produced by the Chartered Institute of Environmental Health reveal a continuing and disturbing upward trend in noise complaints.[2] Over the five year period between 1992/93 and 1997/98, domestic noise complaints rose to 5,050 per million population.[3] This would be about 148,000 per year, or a 60% per year increase since 1992/93. Industrial and commercial noise complaints, whilst reported at significantly lower levels, show a rise of around 100% over the ten years from 1987/88 to 1997/98, with complaints about construction noise over the same period remaining relatively static. In its *National Noise Survey 2001*, the National Society for Clean Air and Environmental Protection (N.S.C.A.)[4] reports that amplified music remains the main source of public complaint in England and is a significant element of complaints in Northern Ireland and Wales. The trend in domestic noise complaints appears to have levelled off in the last two to three years, with 169,810 such complaints being reported in 2000/2001.[5]

---

[1] Now Chartered Institute of Environmental Health.
[2] Analysed in Grimwood, C. and Ling, M., *Domestic Noise Complaints*, B.R.E. Report No. 204732, December 1999.
[3] 225 local authorities responded to the request for information.
[4] *N.S.C.A. National Noise Survey 2001*, N.S.C.A., June 2001.
[5] C.I.E.H. statistics from 249 local authorities (66% response).

Both the Building Research Establishment and the N.S.C.A.[6] emphasise the importance of regulatory control, mediation, public education and awareness, good land use planning, improved technical controls and the development of a national noise strategy to address the continuing problems of environmental noise.

This third edition of *Noise Control: the law and its enforcement* seeks to update the law and practice relating to environmental and occupational noise. My intention is to provide a reliable and useful text containing practical advice, without delving into highly technical matters – the bibliography will direct the reader to some helpful technical and advisory publications. The law remains complex. The effect of many significant legal judgments is to place an increasing demand on employers, developers, planners, architects and lawyers to consider the impact of noise on the external and working environment. Although the text contains brief summaries of some relevant legal decisions, the reader is urged to examine the judgments in those cases relevant to their particular interest or concern; they contain valuable information on the attitude of the courts to noise issues. The increasing number of local government ombudsman decisions also give an insight into what the ombudsman finds unacceptable practice in local authorities. The Government has also produced valuable guidance on noise control in its various circulars and Planning Policy Guidance notes.

The law affecting noise control continues to change. Since the last edition of this book in 1995, the Government has issued many consultation papers on proposals or options to change the law on noise. Many of the proposals are influenced by E.U. developments and they continue to be published thick and fast. The Noise Act 1996 was introduced to try and provide a swift remedy to the problem of disturbance by noise from dwellings at night. The adoptive powers in the Act provide for the issue of warning letters to abate the noise and the confiscation of noise producing equipment. Although the Act has only been adopted by a limited number of local authorities, it appears to have been a lever for improvements in local authority services across the U.K., with 70% in England and Wales having a night-time service, although the proportion in

---

6   *N.S.C.A. National Noise Survey 2001*, N.S.C.A., June 2001.

Northern Ireland is around half of this. The implementation of the Act is currently the subject of a Government review with three options identified:

1. Maintain the existing situation but encourage all authorities to provide an out-of-hours service through other channels such as Best Value.

2. Adjust the Act to make it less prescriptive and non-adoptive.

3. Make adoption of the powers mandatory and require all authorities to provide an out-of-hours service every night of the year.

The Government intends to make the application of the Act more flexible but, at the time of writing, a formal decision is still awaited.

The Crime and Disorder Act 1988 has been used by local authorities to deal with the problem of anti-social behaviour, which may also involve noise problems, in many cases where specific noise control legislation may be inappropriate or unenforceable.

Transport noise continues to have a significant environmental impact in particular areas of the country and research is ongoing to try and reduce the impact of road traffic and aircraft noise. Aircraft noise control is heavily influenced by the International Civil Aviation Organisation because of the international use of aircraft and the Government white paper *A New Deal for Transport: Better for Everyone*[7] promises new enforcement powers to mitigate noise at airports. The subsequent consultation document *Control of Noise from Civil Aircraft*,[8] published in July 2000, should result in new statutory controls.

A system of Integrated Pollution Prevention and Control (I.P.P.C.) has been introduced which applies an integrated environmental approach to the regulation of certain industrial activities. This system, introduced by the Pollution Prevention and Control (England and Wales) Regulations 2000, requires consideration of a range of

---

[7] Cmnd. 3950, H.M.S.O., July 1998.
[8] D.E.T.R., July 2000.

pollutants, including noise emissions, in authorising the operation of specified industries and processes through a permit system. The system is enforced primarily by the Environment Agency and results in the transfer of environmental noise control from local authorities to the Agency in respect of some industries and processes. The permit system will control background noise and noise nuisance from those activities, and local authorities' powers to deal with related noise nuisance will therefore change, although an individual's right to proceed by way of the magistrates' court will continue.

In its Rural White Paper,[9] the Government announced its intention to consult on a national noise strategy. Its consultation paper *Towards a National Ambient Noise Strategy*[10] draws attention to the fact that ambient noise has been addressed by reducing noise from individual vehicles, aircraft, etc., traffic management schemes and planning controls, yet overall ambient noise has not been significantly affected because of other factors such as the growth in the number of vehicles on the road. Accordingly, the Government is looking to a strategic approach to control ambient noise, having regard to a proposal by the European Commission for a Directive relating to the assessment and management of environmental noise.

Research is continuing into the effects of ambient noise and into ways of reducing transportation noise. The D.E.T.R. and the Department of Health are undertaking a number of research projects looking variously at the effects of noise on sleep, morbidity and mortality, educational performance of school children, and the behaviour and development of young children. In relation to specific transport sources, investigation is ongoing into the noise impact of road humps; the feasibility of in-service vehicle noise testing; and accelerating the use of quieter road surfaces on the strategic road network. Quieter surfaces are to be installed on over 60% of the network by 2010. Railway noise is being reduced by modifications such as engine shrouding and exhaust silencers in the case of older diesel engines; continuously welded rails; and operational controls such as limiting the amount of engine idling.

---

[9] *Our countryside: the future – a fair deal for rural England*, Cmnd. 4909, H.M.S.O., November 2000.
[10] D.E.T.R., November 2001.

Research is being undertaken by the European Rail Research Institute on the Silent Track and Silent Freight Projects, and by the Government in association with the European Commission to develop type testing for noise emissions from railway rolling stock, and standards for type testing and monitoring of noise from railway vehicles.

The planning system plays an important role in noise prevention in two ways: by preventing the development of noisy activities in inappropriate locations and by setting appropriate conditions to prevent intrusive noise occurring where potentially noisy developments are approved. The relationship between the planning system and Integrated Pollution Prevention and Control will be an increasingly important one as I.P.P.C. is progressively introduced to cover all relevant industrial sectors by 2007. The planning authorities and the I.P.P.C. regulators are expected to liaise closely to ensure that the I.P.P.C. permit system adequately takes account of planning conditions, resulting in comprehensive environmental pollution prevention and control. The need for close liaison will be even more important as the Government proposes fundamental changes to the planning system during the same period. The Government's Green Paper[11] expresses the view that "Planning is complex, remote, hard to understand and difficult to access". It anticipates a number of changes, including simplifying the complex hierarchical system of plans and the replacement of local plans with new Local Development Frameworks. Improved community involvement is proposed in the preparation of the new Local Development Frameworks and local action plans. The Local Development Frameworks will replace structure plans, local plans and unitary development plans. All Planning Policy Guidance (P.P.G.) notes and Minerals Planning Guidance (M.P.G.) notes are to be reviewed, as is the General Permitted Development Order and the Use Classes Order. Planning obligations, otherwise known as section 106 agreements, are also the subject of review[12] as the Government appears to see a wider role for this system, including greater emphasis on sustainable development and environmental benefits to the community as a whole.

[11] *Planning: delivering a fundamental change*, D.T.L.R., December 2001.
[12] *Reforming Planning Obligations: a consultation paper*, D.T.L.R., December 2001.

In relation to the workplace, in 1995 it was estimated that there were around 170,000 cases of self-reported deafness, tinnitus or other ear conditions associated with working conditions.[13] More recently, research conducted by the Royal National Institute for the Deaf and the T.U.C.[14] states that more than half of the workers surveyed had not received information or training on the risks of noise at work. Other findings were that 25% of employees concerned about noise had approached their employers, and many workers provided with ear protection do not use it properly. A Medical Research Council survey in 1997–98 estimated that 509,000 people in Great Britain were suffering from hearing difficulties associated with noise at work. Despite this clear problem, it has taken the period since 1993 for the European Commission presidency to reach political agreement on a common position on a Physical Agents (Noise) Directive. The Regulatory Impact Assessment of the agreed text is likely to affect some 2.3 million workers and the transposition into national legislation should be completed some time in 2005. A similar timescale is anticipated for a Physical Agents (Vibration) Directive.

In June 2000, the Deputy Prime Minister launched *Revitalising Health and Safety*, a strategy document that included health and safety targets, a 10-point strategy statement and a 44-point action plan. It is possible that this will result in the removal of Crown immunity from statutory enforcement, greater sentencing powers for the courts and increasing penalties for offences against health and safety legislation. The strategy document also included a commitment for the Health and Safety Commission to consider whether the Health and Safety at Work etc. Act 1974 should be amended, and in particular to give consideration to ensuring the same protection is provided to all workers, regardless of their employment status.

The Royal Commission on Environmental Pollution's twentieth report drew attention to the rising number of complaints about

---

[13] *Health and Safety Statistics 2000/01*, Health and Safety Commission, H.M.S.O., 2001.

[14] Reported in *Croners Health & Safety Case Law Briefing*, Issue No. 23, 10th June 1999.

traffic noise and the forecast traffic increases of between 32% and 73% between 1996 and 2026. Although the Government, in its White Paper *A New Deal for Transport: Better for Everyone* explicitly recognised the problems of traffic noise, apart from further research it appears to be depending primarily on E.U. initiatives to secure traffic noise reduction measures.

The principal guidance used for assessing environmental noise complaints remains British Standard 4142, first published in 1967 and revised in the intervening years. A further revision is expected shortly. Valuable though it is, the standard is often used outside its scope and as a set of inflexible rules. This is quite wrong. The subjective response of individual complainants to a particular noise source is bound to vary. Those who investigate noise complaints need to have regard to the range of tonal and other features of noise, together with the varying subjective responses of individuals and the numbers of people affected.

In October 1994 the Government, in response to the worst ever statistics on neighbour noise, announced an urgent review of existing controls over this type of noise. The Environment Minister acknowledged the worrying trend in neighbour noise complaints and accepted that the data on complaints understated the true scale of the problem. A working group subsequently established to review the existing legal procedures was to look "at how these procedures could be simplified and made more effective and at whether there are alternative approaches which make better use of scarce local authority and police resources, while offering the citizen a more certain and reliable remedy for problems which, if not resolved, can lead to violence." Despite welcome developments such as the Noise Act 1996 and the Crime and Disorder Act 1998, there will be no significant reduction in the neighbour noise problem without the continuing combination of strict law enforcement, properly targeted local authority and police resources, the use of mediation schemes and buildings constructed to sound insulation standards that work in practice.

European Community Directives increasingly impact on noise legislation. Most statutes now reflect the requirements of these Directives, and European requirements relating to the harmonisation of noise levels from road traffic, aircraft, construction plant, and other equipment used in the open air and the workplace environment are now embodied in U.K. law. In 1996, the European Commission issued a Green Paper in which it was stated that an estimated 20% of E.U. citizens were exposed to noise levels that scientists and health experts considered to be unacceptable – at which most people became annoyed, sleep was disturbed and health might be at risk. Although there are a number of Directives in place to control noise, the Green Paper proposed a more strategic approach to control by concentrating on those exposed to environmental noise. The paper suggested that "noise mapping" had the potential to be an effective and relatively inexpensive method for assessing noise data, for the presentation of noise data to the public and politicians, and to serve as a basic planning tool. Subsequently, the E.C. issued a Draft Framework Directive on the Assessment and Reduction of Environmental Noise. The subsequent Directive is likely to require noise mapping and noise reduction action plans for urban areas with more than 250,000 inhabitants, within four years of the Directive coming into force. The E.U.'s commitment to these proposals is contained in its document _The Noise Policy of the European Union – Year 2 (1999–2000)_. The proposals are limited to road transport, railway, aircraft and industrial noise. Several working groups are looking at the costs and benefits; research needs; noise indicators; improvements to the Directive's technical annexes; and guidelines on the implementation of the Directive.

On the 2nd October 2000, the Human Rights Act 1998 came into force, with the European Convention on Human Rights becoming part of our domestic legislation. The Convention does not specifically mention the environment but the human rights that are particularly relevant are contained in Article 2 (the right to life) and Article 8 (the right to respect for private and family life). The Act will have an increasingly important impact on domestic legislation and decisions in the courts. The Human Rights Act 1998 basically operates so that:

(a) as far as possible, primary and subordinate legislation, whenever passed, must be read and given effect in a way which is compatible with the Convention (section 3);

(b) no power is given to the courts to strike down legislation which cannot be read as being compatible with Convention rights;

(c) the courts may make a declaration of incompatibility (section 4) which should encourage governments to consider urgent amendments to the law to make it compatible with the Convention;

(d) public authorities cannot act in a way which is incompatible with Convention rights (section 6) and, if they do so, there may be a case for action under section 7. This allows the illegality to be raised in public law or criminal proceedings, except where the public authority is obliged by primary legislation to act in that way (section 6(2));

(e) domestic courts must take account of any judgment of the European Court of Human Rights in Strasbourg when interpreting a Convention right.

Courts and tribunals are defined as public authorities and are therefore required to uphold a person's Convention rights. It will be interesting to see how this requirement will affect common law precedents on the law of nuisance.

The environmental obligations under Article 2 were considered in *Guerra v Italy* (1998) 26 E.H.R.R. 357, the effect of which was to indicate that "If information is withheld by a government about circumstances which ... present a real risk of danger to health ... then such a situation may ... be protected by Article 2 of the Convention." The circumstances do not have to be created by the government or public authority involved, it is that they had the power to halt or prevent a problem but failed to do so that is relevant. Article 2 might, therefore, apply to an enforcement authority which is aware of a significant environmental hazard but fails to exercise its statutory powers of control.

However, Article 8 (right to privacy and home life) is the most likely Article to be used by anyone who has a complaint about the environment near to their home. The Article states:

1. Everyone has the right to respect for his private and family life, his home and his correspondence.

2. There shall be no interference by a public authority with the exercise of this right except such as is in accordance with the law and is necessary in a democratic society in the interests of national security, public safety or the economic well-being of the country, for the prevention of disorder or crime, for the protection of health or morals, or for the protection of the rights and freedom of others.

The first significant environmental case in this country was that of *Powell & Rayner v United Kingdom* (1990) 12 E.H.R.R. 355, involving complaints of noise from Heathrow Airport. The court held that Article 8 was material because the quality of the applicants' private lives and the scope for enjoying the amenities of their homes had been adversely affected by the noise. However, the policy adopted, the noise abatement steps and the economic importance of Heathrow enabled the U.K. to justify this interference under Article 8(2). However, in the later case of *Hatton and Others v The United Kingdom* (application no. 36022/97), Judgment of the European Court of Human Rights, Strasbourg, 2nd October 2001, whilst the court found against the Government for failing to protect people adequately from night-time aircraft noise, it also ruled that the Government had failed to strike a fair balance between the U.K.'s economic well-being and the applicants' right to enjoy their homes, their private and family lives. This decision is subject to appeal by the Government (in October 2002).

The Human Rights Act 1998 also impacts on planning law (see *Alconbury v D.E.T.R.* (2001, House of Lords), and the impending ratification of the 1998 Aarhus Convention on Access to Information, Public Participation in Decision-Making and Access to Justice in Environmental Matters may also promote more widespread involvement in environmental issues. Indeed, the Government's fundamental review of the planning system anticipates more public involvement.

The Government eventually issued a consultation document on proposals for a national noise strategy in December 2001. The paper *Towards a National Ambient Noise Strategy* attracts criticism because it only applies to England and not the devolved regions of Scotland, Wales and Northern Ireland. Arguably, the only new development will be the production of noise maps to be used to inform the development of action plans and policy measures and test the effect of various scenarios on the noise climate. Neighbour noise is to be excluded from the final strategy. The process of developing the strategy will not be completed until 2007 and, over forty years after the Wilson committee were charged with a similar task, many people will be wondering if any real progress has been made in resolving the problem of noise in the interim period. In the meantime, no doubt, we can expect the noise climate in the U.K. to deteriorate, especially in the absence of a coherent and effective transport policy.

Noise can irritate and annoy, interrupt sleep, increase stress, disrupt concentration at work and cause irreparable hearing damage. Although some noise is inevitable, it is a continually increasing problem. By proper design and planning of work activities, buildings and urban and industrial development, much can be done to minimise its effects. In this respect prevention is better than cure and significantly cheaper. A little care and consideration for neighbours can also avoid neighbour noise problems. Increasing public demands for a quieter environment, the reduction of public complaints and occupational hearing loss, and the general lowering of environmental noise levels may be addressed in part by industrial noise audits, hearing conservation programmes, good building design and construction, effective planning, positive law enforcement and consideration by one neighbour for another. Unfortunately, not enough of this takes place. Unless there is a concerted and continuing effort to address these issues, not least by the Government, noise will remain a major and escalating intrusion in our lives.

Chapter 1

NOISE CONTROL

WHAT IS NOISE?

Noise has been given a variety of definitions depending on the circumstances in which it occurs and the effect it produces. It has been defined as "a number of tonal components disagreeable to man and intolerable to him because of the discomfort, fatigue, agitation and, in some cases, pain it causes".[1] Noise may have various effects on human beings exposed to it ranging from discomfort and annoyance to various psychological and pathological conditions. The degree to which it affects people depends on its nature and intensity, its duration, the frequency and time of its occurrence, the activity being undertaken by different individuals at the time of exposure, and their degree of sensitivity. Noise can be measured by its sound energy and frequency characteristics. However, sound measurement does not necessarily give a guide to what is noise – noise is subjective and depends on the factors mentioned above. It is matter of human values and therefore, in the author's opinion, the most appropriate definition of noise is "sound which is undesired by the recipient".[2]

The susceptibility of people to noise, and the level of annoyance they experience, varies widely; indeed the sources of noise in society are equally widespread and varied. The degree of annoyance is dependent on the quality of the sound and the recipient's attitude towards it. The sound of a jet engine may be music to the design engineer but intolerable to people living near an airport. The variety of noise sources and their complexity are such as to require different legal and technical controls to minimise their effect. Because it is difficult to predict precisely the reaction of a particular

---

[1]   *Environment Programme 1977–1981. Draft resolution on the continuation and implementation of a European Community policy and action programme on the environment,* Commission of the European Communities, 1976.

[2]   *Noise,* Final Report of the Committee on the Problem of Noise, 1963, para. 6. For the purposes of law enforcement, noise includes vibration.

individual to a noise, there can be no guarantee that any one set of control measures will improve a particular situation sufficiently to produce a satisfactory environment for all people exposed to it. However, enforcement of legislation and adherence to certain standards and guidelines have, over the last four decades, enabled improved control to take place over the noise produced as a consequence of technological developments.

Measurable psychological and pathological effects have been shown to be attributable to noise. They include effects on health, sleep, communications, working efficiency, industrial accidents and mental stress. Despite these developments, noise complaints are increasing. Between 1976 and 2000/1, general noise complaints to local authorities rose from 6,325 to 238,522.[3]

WHAT IS SOUND?

Noise is unwanted or undesired sound and it is therefore necessary to define sound in simple terms. Sound may be defined as any pressure variation (in air, water or another medium) that the human ear can detect. If the variations in atmospheric pressure occur rapidly, at least 20 times per second, they can be heard and are therefore called sound. The number of pressure variations per second is called the frequency of the sound and this is measured in Hertz (Hz) – previously called cycles per second. The range of human hearing extends from around 20 Hz–20,000 Hz (or 20 kiloHertz). The number of pressure variations per second determines the pitch of the sound we hear. The higher the number of pressure variations (the frequency), the higher the pitch; the lower the frequency, the lower the pitch. If the speed and frequency of a sound is known, its wavelength can be found, i.e. the distance in air between one wave and the next. The speed of sound in air is 344 metres per second at room temperature (20°c).

$$\text{Wavelength} = \frac{\text{speed}}{\text{frequency}}$$

---

[3]   The latter figures provided by the Chartered Institute of Environmental Health.

e.g. for a sound at 20 Hz

$$\text{Wavelength} = \frac{344}{20} = 17.2 \text{ metres}$$

A sound with a frequency of 20,000 Hz (20 kHz) will have a wavelength of 1.7 cm.

Fig. 1. Characteristics of a sound at one frequency (pure tone)
(*courtesy B. & K. Laboratories Ltd.*)

If a sound occurs at only one frequency, it is said to be a pure tone. Pure tones are not common, however, although when they do occur in an environmental situation they can often be difficult to eliminate satisfactorily. Audible pure tones occur in noise from turbine generators, air-moving equipment, power transformers and high speed machinery. The sound of a tuning fork is a good example of a pure tone.

Most sounds have components at several frequencies and the character of the sound is determined by the pressure amplitude at the different frequency components.

Fig. 2. Characteristics of a sound with different frequency components
(*courtesy B. & K. Laboratories Ltd.*)

If more detailed information is required about a particular sound, the frequency range from 20 Hz–20 kHz can be subdivided into sections one octave or one-third octave wide. This is done by electronic filters in sound measuring equipment which reject signals of frequencies outside the selected band. This is called frequency analysis and is of great value in identifying the source of a particular sound and determining the correct degree of sound reduction required.

A sound of short duration, less than a second, is an impulsive sound, examples being hammering and clapping. The characteristic of such a sound is illustrated below.

Fig. 3. Characteristics of an impulsive sound
(*courtesy B. & K. Laboratories Ltd.*)

The decibel

Sound is measured in decibels. The weakest sound pressure that a normal healthy human ear can detect is 20 millionths of a pascal (or 20 μPa) which is a factor of 5,000,000,000 less than normal atmospheric pressure. This pressure change is so small that it causes the membrane of the human ear to be displaced by a minute fraction. The ear can also tolerate sound pressures more than a million times greater. Measurement of sound in pascals would therefore produce quite unmanageable numbers and a simpler scale has therefore been devised – the decibel (dB) scale.

The decibel scale uses the hearing threshold of 20 μPa as its start point or reference pressure, viz.

$$20 \ \mu Pa = 0 \ dB.$$

The decibel scale is logarithmic and every time the sound pressure in Pa is multiplied by 10, 20 dB is added to the dB level. Therefore

$$200 \ \mu Pa = 20 \ dB$$
$$2{,}000 \ \mu Pa = 40 \ dB \ etc.$$

The whole decibel scale compresses the million to one range into a 120 dB range. The following table shows the approximate sound pressure levels in dB of some more familiar sounds.

Sound level in dB   **Environmental noise**

Sound level in dB	Environmental noise
140	
	Threshold of pain
130	
	Pneumatic road breaker
120	
	Loud motor horn
110	
100	
	Inside underground train
90	
	Inside bus
80	
	Average traffic on street corner
70	
	Conversational speech
60	
	Busy office
50	
	Living room in suburban area
40	
	Library
30	
	Bedroom at night
20	
	Broadcasting studio
10	
	Threshold of hearing
0	

Another important feature of the decibel scale is that it gives a much better approximation of the response of the human ear to loudness as the ear responds to the percentage change in level. 1 dB is the smallest detectable change the human ear can record, although 3 dB is usually regarded as the change in level that the average human ear can normally detect. A 6 dB increase represents a doubling of the sound pressure level but a 10 dB increase is required to make it appear twice as loud.

The propagation of sound in air can be compared to the waves on calm water after a stone has been thrown in. The waves spread uniformly in all directions, decreasing in amplitude as they move away from the source. Sound from a single point source is radiated in this way and, in air, each doubling of the distance from the source results in the sound pressure level decreasing by 6 dB. Therefore, if a move from one metre to two metres from the source occurs, the sound level will drop by 6 dB. A further move to four metres from the source will result in a total drop of 12 dB, to eight metres in a total drop of 18 dB, and so on. However, this reduction in amplitude only occurs in "free field" conditions, i.e. when there are no obstructing or reflecting obstacles in the path of the sound. When an obstacle occurs in the sound path, part of the sound will be reflected, part absorbed and the rest transmitted through the obstacle. The degree of sound reflection, absorption or transmission depends on the absorption properties of the obstructing object. Generally, the object must be larger than one wavelength to affect the sound significantly. For example, at 20 kHz the wavelength is only 1.7 cm and there it is relatively easy to achieve sound absorption and isolation. At 100 Hz the wavelength is 3.4 metres and sound isolation is considerably more difficult.

The human ear

It may be helpful to consider how the human ear operates. The ear responds to sound and analyses it to identify the sound, be it speech, sound emitted from machinery, birds, or a whole variety of natural and man-made sounds. The ear is divided into three sections: the outer, middle and inner ear.

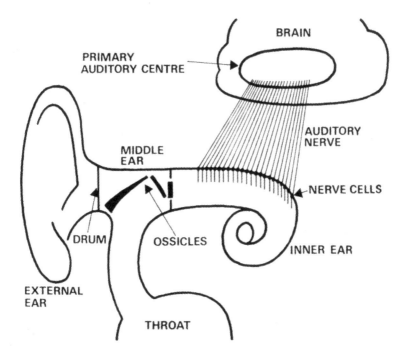

Fig. 4. Simplified diagram of the human ear

A sound wave impinging on the ear drum causes it to vibrate at the same frequency as the sound wave. The vibration of the ear drum is passed on through three small bones (ossicles) into the fluid (lymph) filling the inner ear, setting up pressure waves. The frequency remains constant but the pressure of the sound increases as a result of the amplifying action of the ossicles. Thousands of very fine hairs protrude into the lymph in the inner ear, each hair being connected to a nerve cell. The nerve cell sends a thread to combine with threads of similar cells to make up the auditory nerve which leads to the main auditory centre of the brain. Each hair is sympathetic to one particular frequency or group of frequencies, dependent on its distance from the oval window at the entrance to the inner ear. On the inner ear being filled with pressure waves transmitted from the ossicles, some hairs will be stimulated in accordance with the frequency of the sound and the brain will determine the pitch of the sound heard by the ear.

The ear is therefore sensitive to changes in frequency and is sensitive to the pressure or intensity of the sound. At the lower extreme the sound may be barely audible, whilst at the other extremity the sound may be so great as to be painful and cause damage to the ear.

The factors determining the subjective loudness of a sound are complex and subject to continual research. One important factor is that the human ear is not equally sensitive at all frequencies. It is most sensitive in the 2 kHz–5 kHz range and least sensitive at low and very high frequencies. To complicate matters further, this phenomenon is particularly pronounced at low sound pressure levels. This is indicated in the following figure which shows a "family" of curves known as equal loudness curves. These show the sound pressure level necessary at any frequency to give the same apparent loudness as a 1,000 Hz tone, e.g. a 20 Hz tone must have a 25 dB higher level to produce the same subjective loudness as a 1,000 Hz tone at a level of 70 dB.

Fig. 5. Equal loudness curves
(*courtesy B. & K. Laboratories Ltd.*)

EFFECTS OF NOISE

There are a number of effects of noise on man that are especially relevant to this book. Those effects are discussed here and the remedial action that may be taken to control noise on a practical basis is discussed in general terms later in this chapter. The legal controls which bring into being the various practical control measures are dealt with in the relevant chapter.

Health

The effects of noise on human health vary according to the susceptibility of the individual exposed to noise, the nature of the noise and whether his exposure to it occurs in his working environment or in the occupation of his home.

Deafness
The primary effect of noise at work is the development of industrial or occupational deafness. This is a permanent loss of hearing arising from continuous exposure to noise. It is a gradual process, reducing hearing ability due to damage to the cochlea of the ear and especially to sensitive hair cells forming part of it. Another type of deafness, blast deafness, can occur which arises out of sudden exposure to very high noise levels and may produce greater damage and hearing loss than continued exposure to lower levels over a longer period of time.

An impulsive noise in excess of 150 dB would probably produce instantaneous hearing damage, whereas a noise in excess of 130 dB would be the "threshold of pain" (the level at which physical pain in the ear would be felt) without necessarily causing hearing damage unless the exposure continued for some time.

The gradual hearing loss arising from continuous exposure to high noise levels is a greater problem than that associated with impulsive noise. Two effects will occur:

(a) *Temporary threshold shift* – exposure to noise levels of, say, 90 dB or above in the middle to high frequency range for a relatively short time, will produce this condition. The normal threshold of hearing may, for example, enable a 4,000 Hz tone to be heard at a level of 5 dB. After exposure to the noise, the level at which that same 4,000 Hz tone can be heard may have to be increased to, say, 20 dB. After a short while, however, the threshold of hearing would return to normal. This condition is known as temporary threshold shift and occurs between 3,000 and 6,000 Hz, and more particularly at about 4,000 Hz.

(b) *Occupational deafness* – if exposure to high noise levels continues, the speed with which normal hearing returns decreases. Not only that, but the threshold of hearing gradually becomes higher and reaches a point where it does not return to the normal level that existed prior to the continuous exposure to noise. As the initial hearing loss occurs at 4,000 Hz, and this is above the frequencies usually involved in speech, i.e. 500 Hz–2,000 Hz, the effect is not immediately noticeable to the individual and only when significant hearing loss has spread beyond the initial effect at 4,000 Hz and started to affect the speech frequencies may the exposed individual become aware of the problem. Irreversible damage may have occurred by this time.

Cardio-vascular system (circulation)
Vaso-constriction, which is "startle reaction" is a well documented circulatory response to noise.[4] A tightening of the blood vessels cuts down the flow of blood to various parts of the body. Adrenalin is released into the body which can lead to fatigue and headaches. This reaction may be noticed by people startled into awakening by a noise occurring during sleep.

Digestive system
There is some evidence to suggest that exposure to prolonged intense noise may be significant so far as gastro-intestinal conditions are concerned.[5] It appears that sudden, unexpected noises may interfere with the digestive system, although the real significance of noise on digestion does not seem to be very well documented.

---

4   *Effects of Noise on Physiological State, Noise as a Public Health Hazard,* A.S.H.A. Report 4, pp. 89-98, 1969.
5   "Public Health Aspects of Housing in the USSR", *W.H.O. Chronicle 20.10,* October 1966, p. 357.

Sleep

Interference with rest or sleep and the factors associated with it – lack of concentration, irritability, reduced efficiency – is one of the most obvious and annoying effects of noise. Sleep is a physiological necessity and therefore health may be adversely affected by insufficient sleep. To consider the effects of noise, it is necessary to look at the nature of sleep. It does not form a uniform pattern but varies throughout the night (or day). Four basic sleep stages exist: dozing (the preliminary stage), followed by three stages of progressively deeper sleep, the deepest being of the greatest benefit.

Sleep is affected significantly by age, younger people tending to spend most of the sleeping period in the deeper stages, with the middle-aged and elderly spending an increased proportion of the sleep period in the dozing stage. This would seem to account for the apparently greater number of complaints concerning environmental noise which are made by people in these latter age groups, as there is a longer period during which they are more likely to be fully woken up. The depth of sleep is related to the likelihood of being woken up. In addition, familiar and constant sounds are less likely to wake people than strange and intermittent sounds.

However, it is not necessary that people have to be woken up to suffer loss of the correct type of sleep. The human ear continues to function and transmit sound to the brain during sleep and all phases of sleep can be disturbed by noise. The waking up of a person by noise is of course important and that person can readily identify the effects of that loss of sleep on the following day. Not so readily identified by people affected by noise, however, is the effect of sleep disturbance which does not waken them. It has been shown that the depth of sleep is altered by exposure to noise at varying levels.[6] People whose sleep pattern is altered so that they do not fully enjoy the benefits of the deeper sleep may show the same effects as those deprived of sleep altogether.

Elderly people appear to have greater difficulty in getting to sleep once awakened and more women than men appear to be adversely

---

[6]   For a very useful summary of research see *Transportation Noise Reference Book,* Ed. Nelson, P., Chapter 5, 1987, Butterworth & Co. (Publishers) Ltd.

affected by sleep disturbance if the ratio of complaints from males and females is anything to go by. It is a fact that people can become accustomed to noise and obtain adequate sleep in a noisy environment which initially made sleep impossible. Individual variations, however, are considerable, some people even finding it difficult to sleep without noise. On the other hand, many people exposed to noise, especially at night, never become accustomed to it.

Communications

The speedy and accurate transfer of information is essential in many situations. One of the most common and significant undesirable effects of noise is interference with communication. The disruption of communication can result in inefficiency and possibly fatal accidents. The noise emitted by road traffic, aircraft and industry can produce communication problems. Noise restricts communication in two main ways:

(a) it may exist at levels high enough to make speech unintelligible and audible warnings unheard;

(b) loss of hearing due to high noise exposure makes the spoken word less easily understood and audible warnings incomprehensible.

A reasonably accurate assessment can be made of the permissible background noise level that can exist before intelligibility of speech is seriously affected. A criteria called the "Speech Interference Level" is used. The level at which background noise interferes with speech depends on the sound pressure level and the distance from the speaker. As a guide, a Speech Interference Level of 75 dB(A) would prohibit telephone conversation; 65–75 dB(A) would affect reliable communication over a two foot distance even with a raised voice. A Speech Interference Level of less than 55 dB(A) is desirable for any office operations.[7] Increasing voice intensity will allow the person listening to hear the spoken word in spite of loud noises, but it is undesirable to have to do this. Reduced hearing

---

7   "Effects of Noise on Man", Cohen, A., *Journal of Boston Society of Civil Engineers 52:1,* January 1965, pp. 83-84.

efficiency will of course have similar effects on the person experiencing the hearing loss. He or she will have difficulty comprehending the spoken word, albeit for a different reason.

Working efficiency

Where certain jobs are concerned, of a physical nature only, it may be that working efficiency is less affected by noise. The Wilson Committee in its report[8] stated that at that time the evidence of the effects of noise on working efficiency showed that no general conclusion had been reached. The work of various researchers indicates that noise in the working environment may, however, significantly affect efficiency in the following ways:

(a) expected noise is less likely to affect the performance of a task but efficiency can be altered by unexpected and unfamiliar noises;

(b) noise above 90 dB causes a significant increase in the number of errors made, particularly after the subject has been working for some time in noise;

(c) the effect of noise on the number of errors committed varies with the conditions of work and the state of the subject, viz.

  (i) noise increases arousal, therefore if people are short of sleep and doing routine, undemanding work, noise may arouse and stimulate them and reduce errors;

  (ii) if work being done requires an alert state, a loud noise may make them jittery and increase errors.

Therefore routine work is generally less affected by loud noise than exacting work which requires the ability to concentrate.

These conclusions are related to the achievement of tasks and have been arrived at on the basis of controlled experiments. However, there is no doubt that concentration, efficiency and output may be affected by noise at a much lower level than 90 dB. The degree to which people may be affected may relate to the character and

---

8   *Noise*, Final Report, July 1963, para. 50.

duration of the noise, the nature of the task being performed and also, it is suggested, by the I.Q. of the exposed people.

Mental stress

The relationship between noise and mental stress is a controversial subject and it may be that noise is just one factor affecting the mental health of any population. Most of us will be aware that exposure to unaccustomed high levels of noise tends to change our emotional responses. We tend to become more sensitive to other matters and may "fly off the handle" more readily than usual. Most Environmental Health Officers will be familiar with complainants who show extreme agitation when subjected to prolonged and excessive noise. Their family relationships may be adversely affected, they tend to break into tears when discussing the problem and occasionally suggest extremes such as suicide.

This sensitivity may be more pronounced in people who express concern for the environment, are worried about air disasters, or otherwise associate noise with the possibility of some adverse affect on their lives.

According to a Council of Europe report,[9] the possibility of mental health impairment due to noise is likely to be greater in individuals disposed to nervousness. Noise may also aggravate an existing neurosis or predisposition to mental stress.

In a number of investigations, minor neurotic conditions have been related to high noise environments, although other investigations show no such relationship. A study of schools near to London Airport revealed symptoms suggestive of "mild affective illness" among the teachers,[10] but a community survey in Switzerland showed no relationship between aircraft noise and minor psychiatric illness. The evidence that noise is associated with psychiatric illness is not free from doubt, although there have been studies carried out which strongly suggest that in certain circumstances noise may be a significant factor.

---

[9]   *Noise Abatement: A Public Health Problem*, 1965, p. 12.
[10] "The effects of aircraft noise in schools around London Airport", Crook, M.A. and Langdon, F.J., *Journal of Sound and Vibration 34*, 1974, p. 221.

In recent years, a worrying number of extreme responses to neighbour noise have been reported in the media. Indeed, a national noise attitude survey[11] revealed that one in three people interviewed said that environmental noise spoiled their home life to some extent, with neighbour noise producing the greatest number of objections relative to the number of people who hear it. The survey also revealed that the most frequently reported personal consequences of exposure to noise in the home are emotional reactions such as annoyance, anger, anxiety and resentment. Similar responses have been reported in response to other research.[12] In several cases, the victims of repeated or continuous noise from sources such as burglar alarms and late night parties have resorted to criminal damage and violent physical assault to try and eliminate the source of complaint.

NOISE MEASUREMENT

Where appropriate, more detailed consideration of specific matters to be taken into account in measuring certain types of noise is included in the relevant chapters in this book. It is intended to give guidance here on the general principles usually adopted in measuring noise.[13]

Sound level meter

A sound level meter is an instrument designed to respond to sound, in approximately the same way as the human ear, and to give objective measurements of sound level. The sound signal is converted to an electrical signal by a microphone. The signal must be amplified before it can be read on a meter. The input amplifier is immediately after the microphone and the amplification stage contains a series of circuits in 10 dB steps that can be progressively

---

[11] *Effects of Environmental Noise on People at Home*, Grimwood, C.J., B.R.E. Information Paper IP 22/93, December 1993.

[12] "Noise, Stress and Human Behaviour", Jones, Dr. Dylan M., *Environmental Health*, August 1990.

[13] Useful guidance is also contained in Technical Guidance Note IPPC H3, Integrated Pollution Prevention and Control (I.P.P.C.) Draft, *Horizontal Guidance for Noise, Part 2 – Noise Assessment and Control*, Version 1, Environment Agency, October 2001.

switched in. After the first amplifier, the signal may pass through a weighting network (A, B, C or D). These weighting networks consist of circuits which can be used to reduce the response of the meter to low and very high frequency sounds and liken it more to the human ear. The A network has been found to provide the most useful comparison with loudness sensations and is therefore the most widely used.

However, the A scale (measurements are called dB(A)) gives only a rough indication of the frequency make-up of a noise and an alternative to the single figure weighting network is an octave or one-third octave filter which is usually attached externally to the meter. This enables the measurement of the sound pressure level to be made in a series of frequency bands, so as to provide more valuable information on the nature of the noise, which will assist in the identification of its source and the type of control measures required.

After further attenuation, the sound signal is fed to a rectifier and indicating meter. The rectifier determines the RMS (root mean square) value. The root mean square is a particular kind of mathematical average value. It is important because it is directly related to the amount of energy in the sound signal. A peak rectifier may be included to determine the peak value of impulsive sound signals, and a "hold" circuit which allows the maximum meter deflection to be held at that point.

When the sound level varies, it is necessary for the meter needle to show the variations. Unfortunately, if the level fluctuates too rapidly, the meter needle may move so erratically that meaningful readings are impossible. Accordingly, two meter response characteristics are included:

Fast – this gives a fast meter reaction enabling the user to observe and measure noise levels which do not fluctuate too rapidly.

Slow – this provides a slower response and helps average out meter fluctuations which would otherwise be difficult to read.

The measurement of impulsive noise requires the use of a sound level meter with an impulse and/or peak characteristic. The "hold" facility makes reading a simple matter.

The sound level meter displays the sound level in dB or another derived unit, e.g. dB(A) (which shows that the sound level has been A-weighted). The sound signal is often available at socket outlets on the meter. This allows it to be connected to supplementary equipment capable of providing a greater amount of information concerning a noisy environment. Automatic meters are available, and facilities such as high quality tape recorders to enable recording and subsequent laboratory analysis to take place, graphic level recorders to provide a visual time related trace of noise events, and continuous noise analysers are all available (at a cost) to assist in noise investigations.

Sound is an energy form and its potential to cause hearing damage depends on its level and duration, both of which have to be measured and combined to assess the energy received by the ear. This is straightforward for constant sound levels. Varying levels must be repeatedly sampled over a defined period. This allows the calculation of a single value having the same energy content as the varying sound level and, therefore, the same hearing damage potential. The single value is the Equivalent Continuous Sound Level (L_{eq}). If it is A-weighted, the symbol L_{Aeq} is used. L_{eq} measurements are also used for other types of measurement including noise nuisance assessments. Integrating sound level meters automatically calculate the L_{eq}.

Taking sound level measurements

The following are general rules applicable to the task of measuring noise:

Measurements in rooms
In practice most sound measurements are made in rooms that neither completely absorb nor completely reflect sound and some difficulty can be experienced in finding the correct measurement position when it is necessary to measure the noise from a specific source. For hearing protection purposes, however, the measurements should be taken at a position corresponding with that of the ear, as the total sound field, including reflections, has to be measured.

Several problems can arise in measuring noise from a single source:

(a) if measurements are taken too close to a machine the sound pressure level may vary significantly with small changes in position. This will occur at distances of less than one wavelength of the lowest frequency emitted from the machine or at less than twice the largest dimension of the machine, whichever is the greater. This is the "near field" and measurements in this area should be avoided if possible;

(b) measurements too far away from the machine may result in reflections from walls and other objects which are just as strong as the direct sound and correct measurements will be impossible. This area is the "reverberant field".

Between these two fields is the "free field" in which the level drops 6 dB for each doubling of distance from the source. Measurements should be made in this area if possible, though conditions may exist where a room is so small or so constructed that a "free field" condition does not exist.

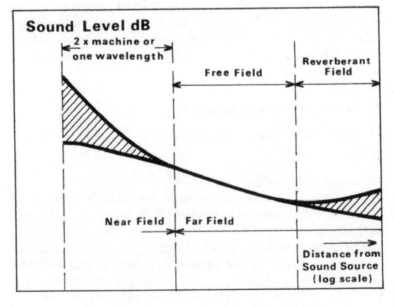

Fig. 6. "Near", "far" and "reverberant fields".
(*courtesy B. & K. Laboratories Ltd.*)

Use of the microphone

A high quality microphone must be used which meets strict standards. It must have uniform frequency response, i.e. be equally sensitive at all frequencies. It must also be equally sensitive to sound coming from all directions, i.e. omnidirectional. This is particularly important when measurements are taken in a diffuse sound field.

Microphones are made with three types of characteristic – free field, pressure and random incidence responses. The type of microphone to be used will depend on the type of sound field encountered. Any microphone will disturb the sound field in which it is used but a free field microphone is designed to compensate for this disturbance. The free field microphone has uniform frequency response to the sound pressure existing before its introduction into the sound field, whereas the pressure microphone has uniform frequency response to the actual sound pressure level, including its own disturbing presence. The random incidence microphone responds uniformly to sound which arrives simultaneously from all directions as in the case of diffuse or highly reverberant sound fields.

In taking measurements in a free field, a free field microphone should be pointed directly at the source, whilst a pressure microphone should be located at 90° to the source so that the sound passes across the front of the microphone. In random or diffuse sound fields the microphone needs to be as omnidirectional as possible. A device called a Random Incidence Corrector may be fitted to the microphone, to improve its omnidirectional characteristics. Determination of the most appropriate microphone may be influenced by relevant national or international standards.

The type of sound field should be checked, i.e. near field, free field or reverberant, to ensure that the correct measurement position is adopted. Several check measurements should be taken before recording actual sound levels to ensure that any factors which may influence the recorded levels are taken into account. If there is doubt about the noise producing the meter readings, headphones connected to the output socket will help identification.

Effect of equipment and operator

The presence of the operator and the instrument may obstruct the sound coming from certain directions, particularly in random or diffuse sound fields, and can also produce reflections which may produce errors in measurement. At lower frequencies, body reflection can produce errors of up to 6 dB at distances of less than one metre. An extension rod is therefore valuable in minimising the effect of the instrument and it is desirable to hold the sound level meter at arm's length or mount it on a tripod. The latter is recommended as it leaves hands free to record sound level readings and other relevant data.

Calibration of instruments
The meter should be properly calibrated at regular intervals, and certainly before and after each set of readings. This is done by putting a portable acoustic calibrator on the microphone, the calibrator emitting a precise sound pressure level to which the meter is adjusted. If recordings are made of noise measurements, the calibration signal should be recorded to provide a reference level on playback.

Batteries
The absence of a spare supply of batteries can be disastrous as batteries do not usually give much advance warning of failure and much time can be wasted unless a spare supply is always kept available. Experience will indicate the expected battery life to be obtained in different circumstances. If continuous or automatic monitoring is to be carried out, it is as well to insert new batteries if there is any doubt about the life of any that have been in use for any length of time.

Standards
Various standards exist relating to the type of instrumentation to be used and the measurement methods to be adopted in certain circumstances. Care should be taken to adhere to these to avoid subsequent disputes about the validity of the information obtained, particularly where legal proceedings are to be taken.

Weighting network/frequency analysis
The type of investigation required must be determined beforehand so that the weighting network (usually the A network) and the type

of frequency analysis can be decided and the correct equipment obtained, e.g. octave band analysis may be of little value in a highly complex sound field or one where pure tones exist. In such cases, more detailed examination of the noise using a narrow band analyser or discrete-frequency analyser may be necessary. The correct meter response, i.e. "fast", "slow" or "impulse" should be used. Before taking readings, an estimate should be made of the range of sound pressure levels so that the meter can be set to record in the appropriate range. Alternatively, the meter should be set at the highest setting. In this way damage and wear to the electrical circuits may be avoided which would occur if the meter was set to record a sound level well below that being produced and the meter consequently overloaded.

Frequency analysis is often required to investigate a noise source and to assess the required insulation characteristics of noise barriers/enclosures, and to measure the noise attenuation between common walls of adjoining buildings. In redesigning existing noise control systems, frequency analysis is a valuable aid in determining the minimum changes needed to meet the revised specification.

Measurements outdoors
The above principles apply together with consideration of other factors:

Wind – wind blowing across the microphone can create a lot of extraneous noise and adversely affect readings. Experience will indicate when measurements are likely to be invalid but measurements in a relatively sheltered position compared with those at the proposed measurement point will give some indication of the effects of wind on measurements of the noise source under investigation. To minimise the effects of wind a special windscreen, usually made of a porous polyurethane sponge, should always be used when taking outdoor measurements. It also helps to protect the microphone from dust and rain.

Rain – in rain or very high humidity (around 90%) special outdoor microphones, rainshields and de-humidifiers may be used.

Temperature – is not usually significant unless sudden changes occur which may cause condensation in the microphone.

Vibration – microphones and sound level meters are not particularly sensitive to vibration but, in environments where strong vibration may occur, it is sensible to mount them on isolating material.

Measurement and investigation reports

It is essential that all results are carefully documented. Experience shows that in the complex task of noise investigation it is not possible to rely on one's memory to recall detailed facts and future comparison will be invalid or impossible without accurate and reliable information. The type of record kept will vary according to the investigation undertaken but the following details will always be important:

(a) details of the noise source being measured – location, type of machinery or other source, speed of machinery, loading, manufacturer, type of work being carried out. Sketch plans or maps are invaluable;

(b) subjective assessment of the character of the noise and whether it is considered to be a nuisance;

(c) type and serial number of measuring instrument;

(d) method and results of calibration;

(e) weighting network and frequency analyses carried out;

(f) background noise levels;

(g) detailed record of measurements taken including location and height of microphone;

(h) date, time and environmental conditions under which measurements taken (e.g. type of sound field, atmospheric conditions);

(i) detailed sketch plan showing location of noise source and location of topographical or other features that may influence measured sound level. Location of machine operators or complainants to the noise source should be shown;

(j) where comparisons are made with relevant standards, and calculations carried out, full details should be recorded;

(k) in the case of public complaint, accurate details concerning interviews, statements taken and observations carried out.

NOISE REDUCTION

The precise noise attenuation measures that may be required in a given situation depend on the circumstances. Many situations are particularly complex and may require very detailed examination to arrive at the correct solution. Many noise problems can also be resolved by the use of relatively simple methods at little cost. It may be necessary to seek the services of a consultant with a qualification in acoustics and/or engineering principles. There are certain basic matters that need to be considered in the examination of any noise problem in order to arrive at a solution.

Any noise problem contains the following ingredients:

> Noise source;
> Transmission path;
> Receiver.

Depending on whether the problem is associated with industry, entertainment, neighbours or other origins, the sources of noise energy are often pieces of machinery or equipment and are usually impact, reciprocating and rotating sources, vibration, turbulent air or gas streams.

The transmission path is the direction taken by the sound waves. Different transmission paths will result in a different sound level at the receiver's ear because of their different properties of attenuation, absorption and radiation. The path of the sound may be direct or indirect, airborne or structure borne, or involve a combination of two or more of these.

The person at the receiving end of the sound may be a worker exposed to potential hearing damage, someone engaged on an intricate task requiring considerable concentration, the occupier of a house wishing to have a decent night's sleep or simply someone trying to complete routine but necessary tasks in a school, office or hospital.

These are the three main components of any noise problem indicated above. Accordingly, there are three main alternatives or combination of alternatives to control the noise and these are:

(a) reduce the noise level at source;

(b) reduce the sound energy transmitted along the transmission path;

(c) protect the recipient by the provision of some form of ear defenders or the introduction of a hearing protection programme.

The main factors to be considered are as follows.

Stop or remove the noise

If the particular process or activity causing the problem can be avoided by alternative less noisy means of carrying out the task, or the activity can be carried out at a time when no nuisance occurs, then this should be considered, e.g. transferring a noisy process from a night shift to a day shift when sleep is less likely to be affected in a neighbourhood and when higher noise levels are likely to be tolerated; the use of the relatively quiet process of welding rather than riveting; using bored piles instead of driven piles on a construction site.

The removal of the noise source, if practicable, to a less sensitive area is likely to achieve beneficial results.

Quieten the source

There are usually three ingredients which result in noise production from machinery: a point of noise generation (e.g. a worn bearing); one or more transmission paths in the machine; connection of these two with a component which radiates the noise. Elimination of one or more of these ingredients will be necessary. In many cases, reduction of noise will be a complicated process affected by the need to ensure that the machinery remains capable of operating efficiently. Noise associated with machinery arises in a number of ways –

Imbalance: rotating parts of machinery such as bearings and drive shafts may become worn due to poor maintenance or exposure to adverse conditions such as dust or rain. Wear or damage may result in incorrectly balanced components which will produce fluctuating loading of the machine and hence noise. Correct and regular maintenance will reduce noise as well as improving the life of the machinery and reducing repair costs.

Friction: this arises from two components rubbing together such as squealing brakes, clutches and belt drives. The remedy is to change the friction coefficient which in effect can involve a change of materials, renewing or relining "glazed" brake shoes and clutch plates, and tightening or renewing slack belt drives.

Impact: impact noise can be reduced in a variety of ways – careful handling of materials to avoid dropping them on to hard surfaces; lining metal containers with resilient material to reduce metal-to-metal contact; fitting internal factory transport with rubber as opposed to solid tyres. Tightening loose parts on machines may be effective. Invariably, major sources of impact noise such as cold heading machines, drop forges and presses are likely to require attenuation of the transmission path but improvements can be achieved by consideration of the type of component being produced and investigating such possibilities as using different dies to produce components which emit lower noise levels, transferring the particularly noisy activities to another area or transferring production to a different time of day.

Turbulence: sources involving gas or air flows including fuel burners, fans, air exhausts and blow-off or control valves are the principle offenders and noise problems may arise from boilers and compressed air escapes from the many types of pneumatic machinery available. In such cases it may be possible to use mufflers on the exhausts, to provide acoustic shrouds, or to reduce the air pressure provided it does not fall below that necessary for the effective operation of the equipment involved.

Transmission paths in the machine: the following diagram shows the manner in which the noise from the source, e.g. worn bearings, may be transmitted along various paths. The elimination of unnecessary solid transmission paths by the introduction of materials with poorer transmission properties such as rubber and felt will help. Insulation of air-solid paths with appropriate absorbent material and the prevention of direct airborne transmission through holes by sealing with high transmission loss materials should be carried out. Where noise is generated as a result of transmission to the building structure to which the machinery is attached, it will be necessary to isolate acoustically the machinery from the building using anti-vibration mounts. In addition, connection to any piping or ducts must be by flexible couplings.

Fig. 7. Typical sound transmission paths in machinery.

Radiating areas of machines: these are the surfaces or holes by which noise is propagated to the surrounding air. The reduction in size of the radiating area will usually reduce the amplitude of vibration. Alternatively, or in addition, it may also be practicable to fit isolated covers with a high transmission loss. Replacement of thin sheet metal covers which are easily vibrated, with substitute materials of a higher transmission loss, will often secure improvements, as will stiffening the panels, adding to the mass, and acoustic damping.

Reducing volume control: where the equipment is capable of noise control by reducing the volume, e.g. on radios, television sets and record players; or by reducing the amplification of loudspeakers such as used in tannoy systems or "pop" groups, this can be a simple and effective expedient.

Screen or enclose the source

If reduction of noise at source is not possible to the desired level, then it may be necessary to screen it. Screening may consist of any one or a combination of the following:

(a) relocation of an external noise source inside a building;

(b) removal of the source if already within a building, to another room where the noise it produces has less effect on the exposed persons. Alternatively, provide the exposed person with a noise refuge or enclosure;

(c) design and construction of an acoustic enclosure.

Whichever of these alternatives is adopted, there are certain basic principles that must be considered to ensure that the screen or enclosure fulfils its purpose of reducing the noise level at the ear of the exposed person. It is important to provide as much sound absorption as possible inside the enclosure. If this is not done there will be a build up of reverberant sound in the enclosure which will in effect increase the sound level to be controlled. The principles to be adopted should include:

1. The source should be *mechanically isolated*. Machinery should preferably be isolated from the building structure or enclosure by anti-vibration mounts and should also be isolated from its services. The enclosure can then be in direct contact with the building structure itself whilst reducing the risk of transmitting sound to the structure. If these factors are not considered the enclosure itself will transmit sound into the building structure, thereby largely negating other work designed to reduce the noise. In the case of doubt, the enclosure can be mounted on suitable absorbent material.

   Pipework and ducts which need to pass through the enclosure must be provided with breaks in the rigid pipework or ducting where it passes through the enclosure. Care will be needed in the selection of the correct materials – dense and relatively stiff rubber may have little effect, whereas some more flexible but thinner materials may be adversely affected by chemicals or extremes of temperature. Where the use of flexible connections is impracticable as in the case of high pressure water, air or oil supply pipes, a clearance hole should be provided in the enclosure wall. This should be packed with suitable felt or mineral wool and sealed with mastic.

2. The structure of the enclosure should have an adequate overall *sound reduction index* and care should be taken to ensure that acoustically weak areas such as windows and access doors and panels are designed and fitted to provide adequate sound attenuation.

3. The maximum internal *absorption* for the relevant frequencies should be provided by the correct type of lining to the enclosure.

These principles are relatively straightforward in the case of simple machinery such as compressors and generators. More complicated machinery, however, may not be so readily enclosed. In some cases, the primary source of noise may be only a small part of a larger machine. If possible, that source only should be treated to reduce the noise by applying a partial enclosure. However, noise may be radiated from other parts of the machine such that the whole machine requires treatment. If complete enclosure can be carried out practically then this should be done. In some cases, it may only be possible to partially screen the source by a barrier. A barrier will generally be less effective than total enclosure because the sound waves which are contained by an enclosure are diffracted around the edges of a barrier. The effect is greater at low frequencies because the sound waves are longer. It is therefore of no benefit fitting a small barrier in front of a noise source producing predominantly low frequency noise.

Increase the distance from the source

Generally speaking, doubling the distance from a point source of noise will result in a reduction of the order of 6 dB. If the recipient of the noise is at a relatively small distance from the source, a reasonable reduction can occur. It may, however, be impracticable if the distance is already considerable. In such cases, screens or barriers may be necessary, or relocation, say on the opposite side of a building to which the noise source is attached so that both the increased distance and the effect of the building as a barrier (provided the building is of adequate dimensions) will improve the situation.

Planning

Many noise problems would be avoided if proper thought was given to the possibility of noise production from plant and machinery or other activities such as fairs, "pop" concerts and similar events. Every engineer, planner, architect, civil engineering contractor, entertainments manager and even the average householder should be aware that their activities, or the activities that they may have responsibility for, may cause noise problems. There are many factors requiring consideration in the planning of development, the introduction of new machinery and processes, the construction of buildings and the organisation of entertainment – noise should also be considered if public complaint, the possibility of hearing damage and communication problems are to be avoided.

The amount of noise transmitted from a site can be reduced by proper layout and the use of well designed and suitable barriers or enclosures. In the open air, increasing distance reduces noise and noisy activities should be sited as far away as possible from sensitive areas such as houses, hospitals, schools and old people's homes.

The timing of certain activities so that noise does not occur at periods when its impact is likely to be greater, i.e. evenings and weekends, is important.

People engaged in noisy activities such as industrialists and civil engineering contractors should make themselves aware of the basic principles of noise control together with the relevant legal controls governing their activities. Close liaison with the enforcing authorities including Environmental Health Officers, Planning Officers, the Health and Safety Executive and the police will enable new proposals to be considered at an early stage to avoid future problems. The relevant officers are invariably willing to provide their expert guidance on noise control measures.

If those responsible fail to plan their activities so as to minimise noise, or disregard the advice of the enforcing authorities, then the cost of carrying out remedial works at a later stage can be far greater than if control measures had been introduced at an early stage.

When a noise problem arises, the person responsible will often be unaware of how to approach the investigation and control of it. The following brief outline of the steps to be taken may be of assistance:

1. The extent of the problem must be established: the amount of noise produced must be determined and the manner in which the noise is transmitted must be assessed.

2. The maximum level of noise that is permissible in the circumstances must be ascertained, i.e. the acceptable level to which workers may be exposed or the level to which noise must be reduced to eliminate public complaint.

3. Having determined the cause and extent of the problem, and the permissible level of noise, it will be possible to determine the remedial work required and the cost of that work. This will enable the financial implications to be determined and a programme of work to be developed. The advice of experts may be necessary and abatement measures should not be entrusted to people without adequate knowledge of the principles of noise control.

4. A programme of works should be implemented, if necessary using temporary expedients whilst a more permanent solution is sought.

5. Once a noise problem has been resolved, care should be taken to ensure that a similar situation does not recur. Therefore regular maintenance of machinery and acoustic enclosures or other control measures that have been adopted should be ensured. Regular assessments of the noise climate in a work area or in the environment surrounding a factory will determine whether a noise problem is likely to develop so that remedial action can be taken at an early stage.

6. Education of staff will make them noise conscious. This is

important as many problems arise due to the carelessness of employees or their failure to appreciate how their activities can adversely affect others.

The reduction of noise from machinery is comparable with other engineering problems in the sense that there may be complicated mechanical and human factors that have to be recognised. If the controlling factors are properly understood there are usually engineering compromises that can be introduced to bring about economical noise control.

The users of machinery can contribute to the reduction of noise by specifying the maximum noise levels that they are prepared to accept from the plant and equipment that they purchase. If all users were prepared to take this attitude, equipment manufacturers would be obliged to give greater consideration to reduction of noise at the design stage. This would ultimately benefit everyone exposed to noise, be it employees or those people seeking to sleep or carry out their normal occupations in their homes or workplaces.

Hearing protection

Personal protection from noise may be obtained by the use of suitable ear defenders; these are dealt with in detail in Chapter 10, pp. 425–427 *post.*

WHAT IS VIBRATION?

A body is said to vibrate when it moves in an oscillating motion about a reference position. The number of times a complete motion cycle occurs during one second is called the frequency and is measured in Hertz (Hz). The motion may comprise a single component occurring at a single frequency, or several components occurring at different frequencies simultaneously, e.g. the piston motion of an internal combustion engine. In practice, vibration signals usually consist of many simultaneously occurring frequencies and the number of components can be identified by plotting vibration amplitude against frequency. This frequency analysis is an essential element of diagnostic vibration measurements. When carrying out frequency analysis of machine vibration, it is usual to find a number of prominent periodic frequency components that are directly related to the fundamental movements of the various parts of the machine. Frequency analysis, therefore, helps to identify the source of the unwanted vibration.

The vibration amplitude shows the severity of the vibration and can be quantified in several ways as shown in the following diagrams.

$$\text{RMS Level} = \sqrt{\frac{1}{T} \int_0^T x^2(t)dt}$$

$$\text{Average Level} = \frac{1}{T} \int_0^T |x| dt$$

Fig. 8. Quantifying the vibration level
(*courtesy B. & K. Laboratories Ltd.*)

The relationship between peak-to-peak level, the peak level, the average level and the RMS of a sinewave is indicated. The peak-to-peak value shows the maximum excursion of the wave. This is valuable where the vibratory displacement of a machine part needs to be considered for maximum stress or mechanical clearance considerations. The peak value is useful for showing the level of short duration shocks. This only indicates the maximum level and does not take account of the time period of the wave. The root mean square (RMS) value takes the time period into account and provides an amplitude value related to the energy content, and accordingly the destructive capability of the vibration.

Vibration can be measured using three parameters – acceleration, velocity or displacement. The velocity or acceleration parameter is usually selected for the purpose of frequency analysis and the overall RMS value of vibration velocity measured over the range of 10–1,000 Hz gives the best indication of a vibration's severity. Displacement is frequently used as an indicator of unbalance in rotating machine parts, as relatively large displacements often occur at the shaft rotational frequency. This is the frequency of most interest for balancing purposes. Some of the environmental and other features to be considered in measuring noise also apply to vibration measurements and the reader is referred to useful detailed texts.[14]

Effects of vibration on the human body

Low frequency vibration (3–6 Hz) can cause the diaphragm in the upper abdomen to vibrate in sympathy. This may produce a feeling of nausea. The phenomenon may be noticed close to large, slow speed diesel engines. Vibration at a frequency of 20–30 Hz may produce a similar response in the head, neck and shoulders, and the eyeball has a resonant frequency of 60–90 Hz. The effects of vibration on the human body depend on the frequency, amplitude and duration of exposure, and many of the effects are similar to those associated with noise.

Vibration reduction

For machines that vibrate badly, the vibrations may travel through the building structure and be radiated as noise (structure borne

---

[14] *Measuring Vibration,* Bruel and Kjaer, September 1982. *Machine Condition Monitoring,* Bruel and Kjaer. *Mechanical Vibration and Shock Measurements,* Bruel and Kjaer.

noise). If the balance of the moving parts cannot be improved, vibration transmission can be reduced in a number of ways. The type of isolation system required should be left to an expert, and may be:

(a) rubber in shear;

(b) rubber in compression;

(c) cork and felt mats or other proprietary materials with similar properties;

(d) inertia blocks;

(e) coiled springs;

(f) flexible couplings.

The chosen method will depend on the weight and size of the machine, the vibration frequency to be controlled and the degree of isolation required. Vibration from machinery is often a complex problem requiring detailed assessment. It can cause damage and create noise. The use of correctly designed anti-vibration mounts can reduce vibration and structure-borne noise but inefficient mounts can increase vibration and noise. The equipment subjected to anti-vibration treatment must remain stable after completion of the work and at the same time the mountings must be as resilient as possible to provide the best vibration isolation. They must also be sufficient to take the weight of the machinery to be treated.

Care should be taken to ensure that the effect is not offset by "bridging", e.g. isolation of a motor or compressor would be reduced by any rigid piping connected to it. Flexible couplings will allow the full benefits of the vibration treatment to be achieved.

Chapter 2

NOISE NUISANCE

WHAT COMPRISES A NUISANCE?

Nuisance may be defined as "an unlawful interference with a person's use or enjoyment of land, or of some right over, or in connection with it".[1]

This fact is important in defining the primary purpose of the tort of nuisance, the protection of the individual's right to use and enjoy his land. Nuisance at law is a tort, i.e. a civil wrong for which courts can provide a remedy, usually damages.

In addition, in 1865 Lord Chancellor Westbury said of such nuisance "with regard to the latter, namely the personal inconvenience and interference with one's enjoyment, one's quiet, one's personal freedom, anything that discomposes or injuriously affects the senses or the nerves, whether that may or may not be denominated a nuisance, must undoubtedly depend greatly on the circumstances of the place where the thing complained of actually occurred".[2]

Clearly, therefore, in attempting to establish nuisance, these two factors are extremely important:

(a) the need for the aggrieved person to establish that his occupation of land is affected by the noise;

(b) each case has to be considered on its merits – many factors may have to be considered in this latter respect which are dealt with later in this chapter.

The slightest noise may be, and often is, considered to be a nuisance by the layman if it annoys him. The legal definition is, however, more restricted. This is inevitable as, where a nuisance at law exists,

---

[1]   *Read v Lyons and Co. Ltd.* [1945] K.B. 216.
[2]   *St. Helen's Smelting Co. v Tipping* (1865) 11 H.L.C. 642.

the law provides a remedy to the person affected by the nuisance and it would be impracticable to provide a remedy against every noise that an individual found objectionable. A case in point is that of *Heath v Brighton Corporation*[3] in which the plaintiff was unsuccessful in his action in respect of noise from a generator because it was shown that he had hypersensitive hearing. It was held that the test for the existence of a statutory nuisance is an objective one to be judged by the standards of the average man. However, this is not to say that the courts would disregard multiple instances of annoyance to an individual who had become sensitised to noise over a long period. All the relevant circumstances would need to be taken into account.

There are in fact three types of nuisance that may be considered. There are two types of nuisance at common law, public and private which are two separate torts, both falling within the term "nuisance"; and there are "statutory nuisances".

(a) *public or common nuisance* – an unlawful act or omission causing inconvenience or damage to the life of Her Majesty's subjects who come within the sphere or neighbourhood of its operation (i.e. it must affect the public at large);

(b) *private nuisance* – an act or omission connected with the use of land and which causes an unlawful interference to another person's use and enjoyment of his land. A single act can never be a private nuisance, there must be either repetition or a continuing state of affairs;[4]

(c) *statutory nuisance* – an act or omission which has been designated a nuisance by statute (e.g. under Part III, Environmental Protection Act 1990).

Common law is law which has not been formulated by Parliament but is the result of hundreds of years of judicial arguments and

---

[3] *Heath v Brighton Corporation* (1908) L.T. 718.
[4] In contrast with a private nuisance, a single noise event may amount to a statutory nuisance. In the case of *East Northamptonshire District Council v Fossett* [1994] Env L.R. 388, D.C., an all night rave was held to be a noise nuisance.

decisions, thus creating a well established body of case law. That is the essential difference between common law and statutory law – common law results from the legal action of individuals or groups of individuals; statutory law is designated as such by Parliament. However, when the Noise Abatement Act 1960 came into force,[5] Circular 58/60 issued by the Ministry of Housing and Local Government advised enforcing authorities that the basis for a decision as to whether noise or vibration was a statutory nuisance was to consider whether the noise or vibration would constitute a nuisance at common law. It is therefore clear that a noise nuisance may be a nuisance at common law (public or private) and also a statutory nuisance, the only difference being the manner in which it is abated. The main principles established by common law are therefore applicable to statutory nuisance.

PUBLIC NUISANCE

A public nuisance is both a tort and a crime punishable by law, whereas private nuisance is a tort, which is a wrong for which there is a remedy by compensation or damages. It is therefore important to establish the difference. The essential difference is the extent to which it affects people and, in this respect, possibly the most important definition is that given by Lord Justice Denning[6] in an appeal trial in which the Attorney General, on the relator action of the County Council and local Rural District Council, alleged that the defendant quarry owners were committing a public nuisance arising from the manner in which they conducted their quarry business. They contended, *inter alia,* that the judge had failed to distinguish between a public nuisance, affecting *all* the subjects of Her Majesty living in the area, or passing through it, and a private nuisance affecting only a limited number of residents and giving rise only to an action for damages. They submitted that the question of dust and vibration should at worst be treated as a private nuisance. It was held that any nuisance which materially affected

---

5   Subsequently repealed by the Control of Pollution Act 1974.
6   *Attorney-General v P.Y.A. Quarries Ltd.* [1957] 1 All E.R. 894; 2 Q.B. 169, C.A. This was a relator action. Such actions do not exist in Scotland where, since 1985 under the Rules of Court, r 260B, the remedy is by application for judicial review.

the reasonable comfort and convenience of life of a class of Her Majesty's subjects was a public nuisance, that the sphere of the nuisance might be described generally as the "neighbourhood" but the question whether the local community within the sphere comprised a sufficient number of persons to constitute a class of the public was a question of fact in every case. Lord Justice Denning said "I decline to answer the question how many people are necessary to make up Her Majesty's subjects generally. I prefer to look at the reason of the thing, and to say that a public nuisance is a nuisance which is so widespread in its range or so indiscriminate in its effect that it would not be reasonable to expect one person to take proceedings on his own responsibility to put a stop to it, but that it should be taken on the response of the community at large."

In considering this definition, therefore, the following matters need to be taken into account:

The number of persons affected – it has been said that the nuisance should be a nuisance "to all persons who come within the sphere of its operation".[7] If it were necessary to prove that *all* of Her Majesty's subjects were affected it would be almost impossible to prove public nuisance, although this principle is sometimes used by defendants.

Trivial matters will not be considered – the rattling of poles and boarding was held not to be a nuisance[8] but isolated acts may constitute public nuisance "if it is done under such circumstances that the public right should be vindicated".[9] An isolated act will never be a private nuisance.

Public nuisance may also be a private nuisance – in the case of *Halsey v Esso Petroleum Co. Ltd.*[10] it was held that a noise nuisance

---

[7]   *Soltau v De Held* (1851) 2 Sim. N.S. 133 per Kindersley V.C. See also *Murdoch and Another v Glacier Metal Co. Ltd.* [1998] Env L.R. 732, C.A. In the original trial, the judge took into account the paucity of complaints from neighbours of the plaintiff in a case alleging noise nuisance from a nearby factory. Other matters were also considered in deciding that there had been no nuisance in law. The decision was upheld in the Court of Appeal.

[8]   *Cooper v Crabtree* (1881) 20 Ch.D. 589.

[9]   *A-G v P.Y.A. Quarries Ltd.* [1957] 2 Q.B. 169.

[10] *Halsey v Esso Petroleum Co. Ltd.* [1961] 2 All E.R. 145.

from the tanker lorries at night on the public highway was both a public and private nuisance for these reasons:

(a) public – it was an unreasonable use of the highway and the plaintiff suffered special damage; and

(b) private – the noise was directly related to the operation of the depot and it was not a prerequisite of private nuisance that the nuisance arose from the defendant's land provided it affected the complainant's property.

Criminal prosecutions can be taken by the Attorney-General or other enforcing bodies (e.g. Local Authority Environmental Health Departments).

Civil Proceedings can be instituted by the Attorney-General, alone or at the relation of a local authority or individual. Section 222 of the Local Government Act 1972 provides that the local authority "in the case of civil proceedings may institute them in their own name".[11]

PRIVATE NUISANCE

A private nuisance is one which interferes with a person's use or enjoyment of land or of some right connected with it. There must not only be an act or omission to cause the nuisance, but also damage. Damage is usually damage to the plaintiff's property, or unreasonable interference with his use and enjoyment of it, e.g.

(a) damage due to vibration

(b) loss of sleep

(c) interference with communication

(d) lowering of property values (possible – certainly not relevant to statutory noise as a common law principle).

Private nuisance actions are more common than public nuisance cases, partly because of the different procedure involved. A private

---

[11] See *City of London Corporation v Bovis* [1992] 3 All E.R. 697, C.A.

nuisance action may be brought by the aggrieved person in the civil court, either the County Court or High Court. Only the occupier of the land, or persons having the requisite interest are entitled to sue (by virtue of the definition above). This may include owner-occupiers and tenants but not relatives or visitors even if living with the occupier.[12] The aggrieved person must have a legal interest in the land.

The following principles have been established in the courts:

1.   There must be material interference with property or personal comfort.

2.   It is no defence for the defendant to show that he has taken all reasonable steps and care to prevent noise.

3.   The noise need not be injurious to health.

4.   Temporary or transient noise will not generally be accepted as a nuisance.

5.   The courts do not seek to apply a fixed standard of comfort.

6.   It is no defence to show that the plaintiff came to the nuisance.

7.   The courts will not interfere with building operations conducted in a reasonable manner.

8.   Contrary to the general rule in the law of tort, malice may be a significant factor.

9.   Noise resulting from a grant of planning permission, where that permission causes a change in the character of a neighbourhood, may not be a nuisance.

10. It is enough to show that a defendant knew or ought to have known of the nuisance.

11. The normal use of a residence may not be a nuisance.

These principles have been established as a result of defendants'

---

[12]   *Malone v Laskey* [1907] 2 K.B. 141.

submissions in the courts that such circumstances as, for example, the fact that his activities began before the arrival on the scene of the plaintiff, should act in his favour. Some of the cases on which these principles are based are therefore worthy of consideration.

THERE MUST BE MATERIAL INTERFERENCE WITH PROPERTY OR PERSONAL COMFORT

Walter v Selfe[13] – nuisance is defined as "an inconvenience materially interfering with the ordinary comfort, physically, of human existence, not merely according to elegant or dainty modes of living, but according to plain and sober and simple notions amongst English people."

Betts v Penge U.D.C.[14] – it was held that it was sufficient to sustain conviction of the appellant to prove that by his act or default his premises were in such a state as to interfere with the personal comfort of the occupier, without necessarily being injurious to health. It was also held that the distinction between public and private nuisance was immaterial to the question of whether a statutory nuisance existed.

Rushmer v Polsue & Alfieri Ltd.[15] – in this case, the defendant introduced a printing press in his premises and operated it at night. The court decided that, having regard to the background noise in the locality, the noise from the printing press was unreasonable. It was held that the working of the machine at night caused a serious additional disturbance to the plaintiff and his family, so as to constitute a nuisance.[16]

It has also been held[17] that night-time factory noise marginally higher than that recommended by the World Health Organisation

[13] *Walter v Selfe* (1851) 4 De G. & Sm. 315.
[14] *Betts v Penge U.D.C.* [1942] 2 K.B. 154; 2 All E.R. 61.
[15] *Rushmer v Polsue & Alfieri Ltd.* (1907) 51 Sol. Jol. 324, H.L.
[16] No scientific evidence was produced in this case and the case may therefore support statutory nuisance proceedings taken in the absence of sound level readings. But see also *R. v Fenny Stratford Justices ex parte Watney Mann (Midlands) Ltd.* [1976] 2 All E.R. 888, Q.B.D., [1976] 1 W.L.R. 1101 when it was also held that justices had discretion to specify noise levels providing they were in sufficiently precise terms.
[17] *Murdoch and Another v Glacier Metal Co. Ltd.* [1998] Env L.R. 732, C.A.

as the level above which the restorative value of sleep could be adversely affected, does not in itself constitute a nuisance; *all of the surrounding circumstances must be taken into account.*

IT IS NO DEFENCE FOR THE DEFENDANT TO SHOW THAT HE HAS TAKEN ALL REASONABLE STEPS AND CARE TO PREVENT NOISE[18]

Rushmer v Polsue & Alfieri Ltd.[19] – Lord Justice Cozens-Hardy stated "It does not follow that because I live, say, in the manufacturing part of Sheffield, I cannot complain if a steam hammer is introduced next door, and so worked as to render sleep impossible, although previous to its introduction my house was a reasonably comfortable abode, having regard to the local standard; and it would be no answer to say that the steam hammer is of the most modern approved pattern and is reasonably worked."

N.B. Clearly, as shown in this case, the fact that the area in which the nuisance occurs may already be an industrial or noisy area, is no defence either.

Halsey v Esso Petroleum Co. Ltd.[20] – Justice Veale said "The making or causing of such a noise as materially interferes with the comfort of a neighbour, when judged by the standard to which I have referred (*Walter v Selfe*) constitutes an actionable nuisance, and it is no answer to say that the best known means have been taken to reduce or prevent the noise complained of, or that the cause of the nuisance is the exercise of a business or trade in a reasonable and proper manner."

In *Macleod-Johnstone-Hart v Aga Khan Foundation (U.K.)* (1981),[21] it was held that any statutory obligation imposed under the Control of Pollution Act 1974, sections 59-74, that is intended to control

---

[18] This may, however, constitute a defence to proceedings under the Environmental Protection Act 1990 if it can be shown to constitute "best practicable means" as defined in those Acts.

[19] *Rushmer v Polsue & Alfieri Ltd.* (1907) 51 S.J. 324, H.L.

[20] *Halsey v Esso Petroleum Co. Ltd.* [1961] 2 All E.R. 145.

[21] *Macleod-Johnstone-Hart v Aga Khan Foundation (U.K.)* (1981) Unreported, cited in *Hawke v Himan* [1988] J.P.L. 84, 85.

noise is not a defence to a nuisance action. Also, the "best practicable means" defence under the Act is not a good defence in common law cases.

THE NOISE NEED NOT BE INJURIOUS TO HEALTH

Vanderpant v Mayfair Hotel Co. Ltd.[22] – an injunction was granted in an action by the occupier of a house abutting on a highway to restrain the owners of a neighbouring hotel from causing a nuisance to the plaintiff by noise arising from the hotel kitchen. One of the principles on which this judgment was based was that the making or causing of such a noise on premises, as materially interferes with the ordinary physical comfort of a neighbour, constitutes an actionable nuisance.

Hampstead and Suburban Properties Ltd. v Diomedous[23] – this case takes into account the principle that noise need not be injurious to health and relates to the fact that the defendant had covenanted not to permit music or musical instruments to be played on his premises in such a manner as to be audible to the extent of causing a nuisance or annoyance to the occupier of any adjoining premises. In the event of complaints being received, at the plaintiff landlord's request he was to discontinue playing until effective sound proofing was completed. The defendant stopped the music but it restarted before completion of the works. Justice Megarry said "...it is of some relevance to consider whether it is more important for the plaintiff's tenants to have the relative peace and quiet in their homes to which they have been accustomed, or for the defendant's customers to have the pleasure of music while they eat, played at high volume. When this comparison is made, it seems to me that it is the home rather than the meal table which must prevail. A home in which sleep is possible is a necessity, whereas loud music as an accompaniment is, for those who enjoy it, relatively a luxury. If, of course, the two can peacefully co-exist, so much the better; but if there is irreconcilable conflict, as there is at present in this case, I think it is the home that should be preferred."

---

[22] *Vanderpant v Mayfair Hotel Co. Ltd.* [1930] 1 Ch. 138.
[23] *Hampstead and Suburban Properties Ltd. v Diomedous* [1968] 3 All E.R. 545.

TEMPORARY OR TRANSIENT NOISE WILL NOT GENERALLY BE ACCEPTED AS A NUISANCE

Leeman v Montagu[24] – the plaintiff purchased a house in a partly rural, partly residential district. The defendant kept a large number of cockerels on a poultry farm about 100 yards away. The plaintiff complained of the dawn chorus of the cockerels which kept him awake. The court found that one dawn chorus of cockerels does not constitute grounds for an action for nuisance but, if it continues in a residential area for weeks, damages and an injunction may be granted.

Andreae v Selfridge[25] – the defendants were developing a large site close to the plaintiff's hotel. Work included demolition, excavation and construction work. It was held that in respect of operations of this character, such as demolition or building, if they are reasonably carried out, and all proper steps are taken to ensure that no undue inconvenience is caused to neighbours, whether from noise, dust or other reasons, the neighbours must put up with it. However, nuisance from pile driving at night has been held to be an actionable nuisance.[26]

Gosnell v The Aerated Bread Co. Ltd.[27] – the plaintiffs, a firm of solicitors, occupied premises adjacent to the defendants who were carrying out internal structural alterations. The plaintiffs sought an injunction restraining the defendants from operating their business between 10 a.m. and 6 p.m. It was held that the work was merely an annoyance "which many people had to put up with temporarily".

Notwithstanding these judgments, however, a noise which lasts for only a short time may be a nuisance if the nature of it is not trivial.[28]

---

[24] *Leeman v Montagu* [1936] 2 All E.R. 1677.

[25] *Andreae v Selfridge* [1937] 3 All E.R. 255.

[26] *De Keysers Royal Hotel Ltd. v Spicer Bros Ltd. and Minter* (1914) 30 T.L.R. 257.

[27] *Gosnell v The Aerated Bread Co. Ltd.* (1894) 10 T.L.R. 661.

[28] In *R. v Shorrock* [1994] Q.B. 279; [1993] 3 All E.R. 917, a public nuisance occurred from noise from a one-night acid house party. In the case of *East Northamptonshire D.C. v Fossett* [1994] Env L.R. 388, a single event, an all-night rave party, was held to be a statutory nuisance.

THE COURTS DO NOT SEEK TO APPLY A FIXED STANDARD OF COMFORT

The following cases illustrate that fixed standards do not apply and each case is determined according to its particular merits.

Rushmer v Polsue & Alfieri Ltd.[29] – if the noise from a printing press results in the occupier of adjacent property being subjected to an increase of noise such as to interfere substantially with human existence according to the standard of comfort existing in the locality, that is sufficient to constitute an actionable wrong entitling the occupier to an injunction.

Halsey v Esso Petroleum Co. Ltd.[30] – it was held that if a man lives in a town, it is necessary that he should subject himself to the consequences of those operations of trade which may be carried out in his immediate locality, which are actually necessary for trade and commerce, and also for the enjoyment of the property and for the benefit of the inhabitants of the town and of the public at large.

Notwithstanding this opinion, however, the court in this case deemed that the plaintiff's complaints of noise from boilers, pumps and heavy tanker lorries was a nuisance, and granted an injunction.

Sedleigh-Denfield v O'Callaghan[31] – it was held that a balance has to be maintained between the right of an occupier to do as he likes on his property and the right of his neighbour not to be interfered with. Consideration has to be given to such matters as the locality, time at which the noise occurs, and its severity and duration.

Colls v Home and Colonial Stores Ltd.[32] – it was held that a person living in towns cannot expect to have as pure air, free from smoke, smell and noise as if he lived in the country and away from other dwellings.

N.B. In Scotland, a material increase of existing noises constitutes a nuisance, whether the district is a noisy one or not.[33]

---

[29] *Rushmer v Polsue & Alfieri Ltd.* (1907) 51 S.J. 324, H.L.
[30] *Halsey v Esso Petroleum Co. Ltd.* [1961] 2 All E.R. 145.
[31] *Sedleigh-Denfield v O'Callaghan* [1940] 3 All E.R. 349, H.L.
[32] *Colls v Home and Colonial Stores Ltd.* [1904] All E.R. 5, H.L.
[33] *Encyclopaedia of the Laws of Scotland,* 10 para, 753.

Dunton v Dover District Council[34] – an injunction was granted prohibiting children's play at night on a housing estate playground due to the effects of their noise on nearby residents.

IT IS NO DEFENCE TO SHOW THAT THE PLAINTIFF CAME TO THE NUISANCE

A defence commonly used, either in legal proceedings or in informal negotiations, is that the defendant has a prescriptive right to carry on his business because of the length of time it has been established. This is no defence and therefore contrary to the "established use right" that may be determined under planning law. The following cases illustrate this point.

Sturges v Bridgman[35] – the defendant had used two large pestles and mortars at the rear of his premises for more than 20 years. The plaintiff, a doctor, built a consulting room at the end of his garden and the noise and vibration from the defendant's equipment caused a nuisance. The defendant claimed a prescriptive right to make the noise, but the court held that:

(a) there must be uninterrupted use for twenty years, *and*

(b) there must also be a nuisance for twenty years.

Therefore the prescriptive right was not present. If a nuisance has existed continuously for twenty years, a prescriptive right to continue it is acquired as an easement appurtenant to the land on which it exists. The nuisance must for 20 years have been a nuisance to the plaintiff or his predecessors in title. The defence of prescriptive right does not apply to a public nuisance, only a private nuisance. It is not a defence to prove that for the period in question, it has been a nuisance to other people occupying the property.

THE COURTS WILL NOT INTERFERE WITH BUILDING OPERATIONS CONDUCTED IN A REASONABLE MANNER

The following case law shows that the courts recognise that a certain amount of noise is inevitable. Most cases, however, appear

---

[34] *Dunton v Dover District Council* (1977) 76 L.G.R. 87, Q.B.D.
[35] *Sturges v Bridgman* (1879) 11 Ch.D. 852.

to relate to construction and demolition works and it is not clear to what degree similar considerations would apply to activities of a more permanent nature, e.g. engineering work in well established factories. Presumably the questions of material interference with property, need to take reasonable care, standards of comfort, etc. will be taken into account.

Andreae v Selfridge[36] – in operations of this nature, if reasonably carried out and all proper steps are taken to ensure no undue inconvenience is caused to neighbours, whether from noise, dust or other reasons, the neighbours must put up with it.

Boynton v Helena Rubinstein and Hall, Beddall and Co.[37] – in this case, building contractors were restrained from using a hoist except between 9 a.m. and 6 p.m. and ordered that the engine be switched off when the hoist was not in use. The brake mechanism was also to be operated to minimise inconvenience from noise and vibration. Injunctions will not be granted, however, in respect of works carried out in a reasonable way and in the case of *Clark v Lloyds Bank Ltd.*[38] a hotel owner was refused an injunction in respect of demolition work which was conducted in a reasonable manner, starting at approximately 6.30 a.m.

Barrette v Franki Compressed Pile Co. of Canada[39] – pile driving operations causing vibration which damaged the plaintiff's building were held to be a nuisance.

MALICE MAY BE A SIGNIFICANT FACTOR

Christie v Davey[40] – the plaintiff gave music and singing lessons for four days per week, totalling seventeen hours. Music and singing practice also took place at other hours and musical evenings were held. It was held that this was not an unreasonable use of the house which could be restrained by an injunction. The neighbour who was aggrieved in the first place had resorted to knocking on the party

---

[36] *Andreae v Selfridge* [1937] 3 All E.R. 255.
[37] *Boynton v Helena Rubinstein and Hall, Beddall and Co.* (1960) 176 E.G. 443.
[38] *Clark v Lloyds Bank Ltd.* (1910) 79 L.J.C.L. 645.
[39] *Barrette v Franki Compressed Pile Co. of Canada* [1955] 2 D.L.R. 665.
[40] *Christie v Davey* [1893] 1 Ch. 316.

wall, beating trays, whistling and shrieking, and so interfering with the music teaching. It was against this person, who out of malice caused a nuisance, that the injunction was granted.

Hollywood Silver Fox Farm Ltd. v Emmett[41] – a farmer was granted an injunction restraining his neighbour from firing his guns so as to scare his silver foxes during breeding time. It was held that the firing of the guns was malicious because it was an act of spite arising from a quarrel.

Fraser v Booth[42] – conversely to the two above cases, the court held that retaliation by the defendant, who set off fireworks to scare away homing pigeons that caused a nuisance, was justified. The court was satisfied that, rather than being motivated by spite, the action of the defendant was taken under stress in an attempt to abate the nuisance.

NOISE RESULTING FROM A GRANT OF PLANNING PERMISSION MAY NOT BE A NUISANCE

Gillingham Borough Council v Medway (Chatham) Dock Co. Ltd. and Others[43] – the council granted planning permission for a change of use from a dockyard to a commercial port operating 24 hours a day. There was substantial interference with local residents' enjoyment of their property. This was due to noisy heavy goods vehicles travelling through a residential area and causing considerable disturbance to sleep. The council, in granting permission, allowed activities which changed the character of the neighbourhood. The judgment was that the alleged nuisance had to be assessed by reference to the character of the neighbourhood after granting permission, not by reference to its character prior to then. In the circumstances the undoubted disturbance was not actionable.

Hunter v Canary Wharf Ltd[44] – this case involved two actions, for nuisance and for neglience, the latter in respect of dust from construction work. In delivering his judgment, Lord Justice Pell

---

41   *Hollywood Silver Fox Farm Ltd. v Emmett* [1936] 2 K.B. 468.
42   *Fraser v Booth* (1949) 50 S.R. (N.S.W.) 113.
43   *Gillingham Borough Council v Medway (Chatham) Dock Co. Ltd. and Others* [1992] 3 All E.R. 923; [1992] 3 W.L.R. 449, Q.B.D.
44   *Hunter v Canary Wharf Ltd* [1996] 1 All E.R. 482.

made reference to the *Gillingham* case and others. He said, in referring to the *Gillingham* case, that "where planning consent for a development is given *and implemented* [author's italics], the question of nuisance will therefore fall to be decided by reference to the neighbourhood with that development and not as it was previously." He preferred to rely on the judgments in *Allen v Gulf Oil Refining Ltd.*[45] and *Wheeler v J.J. Saunders Ltd.*[46] in forming the opinion that "The powers and duties conferred on planning authorities ... are not such that in granting planning permissions under their delegated powers they are conferring an immunity in nuisance upon works pursuant to the permissions" (i.e. in this case the nuisance associated with the construction work).

IT IS ENOUGH TO SHOW THAT A DEFENDANT KNEW OR OUGHT TO HAVE KNOWN OF THE NUISANCE

R. v Shorrock (Peter)[47] – the defendant let a field on his farm to three people for a weekend and then went away for the weekend. An "acid house" party on the field lasting 15 hours caused a major noise nuisance, producing 275 complaints from people living up to four miles away. The land owner and the organisers were convicted of the offence of public nuisance. The land owner appealed on the ground that he had no knowledge of the events that had occurred. It was held that it was not necessary to prove he had actual knowledge of the nuisance; it was enough to show that he was responsible for the nuisance and knew or ought to have known of it. He should have been aware there was a real risk of the sort of nuisance that was created and so he had constructive knowledge of the nuisance.

THE NORMAL USE OF A RESIDENCE MAY NOT BE A NUISANCE

London Borough of Southwark and Another v Mills and

---

[45] *Allen v Gulf Oil Refinery Ltd.* [1981] 1 All E.R. 353; [1981] A.C. 1001; [1981] 2 W.L.R. 188, H.L.

[46] *Wheeler v J.J. Saunders Ltd.* [1995] 2 All E.R. 697; [1995] 3 W.L.R. 466. In this case, Gibson L.J. stated "... I am not prepared to accept that the principle applied in the *Gillingham* case must be taken to apply to every planning decision."

[47] *R.v Shorrock (Peter)* [1993] 3 All E.R. 917, C.A.

Others[48] – the sound insulation of a number of flats was so poor that neighbours' everyday activities could be clearly heard, including "normal conversation, singing, arguments, the television, snoring, coughing ... bed springs ... creaking floorboards ... taps running ...". In this case, the sound insulation standards of the Building Regulations did not apply. The neighbours were not acting unreasonably and the tenants therefore sought a remedy against the landlords under the terms of their tenancy agreements, which included clauses to the effect that the landlord would not interfere with a "tenant's right to quiet enjoyment of the premises during the continuance of the tenancy". The House of Lords considered that the real complaint was about the *condition of the premises at the time of letting* and the covenant of quiet enjoyment could not apply in law, and therefore the landlords were not in breach of the covenant for quiet enjoyment. It was also held that the ordinary and reasonable use of residential premises by its occupier was not in itself an actionable nuisance; that where a tenant complained of noise nuisance from a neighbouring tenant's premises, their common landlord could not be liable in tort for having authorised the commission of an actionable nuisance if the noise arose from that ordinary and reasonable use for which the neighbouring tenant could not be liable.

Having established the principles by which an action is likely to be tried under common law, it is necessary to establish the difference between a private and public nuisance at common law and accordingly to consider who can take action.

Common law: liability to proceedings

It is not intended here to discuss the manner in which proceedings are taken, but the persons against whom proceedings may be instituted and the defences that may be applicable.

The person causing the nuisance will be responsible, whether or not the nuisance arises from property he occupies, provided it affects the plaintiff's property.[49]

---

[48]   *London Borough of Southwark and Another v Mills and Others* [1999] 3
        W.L.R. 939, H.L.
[49]   *Halsey v Esso Petroleum Co. Ltd.* [1961] 2 All E.R. 145.

Ownership of land does not necessarily mean that the owner will be held responsible for the actions of others who may cause nuisance. In one case,[50] a resident complained of the noise from model aircraft in a public park. The court held that the park owners were not responsible for the nuisance as they were not in occupation and had no right to interfere unless the members of the public creating the alleged nuisance contravened any law relating to the flying of model aircraft (such a defence would not be applicable for the purpose of proceedings in respect of a statutory nuisance).[51]

Occupiers of property may be responsible under different circumstances. It has been said "The ground of responsibility is the *possession and control* of the land from which the nuisance proceeds".[52] In the case above, the park owner clearly did not have the necessary control but the occupier of property may be liable for the nuisance if, even though he did not cause it, he allows it to continue during his occupation. In this respect a local authority may be liable for noise generated as a result of activities conducted by another person on its land and with its consent. In *Tetley v Chitty*[53] a local authority authorised go-karting on its land, knowing the activity was likely to cause nuisance from noise, and residents were granted an injunction and damages in respect of the noise.

An occupier engaging a contractor may also be liable if that contractor's activities cause a noise nuisance,[54] as the occupier has possession and control.[55]

Remedial action

Remedial action is principally an injunction and damages. An injunction is a court order restraining the convicted person from committing or continuing the act or omission complained about. It is discretionary and generally will not be used where the granting

---

[50] *Hall v Beckenham Corporation* [1949] 1 K.B. 716.
[51] See Environmental Protection Act 1990, s. 80(2)(a) and (c).
[52] *Sedleigh-Denfield v O'Callaghan* [1940] 3 All E.R. 349, H.L.
[53] *Tetley v Chitty* [1986] 1 All E.R. 663, H.L.
[54] *Matania v National Provincial Bank Ltd. and the Elevenist Syndicate Ltd.* [1936] 2 All E.R. 633.
[55] *Sedleigh-Denfield v O'Callaghan* [1940] 3 All E.R. 349, H.L.

of damages is a sufficient remedy. In the case of minor injury, the value of which can be established in financial terms, and where it would be particularly oppressive to grant an injunction against the defendant, damages may be substituted for an injunction.

If the nuisance has been abated between the time of issuing the writ and the trial, the court will usually withhold action and allow the plaintiff leave to apply for an injunction if the nuisance recurs[56] A court may at the same time grant, but suspend, an injunction subject to remedial work being carried out by the defendant. In the case of a night time nuisance, an order restraining the defendant from carrying out his business between certain hours may be granted.

An aggrieved person has the right to abate the nuisance himself without taking legal proceedings. There are difficulties associated with this and, in particular, it will destroy any right of subsequent action in the courts. Only in exceptional cases might this course of action be recommended, e.g. where a burglar alarm is set off and continues throughout the night. It should also be understood that this kind of action, if deemed unlawful, could render the aggrieved person liable for trespass.

N.B. In Scotland, an owner of land or premises (in private or public ownership) even if not in actual possession, may sue in respect of operations by a third party complained of by his tenant and lowering, or reasonably calculated to lower, the letting value.

STATUTORY NOISE NUISANCE

Prior to the introduction of noise as a statutory nuisance,[57] action under common law or a limited number of local Acts was the only way to deal with noise nuisance. The Environmental Protection Act 1990[58] and the Control of Pollution Act 1974 recognised the fact that undue noise can cause serious annoyance and therefore many

56   *Halsey v Esso Petroleum Co. Ltd.* [1961] 2 All E.R. 145.
57   In the Noise Abatement Act 1960 (now repealed).
58   The Environmental Protection Act 1990, s. 162 and Sch. 16 repealed the provisions in ss. 58 and 59 of the Control of Pollution Act 1974 dealing with statutory noise nuisance in England and Wales; ss. 58 and 59 were repealed totally by the Environment Act 1995, s. 120(3), Sch. 24.

of the nuisances that previously existed at common law became controllable under statute. It is still necessary, in taking proceedings for statutory noise nuisance, to be able to establish a nuisance at common law, although it does not matter whether the nuisance would be regarded as public or private. The 1974 Act also takes into account the fact that temporary or transient noise from construction works, etc. may not be adequately controllable using the nuisance procedures even though such noise may cause serious annoyance. Control of this type of activity, irrespective of whether nuisance is caused, is through the powers in sections 60 and 61 of that Act.

The earlier legislation[59] did not provide control over noisy activities which could be foreseen (e.g. brass band concerts, the installation of noisy compressors and drop hammers, etc.) This situation was rectified in the Environmental Protection Act 1990 to provide for the most comprehensive control of environmental noise yet produced. The noise control provisions contained in Part III of the Control of Pollution Act 1974 and the Environmental Protection Act 1990 were largely derived from the recommendations of the Scott Committee report *Neighbourhood Noise.*[60]

The C.B.I. in that report proposed that, whilst the control of most noise problems should be the responsibility of local authorities, the responsibility for control of certain activities "in which noise abatement inherently calls for a high degree of technical skill" should be with central government. A highly qualified Noise Inspectorate in the Department of the Environment was suggested. This idea was rejected by the Association of Public Health Inspectors (now Chartered Institute of Environmental Health) because noise was and is an essentially local issue requiring control through those with detailed local knowledge.

This was accepted by the Scott Committee who recommended that the responsibility for noise remain with local authorities. However,

---

[59] The Noise Abatement Act 1960.
[60] *Neighbourhood Noise,* Noise Advisory Council, 1971, H.M.S.O. The Noise Advisory Council was abolished as a Government quango in the early 1980s. The Noise Council was subsequently created by the professional noise bodies dealing with such issues and makes a valuable contribution to Government views on noise control.

the fifth report of the Royal Commission on Environmental Pollution suggested that a new central inspectorate (Her Majesty's Pollution Inspectorate) be formed to deal with pollution problems of a large scale, and included noise as part of this concept.

It was felt by many local authorities that any move such as this would remove the essential element of local control and could conflict in particular with the power to declare Noise Abatement Zones (see Chapter 4). In the event, when Her Majesty's Inspectorate of Pollution (now the Environment Agency) was formed, environmental noise control was not included in its remit but remained the responsibility of local authorities.

However, noise control is now included in the Integrated Pollution Prevention and Control (I.P.P.C.) regime operating in the U.K. This is a regulatory system which adopts an integrated approach to control the overall environmental impact (air and water pollution, waste disposal, and noise/vibration control) of specified industrial activities and processes. It provides for a permit process designed to ensure that those industries operate their activities in accordance with Best Available Techniques (B.A.T.). The regulation of noise under I.P.P.C. brings together different legislative approaches to the control of noise and, in the case of noise from certain large and complex industrial installations, a co-ordinated approach will be required between the I.P.P.C. regulator[61] and those responsible for environmental health and planning functions in local authorities.[62] The I.P.P.C. regime will, therefore, effectively transfer the traditional local control of noise for some industries to a more centralised body.

Duty to inspect

Section 79 of the Environmental Protection Act 1990 (the 1990 Act) includes in its definition of statutory nuisance "noise emitted from premises so as to be prejudicial to health or a nuisance" and "noise that is prejudicial to health or a nuisance and is emitted from

---

[61] The Environment Agency for England and Wales, the Scottish Environment Protection Agency, and the Northern Ireland Environment and Heritage Service.

[62] A more detailed explanation of I.P.P.C. is contained in Chapter 7.

or caused by a vehicle, machinery or equipment in a street".[63] It places a duty on local authorities to inspect their areas from time to time to detect any statutory nuisances which ought to be dealt with under the duty to serve abatement notices contained in sections 80 and 80A.[64] There is also a duty to take such steps as are reasonably practicable to investigate complaints of noise. A similar requirement applies in Scotland.[65]

No guidance is given as to how these inspections should be carried out,[66] presumably because it is an essential part of local control by the enforcing authorities to decide how to apply this requirement to their local circumstances. There are a number of ways in which these duties may be met in the absence of more specific guidance:

1. To respond to public complaint, the first step preceding the service of abatement notices. This invariably results in interviews with local residents in the area of complaint to determine the extent of nuisance. The methods indicated under "Investigation of Complaints" will usually be employed.

2. The implementation of the requirement under section 57 of the Control of Pollution Act 1974 "to decide how to exercise its powers concerning noise abatement zones"[67] may also reveal matters constituting a noise nuisance which require to be actioned under the statutory nuisance procedure. Some of the survey methods that may be used in respect of the noise abatement zone provisions are included in that chapter.

---

[63] ss. 79(1)(g) and (ga) respectively. Subsection 79(1)(ga) was inserted by the Noise and Statutory Nuisance Act 1993. It is intended to deal with noise from car burglar alarms and other particular cases of this type of noise pollution. It is not intended to deal with general traffic noise from vehicles.

[64] If a local authority fails to discharge this function, default powers in Schedule 4, para. 3 may lead to an order of direction by the Secretary of State enforceable by mandamus, or an order transferring the relevant functions to himself. There is no such default power in respect of the Control of Pollution Act 1974.

[65] These sections were extended to Scotland by the Environment Act 1995, s. 107 and Sch. 17.

[66] The D.O.E. Circular 2/76 which accompanied the 1974 Act was silent on this issue.

[67] s. 57(b).

3. In the case of premises where varied noises are a frequent
    source of complaint, it may often be the case that the owner or
    occupier chooses to disregard his neighbours and introduces
    new plant or equipment producing unacceptable noise levels;
    to alter his working pattern (e.g. the introduction of a night
    shift); to allow equipment maintenance procedures to deteriorate
    to the extent that subsequent defects produce an unsatisfactory
    level of noise; or to do other things which may increase noise.
    In such cases, Environmental Health Departments may feel it
    appropriate to survey by monitoring at regular intervals the
    noise emission from premises where those sort of problems
    occur. This may then allow remedial action to be promptly
    introduced by the service of an abatement notice where nuisance
    exists or is likely to occur.

The above steps will deal with the requirement to survey for the
detection of noise nuisances and the latter will also deal with the
likely occurrence or recurrence. There are, however, other factors
to be considered in determining whether nuisance is likely to occur
or recur and these may not necessarily be detected by a district
survey. The detection of potential nuisance may arise from:

(a) Checking on work specified by an abatement notice,[68] e.g. the
    nuisance may be abated not by executing works but by ceasing
    the particular activity causing nuisance. The possible
    recommencement of that activity at a future date may, according
    to information obtained by the investigating officer, identify
    the likelihood of a recurrence.

(b) Regular but temporary activities which come to the notice of
    the local authority as being a noise nuisance may, if those
    activities are likely to recur, justify the view that a nuisance will
    occur at that time. Noise from a fairground, e.g. loudspeaker
    system, generator noise or piped music, may fall into this
    category. It may be justifiable to serve notice restricting the
    nuisance from this type of activity. Regular brass band concerts
    or other entertainment activities at established venues may also
    fall into this category.

---

[68]   s. 80 Environmental Protection Act 1990.

(c) Area surveys may reveal the introduction of new equipment in factories, the construction of factory extensions, or the construction of known sources of potential noise nuisance, for example discotheques, stadia, dog kennels, bus depots, etc. which may require control due to their nuisance potential. Some of these matters may also be controllable by other legislation such as planning and licensing laws.

(d) Liaison between Environmental Health Departments and other enforcement departments may also reveal activities with a noise nuisance potential requiring action under the statutory nuisance provisions, viz:

  (i) applications for Building Regulation approval may indicate potential noise nuisance from proposals not controllable under planning law (Building Regulation approval has to be given if the details submitted comply with the law, whether or not planning permission is required). This could include the construction of a building or building extension to accommodate a noisy activity falling within the existing planning use class for those premises;

  (ii) applications to the licensing justices for extending the hours during which music may be played at licensed premises, or for new music and singing licences, may reveal a potential nuisance source, for example in respect of acoustically poor prefabricated buildings used for community associations and licensed clubs. Applications in respect of multi-purpose buildings where only part is used for noisy activities may result in ready transmission of low frequency sound from live groups and discotheques.

What is reasonably practicable?

There is no case law as to what constitutes steps that "... are reasonably practicable to investigate complaints of noise".[69] However, a significant number of complaints have been made to the Local Government Ombudsman and his comments in certain

---

[69] Environmental Protection Act 1990, s. 79(1)(h).

published reports may provide guidance on what could be considered unreasonable in dealing with noise complaints from members of the public, viz:

(a) A delay of five months between an initial visit to interview a complainant and then carrying out a technical evaluation.[70]

(b) It is not acceptable to assume that a complainant's problem has ceased because he has allegedly not contacted the investigating officers to find out what is going on. Local authorities must pursue investigations and keep complainants advised of the action being taken.[71]

(c) Proper records of correspondence and telephone calls must be kept. A system should be used to ensure that progress on investigations is checked and necessary action taken at the appropriate times.[72]

(d) If a statutory nuisance exists, an abatement notice must be served; in one particular case the noise (and vibration) nuisance appeared to have occurred because the council's development officer may have encouraged the location of a forging business next to a residential property.[73]

(e) Where a local authority has planning, economic development and noise control responsibilities, they should work together to avoid or minimise noise problems. It is not justified to suggest that lack of action in serving an abatement notice is because the "lead officer" is someone else or the problem arose from another department's lack of foresight in allowing or encouraging noisy activities in a sensitive area.[74]

(f) It is unacceptable, 20 months after deciding a nuisance exists,

---

[70] Report by the local Ombudsman on an investigation into complaint 88/A/1864 against the London Borough of Barnet, 3rd May 1990, Commission for Local Administration in England.

[71] *Ibid.*

[72] *Ibid.*

[73] Report by the local Ombudsman on an investigation into complaint 88/C/1373 against the Sheffield City Council, 19th September 1989, Commission for Local Administration in England.

[74] *Ibid.*

not to have served an abatement notice.[75]

(g) The defence of "best practicable means" is strictly a matter for the courts to decide. Unduly delaying action to try and decide whether this defence could successfully be used is unsatisfactory.[76]

(h) Failure or excessive delay in responding to requests to monitor noise (in this case from a clay pigeon shoot) because it occurs on a Sunday, is a breach of the duty laid upon the local authority. In this case, the authority was short-staffed, did not allow payment or time-off-in-lieu of overtime worked, nor did it employ consultants as an alternative.[77]

(i) Where a considerable number of complaints and evidence from the complainants existed, a council did not act properly, in only conducting two monitoring exercises during a period of two years.[78]

Failure of a local authority to take effective action may result in the Ombudsman recommending the payment of compensation.[79]

Summary proceedings

The statutory nuisance requirements provide that where a local authority is satisfied that a noise[80] amounting to a nuisance[81] exists,

---

[75] Report by the local Ombudsman on an investigation into complaint 88/C/1373 against the Sheffield City Council, 19th September 1989, Commission for Local Administration in England.

[76] *Ibid.*

[77] Report by the local Ombudsman on an investigation into complaints 88/C/1571 and 88/C/182 against Rotherham Metropolitan Borough Council, 26th November 1990.

[78] *Ibid.*

[79] Report by the Local Government Ombudsman on an investigation into complaint 92/B/1821 against Wychavon District Council. This resulted in the authority paying £8,000 compensation to the complainant for failing to take effective action against noise nuisance caused by a light industrial concern.

[80] Noise includes vibration, and nuisance must be understood in its common law sense, i.e. it must materially interfere with the comfort and convenient enjoyment of land. See page 36 ante, *Thompson-Schwab v Costaki* [1956] 1 All E.R. 652; (1956) 1 W.L.R 335, cited in *Clerk and Lindsell on Torts* (13th edn., page 782).

[81] The common law standard as to what constitutes a nuisance applies but only the statutory defences apply to an appeal. *A. Lambert Flat Management Ltd. v Lomas Ltd.* [1981] 2 All E.R. 280; (1981) 1 W.L.R. 898 D.C.

or is likely to occur or recur, they *must* serve a notice[82] on the person responsible for the nuisance or, if that person cannot be found or the nuisance has not yet occurred, on the owner or occupier of the premises from which the noise is emitted or would be emitted.[83] The notice can require that the nuisance be abated, or prohibit or restrict its occurrence or recurrence. It may require works or such other steps as may be necessary for the purpose of the notice or as may be specified in the notice. The notice must specify the time or times within which the requirements of the notice are to be complied with.

The local authority duty to act in respect of a statutory nuisance applies even though the activity giving rise to the nuisance may be subject to regulation by another body.[84] Abatement notices served in respect of noise from premises need not specify whether the noise is "prejudicial to health or a nuisance"[85] and, although it is common practice to consult on the nuisance and appropriate remedial steps with the alleged offender prior to the service of a notice, there is no such legal duty.[86]

A number of legal cases should help to decide the scope of an abatement notice's requirements when dealing with noise. Several principles emerge:

1. If an abatement notice requires positive action to be taken to abate the nuisance (i.e. not just requiring its cessation), the

---

[82]   Environmental Protection Act 1990, s. 80(1). Notice should be served in accordance with the Local Government Act 1972, s. 233 or Local Government (Scotland) Act 1973, s. 192.

[83]   Environmental Protection Act 1990, s. 80(2).

[84]   In the case of *R. v Carrick District Council ex parte Shelley* [1976] J.P.L. 857, it was held that (in a case associated with sewage debris) the existence of a statutory nuisance was a question of fact for the local authority to decide and that the law of statutory nuisance did not cease to apply because the consent system under the Water Resources Act applied. The court said that the duties were separate and a local authority committee resolution that it would not be "appropriate" to proceed by way of statutory nuisance proceedings in view of an appeal pending against the National Rivers Authority action was legally invalid insofar as the word "inappropriate" suggested the exercise of a power rather than a duty.

[85]   *Lowe v South Somerset District Council* [1998] Env L.R. 143, Q.B.D.

[86]   *R. v Falmouth and Truro Port Health Authority ex parte South West Water Services* [2000] 3 All E.R. 306, C.A.

notice must specify the works or other steps.[87]

2. Steps to be taken must be specified in meaningful terms and with sufficient clarity.[88]

3. Steps required may include action the local authority wants to be taken by a person other than the recipient of the notice, including a local authority officer.[89]

4. No steps need be indicated on the notice where the action, or choice of action, is obvious.[90]

5. In cases arising under section 79(1)(g), although the abatement notice must specify that the act is a nuisance, it need not specify whether it is "prejudicial to health or a nuisance".[91]

Purely subjective assessments of whether noise is a nuisance should be avoided. It is not sufficient for witnesses merely to allege that a nuisance exists; there must be applied an objective standard.[92]

---

[87] *Sterling Homes v Birmingham City Council* [1996] Env L.R. 121, Q.B.D.

[88] *R. v Falmouth and Truro Port Health Authority ex parte South West Water Services* [2000] 3 All E.R. 306, C.A., requirements applied in *Lambie v Thanet District Council* [2001] Env L.R. 397, Q.B.D. The latter case dealt with specified controls over noise from voices and amplified music in a public house.
In *Brighton and Hove Council v Ocean Coachworks (Brighton) Ltd.* [2001] Env L.R. 77, Q.B.D., the simple requirement to keep garages closed to control noise from a vehicle repair workshop was held to be reasonable.

[89] *Lambie v Thanet District Council* [2001] Env L.R. 397, Q.B.D. In this case the authority required installation of noise limiting equipment by one of its officers.

[90] In *Budd v Colchester Borough Council* [1999] Env L.R. 739, C.A., a case of barking greyhounds, the choices were obvious, i.e. get rid of the dogs, insulate the premises or treat the dogs differently.
In *Sevenoaks District Council v Brands Hatch Leisure Group Ltd.* [2001] Env L.R. 86, Q.B.D., referred to in *Lewis* [2000] J.P.L. 1013, it was held that noise levels set for squealing tyres on a racetrack were valid although the notice did not specify what steps should be taken to comply with the notice.
In *Surrey Free Inns plc v Gosport Borough Council* [1999] Env L.R. 750, C.A., it was held that there was no need to specify the steps to abate a nuisance from live and recorded music in a bar.
For analysis of these and other cases, see *Malcolm* [2000] J.P.L. 894, *Pointing* (2000) 150 N.L.J. 340 and *Lewis* [2000] J.P.L. 1011.

[91] *Lowe v South Somerset District Council* [1998] Env L.R. 143, Q.B.D.

[92] *Greenline Carriers (Tayside) Ltd. v City of Dundee District Council* (1991) S.L.T. 673, Ct. of Sess.

It may not always be necessary, however, to measure the precise noise level to establish a statutory nuisance.[93] However, in establishing that noise amounting to a nuisance has occurred contrary to an abatement notice, expert evidence of the measured level given by an Environmental Health Officer might be sufficient to establish that the noise interfered with reasonable enjoyment of property without having to call on the occupier of the property to give evidence.[94]

The power to control the future activities of people or the premises they are responsible for is a valuable form of nuisance control. Generally, local authorities will satisfy themselves of the existence or otherwise of a noise nuisance through their Environmental Health Department. The Environmental Health Officers must decide on the basis of investigation, as noise subject to complaint may not always be upheld as such in the courts. Many of the noises subject to complaint, e.g. noisy parties, barking dogs and minor property repairs, may not be considered a nuisance if merely transient, but their intermittent recurrence over a long period may constitute a nuisance although it would stretch local authority resources to confirm every incident. In such cases reliance solely on witness statements may be necessary, since the 1990 Act does not specify the information required before notice is served. If satisfied that the evidence of witnesses alone is reliable, it may be that proceedings can be taken on the basis of that evidence. In such cases the corroborative evidence of more than one aggrieved person is advisable.[95]

---

93   In the case of *Godfrey v Conwy C.B.C.* [2001] E.H.L.R. 10, Rose L.J., Q.B.D., it was held that measurement of noise levels was not a prerequisite to a finding of statutory nuisance. The appropriate test was identical to that used to establish private nuisance at common law, namely whether the noise constituted an unreasonable interference with the use and enjoyment of the complainant's land.

94   *Cooke v Adatia* (1988) 153 J.P. 129 D.C.

95   However, be aware that the mere fact that witnesses asserted that noise amounted to a nuisance does not of itself entitle the court to conclude that a nuisance for the purpose of the section has been proved. *Greenline Carriers (Tayside) Ltd. v City of Dundee District Council* (1991) S.L.T. 673, Ct. of Sess. It is also worth noting that in establishing that a nuisance has occurred contrary to an abatement notice, expert evidence of the noise level given by an Environmental Health Officer might be sufficient to prove a nuisance without having to produce evidence from the occupiers of property. *Cooke v Adatia* (1988) 153 J.P. 129, D.C.

Appeals

Appeal against a notice must be made within 21 days of service and the conditions of appeal[96] need to be considered *prior to* the service of notice if appeals are to be avoided or successfully defended. Local authorities also have to consider whether they will suspend a notice in accordance with the appropriate appeals regulations, having regard to the relevant conditions. The procedure for appeal is by complaint for an order and the Magistrates' Courts Act 1980 applies to the proceedings.

The Statutory Nuisance (Appeals) Regulations 1995 make provision with respect to appeals to the Magistrates' Court under the 1990 Act.[97] The grounds on which an appeal may be made include:[98]

(a) the notice is not justified by the terms of section 80 (of the 1990 Act);

(b) there has been some informality, defect or error in, or in connection with, the notice;

(c) the authority have refused unreasonably to accept compliance with alternative requirements, or that the requirements of the notice are otherwise unreasonable in character or extent, or are unnecessary;

(d) the time or times for compliance with the notice are not reasonably sufficient;

(e) the noise to which the notice relates is noise arising on industrial, trade or business premises, or is noise emitted from or caused by a vehicle, machinery or equipment being used for industrial,

---

[96] s. 80(3) Environmental Protection Act 1990 and the Statutory Nuisance (Appeals) Regulations 1995, S.I. 1995 No. 2644 (in England and Wales); and the Statutory Nuisance (Appeals) (Scotland) Regulations 1996, S.I. 1996 No. 107.

[97] The Control of Noise (Appeals) (Scotland) Regulations 1983 apply in respect of appeals in Scotland. Appeals are made to the sheriff and the grounds of appeal are similar to those applying to the Environmental Protection Act 1990.

[98] Reg. 2.

trade or business purposes, and the best practicable means[99] for preventing or countering its effects have been used;

(f) the requirements of the notice are more onerous than the requirements imposed, in relation to the noise, by

    (i) any notice under section 60 (control of construction site noise) or 66 (noise reduction notice in a Noise Abatement Zone) of the 1974 Act;[100]

    (ii) any consent under section 61 (prior consent for work on construction sites) or 65 (consent to exceed the registered noise level from premises in a Noise Abatement Zone), or determination under section 67 (new buildings to which a Noise Abatement Order will apply);[101]

(g) in the case of nuisance under section 79(1)(ga) of the 1990 Act (noise emitted from or caused by vehicles, machinery or equipment), the requirements are more onerous than the requirements of any consent given under the Noise and Statutory Nuisance Act 1993 (loudspeakers in streets or roads);[102]

(h) and (i) the notice should have been served on some other person as well as, instead of, or in addition to the appellant, being the person responsible for the noise, or being the owner or occupier of the premises from which the noise is emitted or would be emitted, or who is the person responsible for the vehicle, machinery or equipment.

The court is obliged to dismiss an appeal based on any informality,

---

[99] "Best practicable means" does not require a person to move his business to another area. An abatement notice should require steps to be taken to abate the nuisance where the business is located: see *Manley v New Forest District Council* [1999] P.L.R. 36, Q.B.D. The material date to be considered in determining whether the "best practicable means" defence applies is the date that the notice was served, not the date of the hearing. See *Surrey Free Inns plc v Gosport Borough Council* [1998] J.P.L. B 86, also *R. v Crown Court at Knightsbridge ex parte Cataldi* [1999] Env L.R. 62, Q.B.D. This decision applies to appeals to the magistrates' court and to the Crown Court.

[100] The Control of Pollution Act 1974.

[101] *Ibid.*

[102] Para. 1 of Sch. 2 to the 1993 Act.

defect or error if these are not material. Where the appeal is based on the grounds that notice should have been served on some other person, the appellant must serve a copy of the notice of appeal on that other person.[103] On hearing the appeal, the court may quash the notice, vary it in favour of the appellant, or dismiss the appeal.[104] On hearing the appeal, the court may make such order as it thinks fit:[105]

(a) with respect to the person by whom any work is to be executed and the contribution to be made by any person towards the cost of the work; or

(b) as to the proportions in which any expenses which may become recoverable by the authority under Part III of the Act are to be borne by the appellant and by any other person.

In exercising this power, the court must have regard to any contractual or statutory conditions of any relevant tenancy, and to the nature of the works required, before imposing a requirement on any person other than the appellant, and that any necessary copies of the appeal required to be served have actually been received by that person.[106]

The Regulations also specify the circumstances in which the operation of notices is to be suspended pending the outcome of any appeal.[107] The Regulations specify two circumstances in which a notice *will be suspended*:

1. When the notice would require expenditure on works before the appeal was heard.

2. When the noise to which the notice relates is caused in the course of the performance of a legal duty (e.g. by a statutory undertaker).

A notice *shall not be suspended*[108] where one or other of the above conditions are met if:

---

[103] Reg. 2(4).
[104] Reg. 2(5).
[105] Reg. 2(6).
[106] Reg. 2(7).
[107] Reg. 3(1).
[108] Reg. 3(2).

(a) the noise to which the notice relates

    (i) is injurious to health, or

    (ii) is likely to be of such a limited duration that suspension would render the notice of no practical effect; or

(b) any expenditure incurred on works before the hearing would not be disproportionate to the public benefit to be expected in that period. The notice must include a statement that it shall have effect notwithstanding any appeal to be determined by the Magistrates' Court.

The case of *Hammersmith London Borough Council v Magnum Automated Forecourts Ltd.*[109] is of value in considering the attitude of the courts on appeals. In this case the Court of Appeal granted an interlocutory injunction restraining a 24-hour taxi cab centre from operating between 11 p.m. and 7 a.m. The subject of residents' complaints involved taxis travelling to and from an automatic service centre at night, with noise arising from engines idling in the forecourt. The local authority served an abatement notice under the Control of Pollution Act 1974 requiring that within 28 days the company cease operations between 11 p.m. and 7 a.m. The notice contained the requisite statement[110] that it would not be suspended pending appeal. The defendant company did appeal and the appeal was not due to be heard for some time. In the meantime the night time activities continued as before. The local authority, however, decided that the situation could not continue and applied to the High Court for an injunction. Two proceedings were therefore being

---

[109] *Hammersmith London Borough Council v Magnum Automated Forecourts Ltd.* [1978] 1 W.L.R. 50, C.A.

[110] Reg. 10(2) of the Control of Noise (Appeals) Regulations 1975 states "that it shall have effect notwithstanding any appeal to a Magistrates' Court which has not been decided by the Court". These Regulations no longer apply to statutory nuisances, but to appeals in respect of notices served under ss. 60 and 66 of the Control of Pollution Act 1974. The Statutory Nuisance (Appeals) Regulations 1995, S.I. 1995 No. 2644 (in England and Wales), deal solely with appeals against abatement notices served under ss. 80 and 80A of the Environmental Protection Act 1990. Reg. 3(3) contains a similar requirement. The Statutory Nuisance (Appeals) (Scotland) Regulations 1996, S.I. 1996 No. 107, are almost identical, with appeals being made to the Sheriff Court.

taken. The defendant company's appeal came before the Magistrates first, who decided that the matter should be contested in the High Court. When the case came before the High Court, it was held that the Magistrates should decide the case. The Court of Appeal held:

1. Section 58(8)[111] of the Control of Pollution Act 1974 (the power to take High Court proceedings)[112] almost provided for this very contingency and seemed to cover the case. The injunction procedure was available even though there was an appeal to the Magistrates.

2. What required consideration was that the notice served by the council and not suspended should be enforced because it was the company's duty to comply with it unless and until the appeal succeeded.

3. The council had to be of the opinion that proceedings for failure to comply with the abatement notice would not supply an adequate remedy.

The injunction was granted. Interestingly, an injunction may differ from and be more extensive than the original notice.[113]

A person served with a notice who contravenes any requirement of the notice shall be guilty of an offence[114] unless he has a *reasonable excuse*.[115] If a local authority consider that proceedings for an

---

[111] Now repealed by the Environment Act 1995, s. 120(3), Sch. 24.

[112] Such proceedings would now be taken under the Environmental Protection Act 1990, s. 81(5). In Scotland, proceedings would be in any court of competent jurisdiction.

[113] *Lloyds Bank v Guardian Assurance plc* (1986) Lexis, 17th October.

[114] See Shaws form PA 71 – *Information* and PA 72 – *Summons*.

[115] s. 80(4). "Reasonable excuse" is not defined, but see:
Wellingborough District Council v Gordon (1990) I.S.S. J.P. 494; [1991] J.P.L. 874 D.C. – it was held that a birthday celebration was not a "reasonable excuse" sufficient to establish a defence to an allegation of noise nuisance contrary to the Control of Pollution Act 1974, s. 58(4). Steps taken to reduce the impact and irritation might be mitigating factors. In a subsequent related case, *Wellingborough District Council v Gordon* [1993] Env L.R. 218, it was held that the fact that the nuisance had occurred three years after the original notice had been served, with no intervening breach, was not a reasonable excuse. This was notwithstanding the fact that the noise occurred on only one

offence of failure to comply with a notice would afford an inadequate remedy, they may take proceedings in the High Court,[116] i.e. an injunction to secure the abatement, prohibition or restriction of the nuisance (this only applies where the noise is a nuisance, *not* where it is only likely to occur or recur). Proceedings are maintainable notwithstanding that the local authority has suffered no damage from the nuisance.

If the requirements of an abatement notice are not complied with, the local authority may do whatever is necessary to abate the nuisance,[117] without first taking proceedings in the Magistrates' Court. Costs incurred may be recovered except those shown to be unnecessary.[118] In proceedings to recover costs, the person in default cannot raise any question that could have been raised on appeal against the notice.

---

night, it was a special occasion, the neighbours had been invited, those who did not attend did not complain, and the only evidence of a breach of the notice was that of two local police officers (these factors might, of course, have been relevant to the primary question of whether the noise represented an actionable nuisance).

A. Lambert Flat Management Ltd. v Lomas Ltd. [1981] 2 All E.R. 280; [1981] 1 W.L.R. 898 D.C. – a matter that could have been raised on appeal against an abatement notice cannot constitute a reasonable excuse.

Saddleworth U.D.C. v Aggregate & Sand Ltd. (1970) 114 S.J. 931 – it was held that lack of finance was not a reasonable excuse for failing to comply with a nuisance order under s. 94, Public Health Act 1936.

Hope Butuyuyu v London Borough of Hammersmith and Fulham [1997] Env L.R. D13, Q.B.D. – it may include personal circumstances, e.g. illness (although the scope for this defence is very limited).

John Polychronakis v Richards & Jerrom Ltd. [1998] Env L.R. 346; [1998] J.P.L. B35, Q.B.D. – the defendant must first provide some evidence of a reasonable excuse. The prosecution must then prove, beyond all reasonable doubt, that it is not a reasonable one.

Failure to comply with an abatement notice in respect of industrial, trade or business premises is subject to a maximum penalty of £20,000. Otherwise, the penalty is a maximum fine not exceeding level 5 on the standard scale (currently £5,000 under the Criminal Justice Act 1991 and the Criminal Procedure (Scotland) Act 1995) and a daily penalty up to one-tenth of that level (currently £500).

[116] In Scotland, any court of competent jurisdiction.

[117] s. 81(3) or, in Scotland, whether or not proceedings have been taken for an offence.

[118] s. 81(4). The burden of proof will of course lie with the person alleging unnecessary expenditure.

Defences

The defences available to a person contravening any requirement of the notice are:

(a) the defendant had a reasonable excuse[119] for the contravention; or

(b) that the "best practicable means"[120] were used to prevent or counteract the effects of the nuisance; or

(c) the alleged offence was covered by a notice served under section 60 (control of noise on construction, etc. sites) or a consent given under section 61 (prior consent for work on construction sites) or under section 65 (approval to increase noise levels from premises subject to control in a Noise Abatement Zone) of the Control of Pollution Act 1974; or

(d) the alleged offence was committed at a time when the premises were subject to a notice under section 66 of the 1974 Act, and the level of noise was not such as to constitute a contravention of the notice under section 66;

(e) the alleged offence was committed at a time when the premises were not subject to a notice under section 66 of the 1974 Act (power to require reduction of noise levels in Noise Abatement Zone) and when a level fixed under section 67 (acceptable noise level from new or altered premises coming within a class covered by a Noise Abatement Order) was not exceeded at that time.

---

[119] *Saddleworth U.D.C. v Aggregate & Sand* (1970) 114 S.J. 931 held that lack of finance was not a reasonable excuse and that it would be difficult to rely on the advice of an independent expert as a defence when his recommendations had not been fully implemented. *Wellingborough Borough Council v Gordon* (1990) I.S.S. J.P. 494; [1991] J.P.L. 874 D.C. – considerations such as previous good behaviour and the frequency, intensity and time of the noise could be taken into account in deciding whether a nuisance had occurred, but they did not contribute to the defence of "reasonable excuse". These were matters of mitigation. In this case, birthday celebrations were held not to be a "reasonable excuse" for noise caused by loud reggae music, air horns and whistles. See also footnotes at pp. 67 and 68.

[120] Defined in s. 79(9). This defence is only available in respect of nuisance arising on industrial, trade or business premises.

Paragraphs (d) and (e) apply whether or not the relevant notice was subject to appeal at the time when the offence was alleged to have been committed.

An appeal can be made against any decision of a Magistrates' Court (other than a decision made in criminal proceedings), to the Crown Court. Any party to the proceedings can take this action.[121]

Duties imposed by law

The test of "best practicable means" in relation to undertakings with statutory duties is applicable "... only so far as compatible with any duty imposed by law";[122] "... only so far as compatible with safety and safe working conditions, and with the exigencies of any emergency or unforeseeable circumstances".[123]

In the case of *London Borough of Camden v London Underground Ltd.*,[124] statutory immunity was unsuccessfully claimed under the Railways Act 1993 which privatised the railways. In particular, reliance was placed on section 122 which provided that, in connection with specified operations, the operator has a defence of statutory authority "in any proceedings whether civil or criminal, in nuisance". In accordance with principles developed in case law, this is not usually an absolute defence. It can only be relied on if the person seeking to invoke it can show the use of reasonable diligence.

For the purpose of controlling noise, the "area" of a local authority which includes part of the seashore also includes the territorial sea lying seawards from that part of the shore.[125] References to premises and occupier include respectively a vessel and its master. This will allow control of noise from hovercraft, pleasure boats, motor boats, etc.

---

[121] Schedule 3.1(3).

[122] Environmental Protection Act 1990, s. 79(9)(c).

[123] *Ibid*, s. 79(9)(d). The specific reference to "statutory undertakers" no longer appears in the statutory provisions of the Act, although it still appears in relation to the noise provisions of the Control of Pollution Act 1974.

[124] ENDS Report 3000, January 2000, D.C. (15th December 1999). This was a provisional judgment.

[125] s. 79(11) of the Environmental Protection Act 1990.

INVESTIGATION OF COMPLAINTS

Most complaints of environmental noise are received by local authorities, and investigation and subsequent proceedings are initiated by Environmental Health Officers. It is probably reasonable to categorise the type of noises generally subject to complaint in respect of which the Environmental Health Officer is empowered to act, as follows:

1. Industrial noise – primarily factories.

2. Entertainment noise – discotheques, fairgrounds, concerts, etc.

3. Noise of human origin – record players, parties, structural alterations in domestic premises, self service garages, etc.

4. Animal noises – barking dogs, bleating goats, crowing cockerels, etc.

   (In the case of 2, 3 and 4 – see Chapter 3.)

Noise from construction type works, aircraft and road traffic are considered later in this book.

The general approach to investigation is basically the same but the assessment of results varies according to the category of noise. The intermittent nature of human and animal noise can present particular difficulties that are discussed in this chapter.

The first indication of a noise nuisance is usually a complaint from a member of the public. There are a number of important factors to consider which dictate the nature of the information that the investigating officer will seek to obtain. These are the common law principles stated earlier.[126] To satisfy these requirements he will interview the complainant to ascertain:

(a) the nature of the noise – continuous, intermittent, frequency characteristics (rumble, whistle, whine, clatter, etc.);

(b) the duration of the noise – when it started, time periods, day or

---

[126] See pp. 39–50 *ante*.

night time problem, if it is seasonal only;

(c) the effects of the noise – how does it affect occupation of the house, does it interfere with sleep, cause lack of concentration, headaches or other physical symptoms, interfere with communications;

(d) the number of people affected – the question of whether a nuisance is public or private is irrelevant as far as statutory noise nuisance is concerned, but it is essential to ascertain the extent of the effects of the noise to ensure that reasonable doubt as to the existence of a nuisance is not shown in subsequent proceedings, whether informal or statutory. It is therefore essential to establish the number of people affected in the household and surrounding area. This will usually involve:

  (i) interviewing the occupants of properties in the area in relation to the above matters; and

  (ii) often requesting that questionnaires be completed in detail concerning instances of excessive noise over a predetermined period following the initial investigation. This may give the officer a clearer picture of the type of noise monitoring exercise he needs to carry out to substantiate the complaints. This is not always entirely successful but is a useful approach.

Noise monitoring

The results of interviews will often establish in the mind of the officer the kind of noise source he has to investigate and, in many cases, it will be clear from the outset that he will be seeking to control specific sources such as drop forging, internal traffic movements or material handling. It is often desirable to consult with the person responsible at the earliest opportunity, as a relatively simple remedy may resolve the problem without committing a lot of time to investigations. However, the most serious noise problems are usually the most intractable and require intensive investigation and noise monitoring. The officer will need to confirm the statements of complainants and he will need to measure and record the noise during the relevant times. His own subjective feelings are extremely important as not all people respond in the same way to similar sounds and the experience and expert opinion of the Environmental Health Officer will enable him to judge whether the complainant's adverse reactions are justified. The trained human ear is undoubtedly the best judge of a noise nuisance but it is also important to consider the measured level of noise and the frequency characteristics of the sound if it is to be reduced to an acceptable level.

To help identification of a noise, especially where the environment is made up of a number of different and complex sounds (e.g. a factory may emit sound from such items of equipment as air conditioning systems, electrical equipment, manufacturing machinery, materials handling, traffic and public address systems), the use of a sound level meter is important. This will enable measurements of the noise to be taken to assess it against the "background"[127] noise and against any future improvements that may be made. It is usual to measure the background noise so that a more scientific assessment can be made as to whether the noise is likely to constitute a nuisance. Most investigations involve an assessment carried out in accordance with British Standard 4142:1997 *Method of Rating Industrial Noise affecting mixed residential and industrial areas.* This standard is intended as a guide to the method of measuring a noise, together with the procedures for predicting whether the noise in question is likely to give rise to complaints. For this reason it is invariably used by local authorities and consultants as an indication of whether complaints are justified. Whilst it is a useful guide, *it may only support complaints in a limited number of cases* and should not be relied on totally. It is of no use in trying to convince an aggrieved person that their complaints are unjustified.[128] The common law tests must be

---

[127] "Background" noise is defined in British Standard 4142:1997.

[128] A number of cases have been decided involving consideration of both this standard and/or those of the World Health Organisation, viz. *Milka v Chetwynd Animal By-Products (1995) Ltd.*, Unreported, Carmarthen County Court, 19 January 2000 – in this private action the judge considered expert evaluations of noise based both on BS4142:1997 and the 1980 World Health Organisation Environmental Health Criteria. He decided that the experts' measurements showed that the guidelines were being met, and the plaintiffs

applied in all cases. Measurement of noise will usually involve the following procedures:

(a) setting up a sound level meter (inside and/or outside the affected dwellings);

(b) measurement of the background noise levels;

(c) recording of the noise subject to complaint for a sufficiently representative period to establish a nuisance. This will usually involve the attendance of the investigating officer to record specific details of the noise, its characteristics and duration.[129]

During this period a subjective impression will be formed as to the source and its nuisance value. It is extremely important to be able to specify the local authority's requirements to abate a nuisance and therefore sufficiently detailed analysis often has to be carried out to determine the precise source, its frequency content, intermittency and duration, and the degree of attenuation necessary. This may involve use of the following additional equipment:

(a) magnetic tape recording – this is of special value for noises which are not constant for sufficient time to allow direct on-site analysis. Digital audio tape is frequently used for nuisance recording. This can be transferred to disks for detailed computer analysis;

(b) graphic level recorders – these allow continuous observations

---

had not proved otherwise, and therefore concluded that even at night the noise was insufficient to amount to a nuisance.

In *Murdoch and Another v Glacier Metal Co. Ltd., The Times, 21 January 1998*, reference was made in this civil action to the 1980 World Health Organisation Environmental Health Criteria. The original trial judge had concluded that the measured noise levels at night were the same as, or marginally above, the W.H.O. recommended levels. However, he took account of other considerations in concluding that the noise was not sufficient to amount to a nuisance. The Court of Appeal upheld this decision.

[129] *R. v Fenny Stratford Justices, ex parte Watney Mann (Midlands) Ltd.* [1976] 2 All E.R. 888; [1976] 1 W.L.R. 1101 – in this case involving noise from the juke box of a public house, the justices specified a maximum noise level of 70 dB. It was held that the nuisance order was imprecise because it did not say where the noise was to be measured. If noise levels are specified in an abatement notice, they must be precise enough to be meaningful.

of the variation of a noise with time and allow analysis to be carried out more quickly;

(c) broad band analysis – using octave and one-third octave filters connected to a sound level meter. This may enable the determination of the main frequencies where noise nuisance exists and therefore acts as a guide to the type of sound attenuation required.

Frequency analysis of a noise enables assessment of its subjective characteristics to be made in two respects – its general character and its loudness. The frequency spectrum will give an idea of its general character – whether it is low pitched or high pitched or contains identifiable single-frequency components. Frequency analysis allows comparison of the noise subject to complaint with the offending machinery or equipment.

Whilst this approach may be time consuming it is often required to identify the annoying components of the noise so that the correct remedial works can be required bearing in mind the need to reduce noise to an acceptable level whilst having regard to the "best practicable means" defence (i.e. it is of no value asking for an exceptionally high degree of sound attenuation if a lesser standard will resolve the problem).

It should be emphasised that it is the experience of the investigating officer which is paramount in assessing nuisance and the use of these investigation techniques is to support his assessment and to enable him not only to justify any legal action, but also to specify remedial measures either informally or in a statutory notice.

REGULATION OF INVESTIGATORY POWERS ACT 2000

This legislation, which is particularly relevant to noise nuisance investigations, was enacted partly as a result of the surge in communications technology, and to protect human rights following the coming into force of the Human Rights Act 1998. Section 6 of the 1998 Act is arguably the most significant, making it unlawful for a public authority to act in a manner which is incompatible with a Convention right. In the case of statutory nuisances, Article 8 of the Convention stipulating the right to respect for private and family life is that most likely to be invoked.

When investigating a noise complaint, local authorities will generally carry out monitoring and recording of noise levels. Whether Article 8 is contravened will be dependent on whether surveillance is being undertaken. This is defined in the Regulation of Investigatory Powers Act 2000[130] as including "monitoring, observing or listening to persons ... their conversations or their activities or communications". It also includes "recording anything monitored, observed or listened to in the course of surveillance". Activities not authorised under the Act are unlawful under section 6 of the Human Rights Act 1998 and accordingly any evidence collected in an unauthorised way may be inadmissible in a court of law.

Part II of the 2000 Act may apply to local authority investigations, although the Act is intended primarily to be associated with police, security services and H.M. Customs and Excise activities. The Act applies to directed surveillance; intrusive surveillance; and the conduct and use of covert human intelligence sources.[131]

"Directed surveillance" is defined as covert[132] but not intrusive, when undertaken as a specific investigation or operation and carried out in such a way as to make it likely that private information is obtained about a person. "Private information" in relation to a person, includes any information relating to his private or family life.[133] "Surveillance" includes monitoring, observing or listening to persons and any recordings made as a result of such activities.[134]

Noise investigations involving residents would appear to be included in this definition when conducted covertly. Whether the evidence obtained is private information is not clear. It might be argued that information merely confirming the existence of excessive noise is not intrusive. Whether such evidence is information relating to family or private life may have to be determined by the courts.[135]

---

[130] s. 48.
[131] s. 26(1).
[132] s. 26(2).
[133] s. 26(10).
[134] s. 48(2).
[135] There is no case law on this issue.

"Directed surveillance" must be authorised in each case by a "designated person", i.e. an Assistant Chief Officer or an officer responsible for the management of an investigation.[136] Authorisation must be obtained for each investigation. Numerous complaints over a short time period, e.g. during weekend/night-time party patrols, may place a significant administrative burden on the local authority and its officers.

"Intrusive surveillance" is covert surveillance if it is carried out in relation to anything taking place on any residential premises or in any private vehicle; and involves the presence of an individual on the premises or in the vehicle or is carried out by means of a surveillance device.[137]

The Act also says that surveillance is not intrusive if carried out without that device being present on the premises or vehicle, unless it consistently provides information of the same quality and detail as might be expected if the device was actually present on the premises or vehicle.[138]

It is important to distinguish between the two types of surveillance, as intrusive surveillance by local authorities is not authorised by the 2000 Act. Whether a noise monitoring device operated in the investigation of a noise problem represents surveillance for the purposes of the Act is not clear cut but, if it were deemed intrusive, the evidence obtained by it may not be authorised by the Act and therefore may be inadmissible in court. If this were to be the case,

---

[136] Regulation of Investigatory Powers (Prescription of Officers, Ranks and Positions) Order 2000, S.I. 2000 No. 2417.

[137] s. 26(3).

[138] s. 26(5). This point was not considered in *Lambie v Thanet D.C.* [2001] E.H.L.R. 3, Langley J., Q.B.D. in a case where the manager of a public house appealed against a notice served by the local authority under s. 80 of the Environmental Protection Act 1990. The notice requiring the abatement of a noise nuisance required, amongst other things, that a local authority officer be allowed to set up a sound restricting device to ensure that the noise did not exceed a specified level as measured in any residential premises. The appeal was dismissed, partly on the grounds that s. 80(1)(b) of the Act was a wide one and could legitimately include a requirement to allow an officer to enter premises (and presumably it may be implied that no problem was found with the idea of measuring noise on the premises and restricting its upper limit).

it could make it very difficult to prove nuisance to the standards of evidence required by the courts. The covert use of tape recordings which record the actual sounds produced could equally well be intrusive surveillance, the undertaking of which by local authorities is prohibited. Similarly, the use of covert human intelligence may also present problems, e.g. using complainants to keep records or "noise diaries" recording their neighbours' activities. As the Regulation of Investigatory Powers Act 2000 was primarily intended to regulate the activities of services more dependent on surveillance, it is not clear whether the type of noise monitoring work undertaken by local authorities was fully considered. If the Act proves a stumbling block to the effective investigation of noise problems, it may require future amendment.

INDIVIDUAL'S RIGHT TO TAKE PROCEEDINGS UNDER THE 1990 ACT

The Environmental Health Officers' Association[139] in its memorandum of evidence to the Noise Advisory Council[140] suggested that the provision requiring three aggrieved persons to invoke the provisions of the Noise Abatement Act 1960 in the Magistrates' Court be repealed. This was sensible as experience showed that many circumstances existed where only one or two people were likely to be affected by noise.

Section 82 of the Environment Protection Act 1990 now provides the right for summary proceedings to be instituted by any aggrieved person[141] in cases of noise which amounts to a nuisance.[142] The nuisance must exist or be likely to recur. *Similar proceedings cannot be taken in respect of a noise likely to occur* and, if a nuisance is likely to occur, the matter should be referred to the local authority for action under sections 79 and 80 of the Environmental

[139] Now the Chartered Institute of Environmental Health.
[140] Published in *Neighbourhood Noise*, Noise Advisory Council, 1971, H.M.S.O. The Council was abolished as a Government quango in the early 1980s.
[141] *Sandwell Metropolitan Borough Council v Bujok* [1990] 3 All E.R. 385 – a person whose own health, or that of his family, is being prejudiced by the nuisance would be a person aggrieved.
[142] The right to take summary proceedings is of course in addition to the individual's common law right in the civil courts.

Protection Act 1990. Where a nuisance exists, proceedings can be taken against the person responsible or, if that person cannot be found, against the owner or occupier of the premises from which the noise is emitted or would be emitted.

Procedure for complaint

The aggrieved person must make a complaint to a Magistrate[143] (in Scotland a summary application to the Sheriff) and, if it is shown that a *prima facie* case exists, a summons may be issued.[144] Before instituting proceedings, the aggrieved person must issue a written notice of intention to bring the proceedings.[145]

The Magistrates have discretion under section 16 of the Prosecution of Offences Act 1985 to award costs to the defendant in the case of an unsuccessful prosecution and therefore the complainant would be liable to pay these if his action failed.

If the court is satisfied at the hearing that the nuisance exists, or although abated is likely to recur, the court must make an order requiring the defendant to abate the nuisance within a specified time and/or to prohibit its recurrence and to execute any necessary works within a specified time. A fine not exceeding level 5 on the standard scale may also be imposed.[146] Contravention of the order without "reasonable excuse" is an offence[147] but the defence of "best practicable means" exists[148] where the nuisance arises on industrial, trade or business premises, or from a vehicle, machinery or equipment in a street.[149]

Where a person is convicted of an offence, the court[150] can, after giving the local authority the opportunity of being heard, direct the authority to carry out anything that it has power to require the

---

[143] See Shaws form EPA 34.

[144] See Shaws form EPA 35.

[145] Environmental Protection Act 1990, s. 82(6). See Shaws form EPA 33.

[146] Currently £5,000 under the Criminal Justice Act 1991.

[147] Subject to a fine not exceeding level 5 on the standard scale and a daily penalty for non-compliance of one-tenth of that level (currently £500).

[148] Environmental Protection Act 1990, s. 82(10).

[149] In Scotland, a road.

[150] In Scotland, the Sheriff.

defendant to do. The court can also award costs against the
defendant. If a person fails to comply with a court order, the
magistrates' court[151] may, after giving the local authority an
opportunity to be heard, direct the authority to take the steps
required by the order.[152]

In either case, costs can be recovered from the person in default,
except any that the defaulting person shows to be unnecessary.[153]

As proceedings under section 82 are criminal in nature (by virtue
of the power to fine, and the initiation of proceedings by summons),
the standard of proof is that required for a criminal prosecution
rather than that for a civil claim.[154] In the case of *Lewisham London
Borough Council v Fenner*,[155] the noise from a humidifier at a local
authority swimming pool kept the complainant awake at night and
he was treated for depression. The complainant won his case in the
magistrates' court but the local authority appealed the decision.
Although the court felt that sleeplessness amounts to an injury to
health, it found against the complainant both on the grounds of
"prejudicial to health" and "nuisance" in respect of statutory
nuisance under section 79. In relation to "nuisance", the court
applied the ordinary principles of private law nuisance. It considered
evidence of other people affected by the noise and that of technical
experts. The court thought it important that the noise fell a long way
below the threshold of 30-40 decibels recommended for intrusive
noise in BS8233 and this was considered important in respect of
both section 79 grounds. So, even though the court accepted the
noise had affected the complainant's health and caused considerable
annoyance to another neighbour, it concluded that, as the noise fell
well below advisory standards, it could not be satisfied that the
criminal burden of proof had been established.[156] In another case,[157]

---

[151] In Scotland, the Sheriff.

[152] Environmental Protection Act 1990, s. 82(11).

[153] *Ibid*, s. 82(12) and (13).

[154] *Lewisham London Borough Council v Fenner* (1995) ENDS Report 248,
p. 44, Knightsbridge Crown Court.

[155] *Ibid*.

[156] There did appear to be inconsistencies in the findings in fact and the eventual
conclusions of the court!

[157] *Bonnell v Murphy* [1995] J.P.L. 470.

a private prosecution was brought under section 82 in respect of the constant barking of dogs and the disturbance caused by children riding small motor bikes in a neighbour's garden. The magistrates decided both matters constituted a statutory nuisance and issued a prohibition order. The defendant was ordered to pay £10,000 prosecution costs.

NOISE AT NIGHT

The Environmental Protection Act 1990 provided streamlined powers to deal with complaints of excessive noise but concerns about the effectiveness of existing legislation to deal with problems of neighbour noise led to the establishment of the Neighbour Noise Working Party in 1994. Having considered concerns about the time that could be taken to deal with complaints under the statutory nuisance procedure, the working party recommended that consideration be given to a specific night noise offence and clarification of the powers to confiscate noise-making equipment. The result was the Noise Act 1996.[158]

The night-time noise offence is additional to and complements the existing statutory nuisance controls, to produce a quick remedy to problems of night-time noise from dwellings. It does not alter the statutory nuisance process. It introduces permitted levels for new night time noise offences, but the circular[159] accompanying the Act says that such levels should not be taken as an indicator of whether or not noise is a statutory nuisance. It is possible that noise which is not an offence under the 1996 Act may nevertheless be prejudicial to health or a common law nuisance, and so may be a statutory nuisance.

The summary procedure for dealing with noise at night may be adopted by any local authority in England and Wales, but it must adopt it for its whole area, give not less than three months' notice of the commencement date, and publish the relevant details in a

---

[158] The Act came into force in two stages, being fully operative on 23rd July 1997. It does not extend to Scotland. It applies to Northern Ireland with certain modifications and omissions in s. 14.

[159] DOE Circular 8/97, Welsh Office Circular 41/97, 23rd July 1997.

Noise nuisance

local newspaper.[160] The Act is not mandatory, but the Secretary of State may make an order requiring a local authority to apply it.

Once the powers are adopted, a local authority must take reasonable steps to investigate a complaint of noise from a dwelling at night, if the complaint is made by any individual present in a dwelling[161] during night hours that excessive noise is being emitted from another dwelling.[162] The complainant does not have to be the occupier.

Warning notices

If the authority's investigating officer is satisfied that noise is being emitted from the offending dwelling during night hours, and the noise, if it were measured from within the complainant's dwelling, would or might exceed the *permitted level*,[163] a "warning notice" may be served.[164] A warning notice must state that the authority's officer considers that noise is being emitted from the offending dwelling during night hours and that the noise exceeds, or may exceed, the permitted level, as measured from within the complainant's dwelling, and give warning that any person who is responsible for the noise in the period specified in the notice may be guilty of an offence. The period specified in the warning notice must begin not earlier than ten minutes after the time when the notice is served and end with the following 7.00 a.m.[165] The warning notice must be served on any person appearing to be responsible for the noise at or near the offending dwelling, or by leaving it at the offending dwelling if the responsible person cannot be ascertained. It must also state the time of service.

---

[160] s. 1.
[161] Unlike the requirement with regard to statutory nuisance, the complainant does not have to be living in the area.
[162] s. 2. "Dwelling" is defined in s. 11. "Night hours" are between 11.00 p.m. and 7.00 a.m. (s. 2(6)).
[163] Permitted levels are specified in directions issued by the Secretary of State in accordance with ss. 5 and 6 of the Act and detailed in the Annex to DOE Circular 8/97. The type of measuring devices to be used and their method of use are also detailed.
[164] s. 3.
[165] s. 3(1), (2) and (3).

Unlike statutory nuisance cases, there is no requirement for a local authority to inspect its area from time to time to detect matters actionable under this Act but the authority must ensure[166] that an officer takes reasonable steps to investigate a complaint. Individual authorities need to decide the arrangements appropriate to their area, based on an assessment of their local needs and circumstances. Different arrangements may be appropriate, e.g.:

(a) officers on standby at central locations;

(b) call-out systems from officers' homes;

(c) use of independent experts on contract to the authority, with the relevant delegated powers to act.

Noise measurement

Those involved need to be skilled in noise measurement, the application of the law, and to be competent in dealing with potentially sensitive situations. Well established liaison procedures with the police authority may be necessary when dealing with some noise complaints. The police may be needed to support the local authority, either in the provision of information or by providing a police presence where violence is anticipated or threatened, or a breach of the peace is likely. The Chartered Institute of Environmental Health has produced valuable advice on such liaison arrangements.[167]

If excessive noise above the permitted level is emitted without reasonable excuse after a warning notice has been served, the *person responsible*[168] is guilty of an offence.[169]

Interestingly, there is no requirement for the investigating officer to measure the noise at the time of the initial investigation. In deciding

---

[166] s. 2(1).
[167] *Noise Liaison Guide – Good Practice for Police and Local Authority Co-operation*, 1997.
[168] s. 4(1) and (2). The "person responsible" is "a person to whose act, default or sufferance the emission of the noise is wholly or partly attributable". This need not necessarily be the person on whom the warning notice was served.
[169] s. 4(3). Subject to a fine not exceeding level 3 on the standard scale if found guilty.

whether or not the noise complained of exceeds, or might exceed, the permitted level, it is for the officer to decide whether to assess the noise from within or outside the complainant's dwelling and whether or not to use any noise measuring device. In many cases, however, the officer will no doubt wish to assess the situation by reference to the "permitted level".[170] If an officer decides, by judgement or by taking noise measurements, that the noise complained of does not exceed the permitted level, or he decides that the noise cannot be measured, or where he feels that action under the Act is inappropriate, he may nevertheless be satisfied that the noise is a statutory nuisance under the Environmental Protection Act 1990 (e.g. by virtue of its tonal character or intermittency). If so, the local authority is under a duty to serve an abatement notice under section 80 of that Act.

Offences

In proceedings for an offence of failing to comply with a warning notice, evidence of measurements, the devices used and the circumstances of measurement may be given by production of a document signed by a local authority officer.[171]

Where an appropriately authorised local authority officer believes that an offence has been, or is being, committed, he can offer the offender the option of discharging liability to conviction by service of a fixed penalty notice.[172] The penalty notice may be given by delivering it to the person or leaving it addressed to him at the offending dwelling.[173] Where notice has been served, proceedings for the offence cannot be instituted for 14 days from service and, if the person pays the fixed penalty within 14 days, he cannot be convicted of the offence.[174] The fixed penalty is £100 and the Secretary of State has the power to change the sum by order. The fixed penalty notice must contain specified information[175] and the

---

[170] See s. 5. Also DOE Circular 8/97, paras 33–41, and Annex to the Circular.
[171] s. 7 and DOE Circular 8/97, paras 42–46 set out precise details.
[172] s. 8(1).
[173] s. 8(2).
[174] s. 8(3).
[175] s. 8(4) and (5).

Secretary of State may specify the form of such notices. He has not done so but the Chartered Institute of Environmental Health has suggested a form of notice. The Act provides for the payment arrangements for fixed penalty notices.

If a fixed penalty notice is issued in respect of noise emitted from a dwelling in any period specified in the warning notice, and noise continues above the permitted level during the same period, no further fixed penalty notice can be served but a person may be convicted of a further offence in respect of noise emitted from the dwelling after the fixed penalty notice is served and before the end of the specified period. Such proceedings can follow without service of a further warning notice. In any event, in cases of persistent or gross noise making, or large scale parties or raves, prosecutions, which can attract penalties of up to £1,000, might be more appropriate.

Power of entry and seizure of equipment

The Act provides a power[176] to enter a dwelling where there is reason to believe excessive noise is still being emitted. Where entry is refused or apprehended, or a request for entry would defeat the object of entry, a magistrates' warrant may be obtained authorising entry by force if necessary.

A similar power of seizure exists as that available under the statutory nuisance provisions of the Environmental Protection Act 1990. In cases where a warning notice has been served, and the noise emitted from the premises has exceeded the permitted level during the specified period, the authority may seize and remove the noise-making equipment that is being, or has been, used in the emission of noise in excess of the permitted level. Where entry is refused or apprehended, a warrant for entry can be sought by application to a Justice of the Peace. In the case of statutory nuisances, 24 hours' notice of intended entry must be given to carry out seizure without a warrant. This requirement does not apply to night-time noise offences under the Noise Act 1996.

---

[176] s. 10.

The Schedule to the Act describes the powers of the local authority in respect of the retention, return, forfeiture and disposal of seized noise equipment.[177] Any seized equipment may be retained for up to 28 days from the date of seizure or, if it is equipment related to legal proceedings commenced within that period, it can be retained until sentencing or the discontinuance of proceedings.[178] Seized equipment cannot be retained if a person has been given a fixed penalty notice, the equipment was seized because of its use after a fixed penalty notice was served and the fixed penalty has been paid within the required period.

On conviction for a noise offence, a court can order the confiscation of any related equipment. The court must have regard to the value of the equipment and the likely financial and other effects on the offender. A forfeiture order deprives the offender of any rights over the equipment. Within six months of the forfeiture order being made, another person may lay claim to the equipment, subject to conditions[179] that he had not consented to the offender having possession of the equipment or did not know or suspect that the equipment was likely to be used in the commission of a noise offence. Under the circumstances, a magistrates' court may order the equipment to be delivered to the applicant if he appears to be the owner. If no such order has been made within six months of the forfeiture order, the local authority may dispose of the equipment.

If, in proceedings for a noise offence, no forfeiture order is made, the court may give such directions as to the return, retention or disposal of the equipment by the responsible local authority as it sees fit.[180]

Part V of the Housing Act 1996 complements the nuisance provisions of the Noise Act 1996 and the Environmental Protection Act 1990 in respect of statutory nuisance. It contains provision for landlords to deal with anti-social behaviour from tenants. Landlords have the power to evict tenants for behaviour likely to cause a nuisance. Such powers have been used by numerous authorities to evict noisy

---

[177] See also DOE Circular 8/97, paras 64–77.
[178] Sch. to the Act, art. 2(1).
[179] *Ibid*, art. 4.
[180] *Ibid*, art. 5.

and troublesome families and individuals. Where the noise is deliberately caused to intimidate or harass people, it may be appropriate to involve the police as they have investigatory powers under the Protection from Harassment Act 1997.

MEDIATION IN NOISE DISPUTES

There is a national and international move towards the use of mediation as a potentially more amicable way of resolving noise disputes than legal proceedings. Mediation, involving a neutral third person, has been used to aid the process of negotiation between conflicting parties. Its use in dealing with neighbour noise disputes has probably been adopted in the United Kingdom since the mid 1980s.

Mediation schemes may form an element of a local authority's system for managing noise complaints and may receive funding from the authority. Such schemes offer their services through trained volunteer mediators. Noise counselling is usually just one of their functions.[181] Mediation is usually face-to-face between the parties in conflict or indirectly through the trained volunteers. It is reported[182] that in the cases where mediation is attempted, the success rate, i.e. where agreement is reached or there is a substantial improvement in the situation, averages at least 59%.

The largest mediation service[183] has a membership of over 500 organisations and individuals who offer this type of facility. They dealt with around 16,000 requests in 2000/01, 45% of which related to problems of noise. Most of those involved noise from D.I.Y. activities, noisy children or music. Mediation has even involved whole streets where noisy and unruly children have annoyed a neighbourhood. Considerable mediation work is done in close liaison with local authorities who make financial contributions to this work or even provide their own services.[184] Indeed, 50% of

---

[181] Others include victim-offender issues, planning disputes, school exclusions, workplace and education needs problems.
[182] Mediation UK Annual Report 2001.
[183] Mediation UK. For the role of mediation in planning matters, see p. 384.
[184] Birmingham City Council, for example, have a dedicated team of mediators dealing with disputes involving their 88,000 council houses.

referrals to mediation services are from local authority housing departments and housing associations.

Mediation is a possible alternative where an aggrieved individual has no wish to pursue action to resolve a noise nuisance by legal means. However, the future of such schemes will depend heavily on long term funding from local authorities, charitable trusts and other sources.

Chapter 3

NOISE IN PUBLIC PLACES

The Noise Advisory Council report *Neighbourhood Noise* referred collectively to "neighbourhood noise" as including all noise except that arising from road traffic and aircraft, and industrial noise affecting workers.[1] Other chapters in this book deal with specific major sources of noise; this one deals collectively with a miscellany of noise problems which usually occur in places frequented by the public. It includes noise from places of entertainment, recreational activities, "country noises", noise from neighbours and public affrays. A number of the matters dealt with may often be controllable under local byelaws or specific Acts of Parliament. Byelaws can be more effective as they can be used to deal with transient noise that it may be impossible to show is a nuisance at common law (and therefore statutory law) but which does cause disturbance. However, the circumstances of each case should be considered carefully in deciding which is the most appropriate course of action.

It is not intended to deal in depth with behaviour at processions, demonstrations and public meetings. These activities may result in disturbance from noise and there are statutory law offences concerning affrays,[2] riot,[3] harassment, alarm or distress[4] and conduct likely to result in a breach of the peace.[5]

Noise from neighbours is now the greatest source of noise nuisance and public complaint. The extent of the problem can be shown by:

1. A survey was conducted by the Building Research Establishment

---

[1] *Neighbourhood Noise,* Noise Advisory Council, 1972, paras. 54 and 55, page 11.
[2] Defined in s. 3, Public Order Act 1986.
[3] Defined in s. 1, Public Order Act 1986.
[4] Defined in s. 5, Public Order Act 1986.
[5] See also Public Order Act 1986, s. 4, concerning fear or provocation of violence, also the Public Meeting Act 1908, s. 1, concerning disorderly behaviour at a lawful meeting, and the Public Order Act 1986, ss. 12, 13 and 14 regarding the imposition of conditions on, or prohibition of, public processions/assemblies.

on behalf of the Department for Environment, Food and Rural Affairs[6] to:

- track changes in community attitudes to environmental noise in England and Wales between 1991[7] and 1999;

- to obtain the best possible estimate of attitudes to environmental noise in the U.K. for 1999/2000.

A total of 2,876 interviews were conducted, 21% of respondents reported that noise spoilt their home life to some extent, with 8% reporting that their home life was spoilt either "quite a lot" or "totally". 18% reported noise as one of the top five from a list of environmental problems that personally affected them. 81% of respondents heard noise from neighbours and/or other people nearby and 26% reported being adversely affected by noise from this source (up from 21% in the 1991 survey). There were also increases in the proportion of people adversely affected by people's voices, children, radio/TV/hi-fi, and lawn-mowers. Unsurprisingly, the evening (1900hrs–2300hrs) and night time (2300hrs–0700hrs) periods were the times when the greatest proportion of respondents reported being particularly bothered, annoyed or disturbed by neighbour noise.

2. The number of noise complaints made to local authorities has risen considerably since the mid 1970s. In 1976, 6,325 complaints were made. By 2000/2001 this had risen to 238,525. Of this total, 169,810 complaints were of domestic noise, 5,172 about vehicles and 6,501 concerned equipment in streets.[8] A study of domestic noise complaints[9] revealed that amplified

---

[6] *The U.K. National Noise Attitude Survey 1999/2000*, Grimwood, C.J., Skinner, C.J., Raw, G.J., Building Research Establishment, May 2002.

[7] The 1991 results of a similar survey were published in Grimwood, C.J., *Effects of environmental noise on people at home*, B.R.E. Information Paper IP 22/93, 1993.

[8] Figures provided by the Chartered Institute of Environmental Health for this period, although only 249 (66%) of local authorities responded to the relevant survey. Between 1986 and 1996 the total number of domestic noise complaints trebled, although a levelling off of complaints occurred post 1996.

[9] *Domestic Noise Complaints – furthering our understanding of the issues involved in neighbourhood noise disputes*, Grimwood, C., Ling, M., B.R.E. Report No. 204732, December 1999.

music was the main source, with the most common secondary sources being noisy parties and barking dogs.

Interestingly, only a small proportion (less than 10%) of respondents complained to their local authority. This suggests that the *real level of domestic noise complaints may well exceed 1.5 million per year*, rather than the figures reported by local authorities to the Chartered Institute of Environmental Health.

NUISANCES UNDER LAW

The principles which govern proceedings for nuisance under common or statutory law are considered in Chapter 2. It is important to ensure that the criteria applicable to these proceedings can be met.

A number of cases concerning statutory proceedings in respect of neighbourhood noise are of interest:

Noise from community centre

In a case taken by Newcastle M.D.C. in 1975,[10] proceedings were taken under the Noise Abatement Act 1960 in respect of noise from a "jazz band" which practised in a community centre on two evenings each week between 6.00 p.m. and 8.00 p.m. and occasionally on Saturday mornings. An abatement notice was served which resulted in a temporary reduction in noise but further complaints were subsequently received. The principal cause of nuisance was the bass drum. Sound level measurements were not taken as it was believed that no useful purpose would be served by measurement – a view reiterated by the Judge in his summing up in the Crown Court! The Magistrates found the case proved and made a nuisance order. On appeal the Judge referred to the case of *Christie v. Davey*[11] where 17 hours of music lessons a week were not held to be a nuisance.[12] The judge concluded "one cannot expect

---

[10] Reported under "Court decision confuses noise nuisance position", *Municipal Engineering,* 16th Jan. 1976, pp. 93/94.

[11] *Christie v Davey* (1893) 1 Ch. 316.

[12] However, the carrying on of music lessons has been held to be a nuisance in the cases of *Waterfield v Goodwin* (1955) 105 L.J. 332 and *Hartland v Mottershead* (1956) 106 L.J. 269.

quiet from a community hall but the noise should not be a substantial interference with the comfort and enjoyment of the surrounding residents in their homes. Has it been proved to be a substantial interference? It is obviously an interference but some things we are bound to put up with, for instance, aeroplanes and bellringers. The question is, what is reasonable in all the circumstances in the case? Is it reasonable to expect residents to accept the amount of noise for the period of time for which it exists to come from the community hall? ... Looking at the expressions used by the witnesses such as 'obtrusive', 'they practise for an hour', 'unsettling', 'interference with our peace and quiet' we have concluded that the extent of the noise is not so unreasonable as to not expect the occupiers of the neighbouring property to suffer it." The court did not consider that substantial interference existed and discharged the nuisance order.

Music nuisance from public entertainment[13]

A case arising from action taken by Babergh District Council[14] under the Control of Pollution Act 1974 followed from the service of a notice under section 58[15] in response to the complainants' representations concerning the regular playing of live or recorded music at an adjacent public house. An appeal was lodged in the Magistrates' Court under the Control of Noise (Appeals) Regulations 1975 on three grounds:

(a) the notice was not justified by the terms of section 58;

(b) the requirements of the notice were unreasonable in character or extent, or were unnecessary;

(c) the noise was caused in the course of a trade or business and the

---

[13] For advice on assessing and dealing with noise problems from pubs and clubs, see also *Draft Code of Practice on the control of noise from pubs and clubs*, Institute of Acoustics, November 1999.

[14] Reported in *Environmental Health*, Sept. 1977, p. 206.

[15] Dealing with summary proceedings in respect of noise nuisance. Now repealed. Decisions made in respect of cases taken under the Control of Pollution Act 1974 will still be relevant to proceedings under the statutory nuisance provisions of s. 80, Environmental Protection Act 1990.

"best practicable means"[16] had been taken for preventing or counteracting the effect of the noise.

The appeal was dismissed in the Magistrates' Court and a further appeal was subsequently considered in the Crown Court.[17] Counsel for the appellant did in fact accept the view that the noise was a nuisance. The Judge felt that the wrong grounds had been chosen in "character or extent" and that it was necessary to choose one or the other. The case then rested on the last of the appeal grounds. The council contended that the trade or business was only the hiring of the room, not the playing of music which was done by the persons to whom the room was let. As the business was derived from the letting only, the "best practicable means" defence did not apply. The Judge found that the noise emanating from private functions was not noise caused in the course of trade or business. The appeal was dismissed.

Brass band concerts

Blackpool District Council received complaints from residents near a hotel that a proposed series of brass band concerts to be held for ten consecutive weeks in the rear garden of the hotel would be a nuisance.[18] A notice was served under section 58 of the Control of Pollution Act 1974[19] prohibiting the occurrence of a noise nuisance from concerts to be held between 27th June and 29th August 1976. An appeal was lodged in the Magistrates' Court on the grounds:

(a) the notice was not justified by the terms of section 58;

(b) the requirements of the notice were unreasonable in character and were unnecessary, having regard to the character of the premises in question;

---

[16] Defined in s. 72 Control of Pollution Act 1974. Similar provision is now in s. 79(9), Environmental Protection Act 1990.

[17] The provisions in respect of appeals are now governed by s. 80(3), Environmental Protection Act 1990 and the Statutory Nuisance (Appeals) Regulations 1995, S.I. 1995 No. 2644.

[18] Reported in *Environmental Health*, May 1977.

[19] Now repealed.

(c) the times within which the requirements of the notice were to be complied with were not reasonably sufficient in any event.

At the hearing in the Magistrates' Court it was submitted for the appellants that to ban concerts without hearing the bands was to prejudge the issue, that the notice, if upheld, could have far reaching effects and that there would be widespread resentment if the classification of brass bands as "pollution" were allowed to stand. An expert witness stated that noise levels were not excessive and were within the limits of the Wilson Committee report.[20]

The council contested this and referred to the powers in the Control of Pollution Act 1974, section 58 to prohibit the occurrence of a noise nuisance. Evidence was given by an Environmental Health Officer of noise levels recorded on two dates in July when the ambient noise levels were exceeded by up to 19 dB(A) during brass band concerts. The officer was satisfied that the noise was of such a nature and volume as to constitute a nuisance. Residents said that they found the noise most annoying and it prevented them following pursuits of their own choice. The Magistrates dismissed the appeal and subsequently imposed fines in respect of four summonses following breaches of the notice.

Decisions of this kind may also serve to indicate the possibility of adequate control over open-air pop festivals.

Local authorities have discretion about the type of notices they serve, i.e. specifying works or a straightforward abatement notice.[21] If specifying works, they must be sufficiently detailed to clarify precisely what the recipient must do to comply with the notice.[22] Alternatively, a simple notice may be served requiring abatement of the nuisance, without specifying works. In this case the recipient must decide how to comply with the requirement. Specifying noise limits in an abatement notice and how the monitoring should be undertaken are not considered to be "steps" under section 80(1) of the Environmental Protection Act 1990,[23] and therefore a notice

---

[20] *Noise,* Final Report, 1963, Cmnd. 2056.
[21] Environmental Protection Act 1990, s. 80(1).
[22] *Sterling Homes (Midlands) Ltd. v Birmingham C.C.* [1996] Env L.R. 121.
[23] *Sevenoaks D.C. v Brands Hatch Leisure Group Ltd.* [2001] Env L.R. 86.

just specifying the noise limits will suffice. In the case of *Surrey Free Inns plc v Gosport B.C.*,[24] the local authority required the company "to cease the playing of amplified music at levels which cause a nuisance at neighbouring premises". How it complied with the notice was up to the recipient: it could stop playing music, reduce the noise level, or undertake works to abate the nuisance. The requirements of the notice were upheld by the Court of Appeal.

Noise from railway work

In February 1993 the Royal Borough of Kensington and Chelsea served a notice under section 80 of the Environmental Protection Act 1990 on the British Railways Board. The notice required the Board not to cause a noise nuisance as a result of its track realignment operations. In the early hours of the 15th/16th March 1993, the noise level from the "tamping" of the stone track base was found to be unbearable and sleep for local residents impossible. A prosecution for contravention of the notice was instigated. British Rail pleaded guilty, was fined £2,000, and ordered to pay £500 compensation to aggrieved residents and £10,211 costs.

BYELAWS

A byelaw is a local law enforceable in the courts provided it is properly made. The power to make byelaws is contained in Acts of Parliament. Most byelaws are now made by local authorities under the provisions of the Local Government Act 1972.[25]

Section 235(1) of the Act enables a district council[26] and a council of a London borough to make byelaws for the good rule and government of the whole or any part of the district or borough, as

---

[24] *Surrey Free Inns plc v Gosport B.C.* [1999] Env L.R. 750. In a similar case, *R. v Crown Court at Canterbury ex parte Howson Ball* [2001] Env L.R. 36, a similar type of notice was served, but the second part of it limited noise levels at two metres from any loudspeaker to 75dBL$_{Aeq}$ (1 minute). This form of notice was also upheld.

[25] Byelaws previously made under the Local Government Act 1933 are by virtue of s. 272(2) of the Local Government Act 1972 preserved and remain in force. *D.P.P. v Jackson* (1990) 154 J.P. 967.

[26] The council of a principal area in Wales.

the case may be, and for the prevention and suppression of nuisances therein. The detailed procedure for making byelaws is contained in section 236 of the Act.[27] Byelaws do not become effective until confirmed by the confirming authority. In the case of byelaws made under section 235(1) of the Act, this is the Secretary of State for the Environment.

Although its seems that there could be considerable variation in local byelaws between authorities, a substantial degree of uniformity exists as a result of the production of "model byelaws" which are often adopted in their entirety by local authorities. Local circumstances may, of course, necessitate variations from these model byelaws but the fact that confirmation by the Secretary of State is necessary ensures uniformity between authorities. The following model byelaws deal with many of the more common noise problems in urban areas. It is clear that the statutory powers to deal with nuisances will not adequately deal with all of these noises, which are mostly likely to be transient, and in many cases the byelaw powers are the more appropriate.

MODEL FORMS OF BYELAWS RELATING TO NOISE

The following forms of byelaws are issued by the Home Office for the guidance of local authorities who may have occasion to make good rule and government byelaws under s. 235 of the Local Government Act 1972.

The matters dealt with include most of those which have formed the subject of regulation by byelaw in different parts of the country according to local needs and circumstances. The object of the collection of forms is to enable a local authority which has found it necessary to make a byelaw on a particular subject to make its proposal in the most appropriate form. It should be clearly understood that the forms are not intended for wholesale and indiscriminate adoption. Local authorities will fully appreciate the strong objection to the making of byelaws which local experience has not shown to be necessary. Many of

---

[27] This section does not apply to byelaws made by the Civil Aviation Authority under s. 29 of the Civil Aviation Act 1982.

the forms recommended are the result of long experience, the wording having been changed from time to time to cure defects found in actual practice and to meet legal criticisms.

It is requested that any proposed byelaw should be submitted to the Secretary of State in draft for his provisional approval before any steps are taken for its formal adoption and publication.

1. *Music near Houses.* – No person shall sound or play upon any musical or noisy instrument or sing[28] in any street or public place within 100 metres of any dwelling-house or office, after being requested to desist by any inmate or occupant thereof, either personally or through a servant, or through a constable, on account of the interruption of the ordinary occupations or pursuits of any such inmate or occupant or for other reasonable and sufficient cause: Provided that this byelaw shall not apply to properly conducted religious services, except where the request to desist is made on the ground of the serious illness of any inmate of the house.

2. *Music near Churches, etc.* – No person shall sound or play upon any musical or noisy instrument or sing in any street or public place within 100 metres of any place of public worship or public entertainment or other place of public assembly in which persons are for the time being assembled, to the annoyance or disturbance of any person or persons so assembled, after being requested to desist by any constable, or by any person so annoyed or disturbed, or by any person acting on his behalf.

3. *Music near Hospitals.* – No person shall sound or play upon any musical or noisy instrument or sing in any street or public place within 100 metres of any hospital, infirmary, convalescent home, or other place used for the reception or treatment of the sick, after being requested to desist by any

---

[28] A person refusing to stop singing at an open air religious service on a public highway in Kent was found guilty of contravening a similar byelaw. *Kruse v Johnson* [1898] 2 Q.B. 91; 62 J.P. 469.

constable, or by any inmate or officer of such hospital or other place, or by any person acting on his behalf.

4. *Organs.* – No person shall in any street or public place, or on any land adjoining or near to any street or public place, use or play, or cause to be used or played, any steam organ or other musical instrument worked by mechanical means, to the annoyance or disturbance of residents or passengers.

4a. *Organs, Alternative Form.* – No person shall, in connection with any roundabout, show, exhibition, or performance, placed or held in any street or on any vacant ground adjoining or near to any street, make or cause to be made any loud and continuous or repeated noise by means of any organ or other similar instrument, to the annoyance of residents or passengers.

5. *Wireless Sets, Gramophones, etc.*

    (1) Any person who by operating or causing or suffering to be operated any wireless set, gramophone, amplifier or similar instrument:

        (a) in or on any street or public place or in connection with any shop, business premises or other place which adjoins any street or public place and to which the public are admitted, makes or causes or suffers to be made any noise which is so loud and so continuous or repeated as to give reasonable cause for annoyance to other persons, or

        (b) in any other premises makes or causes or suffers to be made any noise which is so loud and so continuous or repeated as to cause annoyance to occupiers or inmates of any premises in the neighbourhood,

    shall be guilty of an offence:

    Provided that:

        (i) no proceedings shall be taken under this byelaw against any person in respect of anything done in any premises referred to in paragraph (b) thereof unless the nuisance does not cease before the expiration of a fortnight from the date of the service on that person of a notice alleging a nuisance, signed by not less than three householders residing within hearing of the instrument in question,

(ii) this byelaw shall not apply to any wireless set, gramophone amplifier or similar instrument used by a police constable in the execution of his duty.

(2) In this byelaw the expression "public place" includes any park, pleasure ground or other like place to which the public are admitted (and any part of a beach to which the public are admitted).

NOTE. The words in parenthesis in paragraph (2) should only be included if relevant.

6. *Noisy Hawking.* – No person shall, for the purpose of hawking, selling, distributing, or advertising any article, shout or use any bell, gong, or other noisy instrument in any street or public place so as to cause annoyance to the inhabitants of the neighbourhood.[29]

7. *Unruly Behaviour in Places of Entertainment.* – No person shall in any place of entertainment to which the public are admitted with or without the payment of money, while the public are on the premises use any threatening, abusive or insulting language, gesture or conduct with intent to put any person in fear or so as to occasion a breach of the peace or whereby a breach of the peace is likely to be occasioned.

8. *Noisy Conduct at Night.* – No person shall in any street or public place between the hours of 11.00 p.m. and 6.00 a.m. wantonly and continuously shout or otherwise make any

---

[29] It has been held that a newsboy calling out for the purpose of selling his newspapers, to the annoyance of only one inhabitant of the neighbourhood, contravened a similar byelaw. *Innes v Newman* [1894] 2 Q.B. 292; 58 J.P. 543.

loud noise to the disturbance or annoyance of residents.[30]

9. *Noisy Animals.* – No person shall keep within any house,
   building, or premises any noisy animal which shall be or
   cause a serious nuisance to residents in the neighbourhood.
   Provided that no proceedings shall be taken against any
   person for an offence against this byelaw unless the nuisance
   be continued after the expiration of a fortnight from the date
   of the service on such person of a notice alleging a nuisance,
   signed by not less than three householders residing within
   hearing of the animal.

Other model byelaws have been prepared dealing with barking
dogs, model aircraft,[31] seaside pleasure boats and bird scaring
devices. The courts have upheld proceedings for contraventions of
byelaws dealing with roundabouts,[32] musical ice-cream vans,[33]
shooting galleries, playing musical instruments in streets,[34] the
making of noise in a street,[35] and the causing of a brawl or otherwise
disturbing the peace.[36]

Contravention of the Byelaws for Good Rule and Government
constitutes a criminal offence for which, unless the enabling
enactment fixes a sum, the penalty on summary conviction is a fine
not exceeding level 2 on the standard scale and in the case of a
continuing offence a further fine not exceeding £5 for each day
during which the offence continues after conviction unless the
byelaw fixes an alternative sum.[37] There is no restriction under the

---

[30] In relation to the use of obscene language in a street, justices are entitled to
infer annoyance in the absence of positive evidence that any person was
annoyed. *Nicholson v Glasspool* (1959) 123 J.P. 229.

[31] A Code of Practice has been published by the Department of the Environment
as an approved Code under the provisions in s. 71 of the Control of Pollution
Act 1974.

[32] *Teale v Harris* (1896) 60 J.P. 744.

[33] *John v Heath* [1958] Crim. L.R. 385; *Raymond v Cook* [1958] 1 W.L.R.
1098.

[34] *Brownscombe v Johnson* (1898) 62 J.P. 326; *Kruse v Johnson* (1898) 2 Q.B.
91; 62 J.P. 469.

[35] *Innes v Newman* [1894] 2 Q.B. 292; 58 J.P. 543.

[36] *Beaty v Glenister* (1884) 51 L.T. 304.

[37] Local Government Act 1972, s. 237, as amended by the Criminal Law Act
1977 and the Criminal Justice Act 1982.

Local Government Act 1972 prescribing that only the local authority may take proceedings in respect of contravention of the byelaws. The police can take proceedings without reference to the local authority. Although the local authority and the police may take proceedings of this kind, it is quite common for contravention of the byelaws to be left to the police to enforce because they are more readily able to undertake immediate investigations into the relatively transient matters covered by the byelaws.

There is no bar on any other person taking criminal proceedings for a breach of a byelaw unless that right is specifically restricted by the enactment under which the byelaws are made. In proceedings for an offence it is a defence to show that the byelaw is invalid. This will be the case if the proper procedure has not been followed and the byelaw confirmed or because it is *ultra vires* (i.e. beyond the scope of the authority). To avoid being *ultra vires,* byelaws must be:

(a) *intra vires* the enactment under which they are made;

(b) consistent with both statutory and common law;

(c) reasonable;

(d) certain.

An important point arises in section 235(3) of the Local Government Act 1972. This provides that byelaws made under the section shall not be made for any purpose as respects any area if provision for that purpose in respect of that area is made by, or is or may be made under, any other enactment. The importance of this is reflected in a case which is also of importance in respect of the legal control over noise nuisance from animals. In the case of *Galer v Morrissey,*[38] proceedings were taken in respect of a byelaw providing that no person should keep within any house, building or premises any noisy animal which would be or cause a serious nuisance to residents of the neighbourhood.[39] In defence it was contended that

---

[38] *Galer v Morrissey* [1955] 1 All E.R. 380.
[39] See Model Byelaw No. 9, p. 100 *ante.* In relation to noise from barking dogs, see also *Clemons v Stewart and Others,* S.L.J., 30th May 1969 in respect of successful proceedings for statutory nuisance.

the matter of noisy animals was already dealt with at that time under the Public Health Act 1936, section 92(1)(b) which included in its definition of statutory nuisance "any animal kept in such a place or manner as to be prejudicial to health or a nuisance". In this case the Lord Chief Justice stated: "No-one doubts that if the statute deals with precisely the same matter, the byelaw would be *ultra vires,* because a byelaw cannot, in effect, cross the t's and dot the i's of a statute. If the byelaw deals with the same matter as the statute there would be no necessity for the byelaw and, if it goes beyond the statute, then the byelaw is bad." The Divisional Court decided that the byelaw was in fact good and section 92(1)(b) did not deal with noisy animals but was intended to deal with nuisances caused by insanitary or defective premises.

If a noise nuisance occurs which is capable of being dealt with under Part III of the Environmental Protection Act 1990 but is also a matter that can be dealt with under Byelaws for Good Rule and Government, then the byelaws will be invalid as being inconsistent with Part III.

LICENSED PREMISES[40]

Liquor licensing

The Licensing Act 1964 requires that any person wishing to retail intoxicating liquor either on or off the premises has to obtain a licence, renewable for a three year period, from the Licensing Justices. Any member of the public, a local authority, the Chief Fire Officer or the Chief Officer of Police, may object to the granting or renewal of the licence. In granting on- and off-licences, the Justices generally have complete discretion to attach conditions they consider appropriate, including conditions intended to deal with noise nuisance. Their discretion in respect of restaurant and residential licences is more restricted. They can only attach conditions to the grant of a new on-licence if it is in the interests of the public. A right

---

[40] In its White Paper *Time for Reform: Proposals for the modernisation of our licensing laws,* Cmnd. 4696, April 2000, the Government proposes extensive reform of all areas of the licensing system. The main objectives considered in framing the proposals include the prevention of nuisance and disturbance to the public. See also the Introduction to this book.

of appeal to the Crown Court exists against most decisions. The kind of conditions that the licensing justices have been known to impose include the control of amplified music to an acceptable external level by a suitable noise limiting device (e.g. the electronic orange) and no music to be played unless controllable in this way (this could mean drums being banned). This procedure is only applicable to public houses and licensed clubs (i.e. when liquor is sold for personal gain).

Any person opposing an application for renewal of a justices' licence must give notice in writing to the applicant and the justices' clerk specifying in general terms the grounds of the objection. Notice of objection on the ground that the premises are "of a disorderly character" may refer to problems of noise and unruly behaviour, either inside or outside the premises, provided it is associated with the use to which the licence relates. If the premises have acquired a "disorderly character" there is ground for refusing the licence, even if the applicant is of good character.

Registered clubs are dealt with under a separate procedure (in these clubs the liquor, which is owned by the club membership, is *supplied,* not sold). In these clubs liquor is supplied under the terms of a registration certificate granted by the Magistrates and not the licensing Justices. Magistrates considering applications for registration certificates do not have the degree of discretion available to the licensing Justices. Registration certificates are initially issued for 12 months but, on the second or subsequent renewals, can be granted for 10 years; grounds for objection to the granting or renewal of a certificate are contained in section 44 of the Act.[41]

Music and dancing licences

Complaints of noise from places of entertainment, particularly

---

[41] The *Report of the Departmental Committee on Liquor Licensing,* Cmnd. 5154 recommended that damage to local amenity be included as a ground for refusing a licence, together with the power to restrict licensing hours. They also recommended that registered clubs be covered by the same conditions as those applicable to public houses and licensed clubs. These recommendations were endorsed by the Noise Advisory Council in its report *Noise in Public Places,* 1974, H.M.S.O.

public houses and clubs continue to increase. The use of amplified music appears to be primarily responsible.

Premises licensed under the Licensing Act 1964 do not require a licence for public entertainment provided by radio or television, by use of a cable programme service, by recorded music, or by not more than two performers.[42] Apart from this, premises used for public dancing, music or similar entertainments normally require a licence. There are several Acts under which these licences may be issued and the law differs in various parts of the country. Controls relate to both public and private places.

Public places

The law relating to music and dancing depends on whether the place is in the Greater London area or elsewhere, although the controls have much in common. The greatest difference is the discretion of local authorities outside London to decide whether or not to apply the licensing provisions to entertainments in the open air or on private land. Music and dancing licences do not cover the performance of stage plays, for which a theatre licence is required, nor in ordinary cases does a theatre licence cover music and dancing. However, a building may have both licences. Unlike a theatre licence, a music and dancing licence does not allow the holder to sell intoxicating liquor without obtaining a justices' licence.

Control is available through:

(a) Music and dancing licences in Greater London. The London Government Act 1963, Schedule 12, paragraph 1, requires the licensing of premises[43] for public entertainment in Greater London. It applies to public[44] dancing or music and any other entertainment of the like kind. Any licence is to be subject to such terms and conditions and subject to such restrictions as may be specified.[45]

---

[42] Licensing Act 1964, s. 182(1).
[43] "Premises" includes any place, Schedule 12 1(7).
[44] The entertainment, to be public within the meaning of Schedule 12, must be one to which all persons have a right of admission on payment or otherwise.
[45] Use of premises without a licence is subject to a fine of up to the level 5 on the standard scale and/or 3 months' imprisonment.

(b) Generally, under the Local Government (Miscellaneous Provisions) Act 1982. Section 1 of the Act applies to the licensing of public entertainments[46] outside Greater London. Schedule 1 relates to public dancing or music or any other public entertainment of a like kind and requires that such entertainment shall not be provided at any place except under the terms of a licence. The requirement does not apply to any music associated with specified religious activities, pleasure fairs or entertainment taking place wholly or mainly in the open air. Licences are also required for premises[47] used for any entertainment which consists of any sporting events to which the public are invited (unless the sporting event is not the principal purpose for which the premises are used on that occasion or the entertainment is held in a pleasure fair).

These provisions do not apply to public musical entertainment held mainly or wholly in the open air, and on private land, unless the licensing authority resolves that they shall apply. If so, a licence is required which may be subject to appropriate terms and conditions and to restrictions imposed "for preventing persons in the neighbourhood being unreasonably disturbed by noise."[48] The licensing authority, for the purposes of the relevant provisions of the Act, is the District Council in England and Wales for the area in which the place is situated. The authority, in considering an application for a licence, may consult with the Chief Officer of the Police and the Fire Authority and must have regard to any observations submitted by them.

It is, generally speaking, an offence to organise a public entertainment without a licence obtained in advance from the local authority where one is required by law or to be in breach of any of the terms,

---

[46] Entertainment provided at an all night dance party attended by some 7,000 people was held to be public entertainment, notwithstanding that those attending were members of a club, since the club was merely a transparent device designed to achieve the effect of circumventing the licensing requirements; *Lunn v Colston-Hayter* (1991) 155 J.P. 384.

[47] "Premises" means a permanent or temporary building and any tent or inflatable structure.

[48] This requirement does not apply to garden fêtes, bazaars, religious meetings and sporting events merely because music is incidental to them.

conditions or restrictions the law allows the local authority to place on a licence. This also applies to private entertainment promoted for private gain where a licence is required. The Entertainment (Increased Penalties) Act 1990 applies maximum penalties on summary conviction of £20,000 and/or 6 months' imprisonment in cases where an event is held without a licence or where a licence condition regarding the number of people who might be present is breached. The Criminal Justice Act 1988 (Confiscation Orders) Order 1990 gives Magistrates the power to order the confiscation of proceeds, where they exceed £10,000, made by people convicted of these particular offences.

The Deregulation (Sunday Licensing) Order 2001 permits "special hours certificates" and "extended hours orders" to be granted on Sundays. These allow premises such as nightclubs, discotheques, casinos, registered members' clubs and restaurants which are licensed to provide music and dancing, gaming facilities or substantial refreshment to the public, to apply for an extension to the permitted hours for the sale of alcohol. However, under the order, the extension on Sundays can only be granted up to 12.30 a.m. on a Monday morning, or 2.00 a.m. (3.00 a.m. in areas of Central London) if the Monday is a Bank Holiday, except Easter Monday. The Order requires licensing justices and magistrates' courts, when considering the relevant applications, to take account of guidance issued by the Secretary of State. The Order also allows local residents to apply to the licensing justices and magistrates' courts to limit or revoke any extensions granted on Sundays on the grounds of disturbance or annoyance. The Secretary of State's guidance[49] says that licensing justices should bear in mind, amongst other things, "the position of those living in the area who would prefer a relatively quiet Sunday evening ... and who would not want to ... be disturbed."

Private places of entertainment
The Private Places of Entertainment (Licensing) Act 1967 can be adopted where there already exists statutory control over premises where public music and dancing takes place. It provides a system

---

[49]　Annex to Home Office Circular 2/2001, *Extended liquor licensing hours on Sundays*.

of licensing control over private places of entertainment which are not open to the public but where the entertainment is provided for private gain. However, premises where intoxicating liquor is sold or supplied and bona fide clubs, being premises controlled under the Licensing Act 1964, the London Government Act 1963 or the Local Government (Miscellaneous Provisions) Act 1982, are not covered by the 1967 Act.[50]

The Private Places of Entertainment (Licensing) Act 1967 enables local authorities to adopt powers requiring the licensing of private events on a similar basis to public entertainments. The powers enable authorities to control events involving music and dancing including so called "acid house" or "rave" parties. The Noise Review Working Party[51] applied the following terminology to large scale parties:

Warehouse party – generally held in warehouses or large permanent structures. Attendance generally ranges between 200 and 2,000.

Acid house party – the most common publicly known term for large scale parties which are generally held out of doors on farmland or in remote areas. Attendance can vary but numbers of 4,000–7,000 are not unusual.

Dance party – synonymous with acid house parties but a better known term used by party goers themselves.

Pay party – smaller scale parties (up to 100 attending) held in domestic premises.

Shebeen – synonymous with pay parties but an older term.

"Private gain" is not defined in the Act.[52] However, in London Boroughs where Part III of the London Local Authorities Act 1991

---

50 A licensed club (for liquor) which wishes to have a special hours certificate (to extend the permitted hours for drinking with meals) must provide substantial refreshment and music and dancing *and* must have a music and dancing licence or a certificate of suitability for music and dancing: Licensing Act 1964, ss. 77–79.

51 *Report of the Noise Review Working Party*, 1990, H.M.S.O., Ch. 6, p.24.

52 But see *Payne v Bradley* [1962] A.C. 343; [1961] 2 All E.R. 882; 125 J.P. 514 concerning the scope of the expression "promoted for private gain".

has effect, an entertainment is to be regarded as having been promoted for private gain for the purposes of the Private Places of Entertainment (Licensing) Act 1967 if, and only if:

(a) any proceeds of the entertainment, i.e. sums paid for admission; or

(b) any other sums (whenever paid) which, having regard to all the circumstances, can reasonably be regarded as paid wholly or partly for admission to the entertainment; or

(c) where the entertainment is advertised (whether to the public or otherwise), any sums not falling within (b) which are paid for facilities or services provided for persons admitted to the entertainment;

are applied for purposes of private gain. If, in criminal proceedings in respect of entertainment where a licence under the 1967 Act was not held, it is proved that the sums indicated above were paid, the entertainment is deemed to have been promoted for private gain unless the contrary is shown.

Similar penalties and confiscation powers apply to contraventions of the Private Places of Entertainment (Licensing) Act 1967, as to the Local Government (Miscellaneous Provisions) Act 1982.

Unruly behaviour

A frequent cause of complaint is the behaviour of people using or leaving licensed premises. The consumption of intoxicating liquor often results in inconsiderate actions – shouting, banging car doors and revving of car engines. This may cause extreme annoyance and is difficult to control. An element of control may be available by:

(a) Control under the Late Night Refreshment Houses Act 1969. A late night refreshment house is "a house, room, shop or building kept open for public refreshment, resort and entertainment at any time between the hours of ten at night and five in the following morning, other than a house, room, shop or building which is licensed for the sale of beer, cider, wine or spirits".[53] If it is

---

[53] s. 1.

considered necessary to avoid unreasonable disturbance to residents
of the neighbourhood (and noise is likely to be a major problem),
the licensing authority may, on granting or renewing a licence,
prohibit the opening or keeping open of the refreshment house for
public refreshment, resort or entertainment at any time between
11.00 p.m. and 5.00 a.m.[54] If the licensee contravenes a condition
an offence is committed. A right of appeal exists to the Magistrates'
Court[55] against any condition imposed by the licensing authority.
Offences are punishable by a fine of not more than level 4 on the
standard scale, or by 3 months' imprisonment, or both.

Illegal and disorderly conduct in late night refreshment houses is
also dealt with under the Act and any person who is drunk, riotous,
quarrelsome or disorderly who refuses or neglects a request from
the manager or occupier to leave the premises will be guilty of an
offence.[56] The police enforce this Act and have powers of entry.
Offences are punishable by a fine of not more than level 1 on the
standard scale. Disqualification orders may also be imposed in
respect of these offences.

Part III of the 1964 Act was amended by the Licensing Act 1988 to
remove restrictions in England and Wales on the sale and supply of
alcohol on weekday afternoons. Licensing Justices or the
Magistrates' Court can make, vary and revoke restriction orders in
respect of licensed premises or registered clubs respectively, using
powers in sections 20A and 67A–D. Applications may be made by
the Chief Officer of Police, persons or representative bodies of
persons living in the neighbourhood, persons carrying on businesses
in the neighbourhood, or by head teachers or other persons in
charge of education establishments in the neighbourhood, for an
order requiring premises which give rise to problems of disorderly
conduct or nuisance to close for all or part of the afternoon period
between 2.30 p.m. and 5.30 p.m., during the days or weeks

---

[54] s. 7.
[55] And subsequently to the Crown Court.
[56] s. 9(4). In the case of *Surrey Heath B.C. v MacDonalds Restaurants Ltd.*
(1990) *The Times,* 3rd July, on hearing an appeal against an early closing
condition on the renewal of a late night refreshment licence, it was held that
Magistrates had to take into consideration any disturbance attributable to a
restaurant being open late.

specified, for a period of up to twelve months.

(b)   Action may be available under the Byelaws for Good Rule and Government in respect of unruly behaviour in places of entertainment[57] or noisy conduct at night.[58]

PRIVATE PARTIES NOT FOR GAIN

Noisy parties are an increasing and major problem for many local authorities. Where private parties are not held for gain and do not come within the scope of licensing legislation, local authority powers are generally restricted to the noise abatement powers of the Environmental Protection Act 1990. These include the power to apply for a High Court injunction if the authority considers that summary proceedings would be inadequate.[59]

High Court injunctions have been obtained to prevent parties taking place and the procedure can be used at short notice to stop parties occurring, even where the local authority has had little prior warning of the date and venue.[60] Where an injunction does not prevent a party taking place, the penalties for non-compliance with the terms of the injunction, i.e. unlimited fine and/or imprisonment, can be a strong deterrent. Injunctions may be sought under the powers of the Environmental Protection Act 1990[61] or those available under section 222 of the Local Government Act 1972 which allows a local authority, if it considers it expedient for the promotion or protection of the interests of the inhabitants of the area, to take legal proceedings in its own name.

The injunction procedure is likely to be expensive and the alternatives should be considered.[62] In the case of pay parties, it is the object of

---

57   See Model Byelaw No. 7, p. 99 *ante.*
58   See Model Byelaw No. 8, p. 99 *ante.*
59   s. 81(5), Environmental Protection Act 1990.
60   See *Brentwood D.C.*: Municipal Journal No. 35, 1st September 1989; *Windsor and Maidenhead R.B.C.*: Municipal Journal No. 37, 15th September 1989; *Newbury D.C.*: Municipal Journal No. 39, 29th September 1989.
61   s. 81(5), Environmental Protection Act 1990.
62   Notice preventing the occurrence or recurrence of a nuisance: s. 80(1)(a), Environmental Protection Act 1990.

the organisers to avoid the regulatory authorities becoming aware of the activity, if possible. Information may, therefore, only become available shortly before a party is to take place. In urgent cases an ex-parte application can be made without the prior service of notice on the person against whom the injunction is sought. The local authority needs to prepare to produce the writ, draft order or affidavit very quickly. In seeking an injunction, the local authority may be required to give "an undertaking as to damages". If a person succeeds in getting the terms of an injunction set aside, the authority will be liable for any losses associated with the interim order including the costs of a cancelled party.

When applying for an injunction, the High Court must be convinced that remedies available under other legislation would not stop the party occurring. It will also need to know:

(a) the location of the party in the local authority's area;

(b) the land owner and/or the party organisers;

(c) that no licence has been granted or that if a licence application were made it would not be granted because the licence conditions could not be met, e.g. anticipated noise problems, inadequate safety arrangements.

(d) if it went ahead the party would cause a noise nuisance.

PRACTICAL CONTROL OF ENTERTAINMENT NOISE

Noise from parties and other entertainment occurs mainly at night. In some large metropolitan areas and London Boroughs the scale of the problem stretches the resources of the local authorities and the police, who frequently work together to deal with such problems. Taking enforcement action when a party is in full swing can lead to public disorder and danger to enforcement officers. The police play a vital role in supporting local authority officers called to deal with noise from parties which are violent or disorderly. Maintaining public order and dealing with associated criminal activities, e.g. drug abuse, sale of alcohol, illegal parking and drunken driving are police responsibilities. If necessary, the police will use their powers to stop or prevent a breach of the peace.[63] The use of the power depends on individual cases and could be open to challenge in the courts. Use of the power to close down a party may be easier to justify where members of the public may be threatening to take matters into their own hands. In such cases, this can provide a stronger reason for action and the threat to stop a party using breach of the peace powers may produce a voluntary cessation of it.

In many authorities, routine night time patrols have been introduced to deal with the increasing problem of noisy parties. Some of the most well established are in the London Boroughs. That operated by Environmental Health Officers in Lewisham has been in existence since 1976. In recent years, the number of domestic noise complaints received by the authority has been increasing by up to 20% per year and is currently around 9,000 per year. The authority employs eight officers operating on a shift basis to provide a seven-day service. Its late shift covers the period 8.00 p.m. to 4.00 a.m., with officers working in pairs. This is to provide increased protection because of an increasing number of threats of violence and actual assaults by people associated with noisy activities. The multicultural team works closely with the police and operates on a rota basis. Diplomacy and discretion is needed and training is required to avoid the violence that can be associated with the work. It is not always easy to discover who is the owner of the property or the person responsible for the party and the service of an abatement notice often has to be by addressing it to the occupier and fixing it on the premises. In the event that a notice is not complied with, as a last resort sound equipment may be seized using the powers in section 81(3) of the Environmental Protection Act 1990[64] or section 10(2) of the Noise Act 1996 (in respect of noise from a dwelling at night).[65] A seizure warrant is required from a Magistrate. Applications for a warrant

---

63   *R. v Howell* [1982] Q.B. 416; [1981] 2 All E.R. 383; [1981] 3 W.L.R. 501 held that there is a breach of the peace whenever harm is actually done, or is likely to be done to a person, or in his presence to his property, or a person is in fear of being harmed through an assault, or affray, a riot, unlawful assembly or other disturbance.

64   Power to abate the nuisance where a notice has not been complied with or do whatever may be necessary in execution of the notice.

65   In Lewisham, the local authority seized 49 sets of noise-making equipment in the last financial year.

have been made in the following cases:[66]

(a) where squatters holding a pay party failed to respond to abatement notices;

(b) a young council tenant regularly left loud music playing in her council flat until 2.30 a.m. in the morning.

Birmingham Council adopted an innovatory approach to the investigation of noise from problem neighbours. In encouraging people to provide their own evidence, the council has developed a tape recorder that records how loud the noises are, when they happen, and their duration. The families affected can switch on the equipment any time they hear noise from problem neighbours. This scheme has resulted in a number of successful prosecutions.[67]

However, in undertaking any surveillance operations, regard must be had to the Regulation of Investigatory Powers Act 2000 and, in particular, Part II which deals with directed and intrusive surveillance and the conduct and use of covert human intelligence sources.[68] Authorisations for such activities have to be obtained[69] from persons entitled to grant them.[70] In the preparation of evidence for legal proceedings, regard must also be had to the requirements of the Criminal Procedure and Investigations Act 1996.[71]

POLICE POWERS

In addition to byelaws, licensing controls and powers to deal with breaches of the peace, there are certain other powers which may be available to the police to control noise.

Metropolitan Police Act 1839

Section 54(14) "Every person, except the guards and postmen

---

[66] See *Environmental Health News*, 31st January 1992, p. 7.
[67] See *Environmental Health News*, 14th August 1992, p. 5.
[68] Defined in s. 26. See also pp. 75–78 for a more detailed explanation of the Act.
[69] ss. 28 and 29.
[70] s. 30.
[71] Part 1 in particular reformed the law relating to prosecution and defence disclosure, as recommended by the Royal Commission on Criminal Justice in its report published in July 1993 (Cmnd. 2263).

belonging to H.M. Post Office in the performance of their duty, who shall blow any horn or use any other noisy instrument, for the purpose of calling persons together, or of announcing any show or entertainment, or for the purpose of hawking, selling, distributing, or collecting any article whatsoever, or of obtaining money or alms" – shall be liable to a penalty of not more than level 2 on the standard scale. This offence applies to any thoroughfare or public place within the limits of the Metropolitan Police district.

Public Order Act 1986

Section 14 provides that in respect of public assemblies,[72] if the senior police officer reasonably believes that the assembly may result in serious public disorder, serious damage to property, serious disruption to the life of the community, or intimidation of individuals, he can give directions with regard to the place, maximum duration, or maximum number of people who may constitute the assembly. Penalties of up to 3 months' imprisonment or a fine not exceeding level 4 on the standard scale may be imposed in the case of offences.

Town Police Clauses Act 1847

Section 28 makes it an offence for any person in a street,[73] to the annoyance of residents, to discharge any firearm, subject to a penalty not exceeding level 3 on the standard scale, or to 14 days' imprisonment.

NOISE IN STREETS

The Noise Review Working Party 1990 identified a number of noisy activities that take place on the highway that were not controllable by the law on statutory nuisance or road traffic legislation, e.g. car repairs on the highway that do not cause

---

[72] s. 16 – public assembly means an assembly of 20 or more persons in a public place which is wholly or partly in the open air.

[73] This includes a public place, or recreation ground belonging to or under the control of the local authority, by virtue of the Public Health Acts Amendment Act 1907.

obstruction but do cause nuisance to local inhabitants; noisy plant such as diesel generators and vehicle refrigerators left on the highway because there was nowhere else to leave them; misfiring vehicle alarms.[74]

Following the Working Party's recommendations, the Noise and Statutory Nuisance Act 1993 amended the definition of statutory nuisance in section 79 of the Environmental Protection Act 1990 to include "noise that is prejudicial to health or a nuisance and is emitted from or caused by a vehicle, machinery or equipment[75] in a street."[76]

Loudspeakers in streets

The operation of loudspeakers in streets[77] is controlled by section 62 of the Control of Pollution Act 1974. By subsection (1) of that section such operation is prohibited as follows:

(a) between 9.00 p.m. and 8.00 a.m. the following morning, for whatever purpose the loudspeaker is being operated;

(b) at any other time, when the loudspeaker is being operated to advertise any entertainment, trade or business.

A person operating or permitting the operation of a loudspeaker in contravention of the section is guilty of an offence and liable on summary conviction to a fine not exceeding level 5 on the standard scale and a daily penalty of £50 after conviction for a continuing offence.[78]

The operation of a loudspeaker for the following purposes is not subject to these restrictions:

---

[74] *Report of the Noise Review Working Party,* 1990, H.M.S.O., Ch. 3, page 10.
[75] "Equipment" includes a musical instrument.
[76] Noise and Statutory Nuisance Act 1993, s. 2.
[77] "Street" means a highway and any other road, footway, square or court which is for the time being open to the public.
[78] See ss. 74(1) and 74(2) for determining whether an offence is a second or subsequent offence. Account is taken of offences which may have occurred under s. 24 of the Public Health (Scotland) Act 1897 or s. 80(4) of the Environmental Protection Act 1990 in relation to England and Wales.

(a) for police, fire brigade or ambulance purposes, by the Environment Agency, a water undertaker or a sewerage undertaker in the exercise of any of its functions, or by a local authority within its area;

(b) for communicating with persons on a vessel for the purpose of directing the movement of that or any other vessel;

(c) if the loudspeaker forms part of a public telephone system;

(d) if the loudspeaker is in or fixed to a vehicle and operated solely for entertaining or communicating with the driver or passengers, or where the loudspeaker is, or is part of, the horn or other warning instrument used solely for giving warning to other traffic, *and is so operated as not to give reasonable cause for annoyance to persons in the vicinity*;

(e) otherwise than on a highway, by persons employed in connection with a transport undertaking used by the public in a case where the loudspeaker is operated solely for making announcements to passengers or prospective passengers or to other persons so employed;

(f) by a travelling showman on land which is being used for the purposes of a pleasure fair;

(g) in case of emergency.

Subsection 62(1)(b) is not applicable to the operation of a loudspeaker between 12 noon and 7.00 p.m. if it is fixed to a vehicle being used for the sale of perishable goods from the vehicle, *and is so operated as not to give reasonable cause for annoyance to persons in the vicinity.*[79]

---

[79] Offences in Scotland can be prosecuted in any court of summary jurisdiction within the meaning of the Summary Jurisdiction (Scotland) Act 1954 having jurisdiction in the place where the offence was committed. This means a court of "summary criminal jurisdiction", i.e. the Sheriff and District Court, Criminal Procedure (Scotland) Act 1975 s. 462(1). In relation to Scotland, see also the Civic Government (Scotland) Act 1982 relating to the playing of musical instruments, singing and the operation of sound-producing devices giving reasonable cause for annoyance. This supplements the provisions of s. 62 of the Control of Pollution Act 1974.

The Noise and Statutory Nuisance Act 1993 does not change the complete ban on loudspeakers for advertising but enables a local authority to adopt a power to grant consent for the use of loudspeakers in the street outside the period of 8.00 a.m. to 9.00 p.m., provided that the loudspeaker is not used for electioneering or advertising.[80] This adoptive power will allow, for example, the relaying of evening entertainment by loudspeakers to a wider audience. Charity events, carnivals or processions are likely candidates for consent and local authorities will wish to consider relevant matters such as the time of day, location of noise sensitive properties, likely noise levels, the planned route and means of noise control.

The Secretary of State has power[81] to amend by order the prescribed times in section 62(1)(a) of the Control of Pollution Act 1974. Whilst the power may be used to shorten the period between 8.00 a.m. and 9.00 p.m. (when loudspeakers used for non-advertising purposes can be used without consent), it cannot be used to prescribe times later than 9.00 p.m. or earlier than 8.00 a.m.

One of the noisiest forms of advertising is ice-cream van chimes. These are subject to the controls of section 62 of the Control of Pollution Act 1974 and a Code of Practice[82] gives guidance on the methods of minimising annoyance by such noise. The guidelines deal with noise levels, the playing time of chimes, their frequency of use and restrictions on use in sensitive areas. The Code does not create offences or have force in law but will be taken into account by local authorities and the courts.

Audible intruder alarms

The *Code of Practice on Noise from Audible Intruder Alarms*[83] provides guidance on the installation and operation of alarms to reduce misfiring and enable their disarming or deactivation with

---

[80] s. 8 and Sch. 2.
[81] s. 7.
[82] *Code of Practice on Noise from Ice-Cream Van Chimes, etc.*, 1982. Made by order under s. 71, Control of Pollution Act 1974 and applicable to the whole of the U.K.
[83] *Code of Practice on Noise from Audible Intruder Alarms*, 1982. Also applicable to the whole of the U.K.

the minimum of difficulty. It suggests alarms be fitted with 20 minute cut off devices and that police be notified of key holders who can give access and deactivate continually ringing alarms. The Code is widely used by the security industry and local authorities. The main British Standard (BS4737) for intruder alarm systems requires compliance with the Code of Practice.

In cases of continually ringing alarms and where key holders cannot be contacted, or are unknown, local authorities can use the statutory nuisance provisions of the Environmental Protection Act 1990[84] to serve notice requiring the abatement of the nuisance, if necessary gaining access by warrant to deactivate the alarm.[85] In London, the London Local Authorities Act 1991[86] provides London boroughs with power to adopt provisions concerning the specification and control of alarms. These are similar to the 1982 Code of Practice and include a duty to notify the local authority of the installation and the police of key holders. A warrant can be secured to deactivate an alarm if it causes annoyance to persons living or working near the premises and it has been ringing for more than one hour. It does not rely on proof of statutory nuisance. The Noise and Statutory Nuisance Act 1993[87] enables local authorities outside London to adopt similar powers in relation to audible intruder alarms on premises. The powers related to these alarms do not come into force until the Secretary of State lays an order and it is approved by Parliament.

Noise from vehicles, machinery or equipment (V.M.E.s) in the street

Prior to the Noise and Statutory Nuisance Act 1993[88] action to deal with a statutory noise nuisance under the Environmental Protection Act 1990[89] was restricted to noise from premises. Noise from

---

[84] ss. 79 and 80.

[85] s. 81(3) and Sch. 3 of the Environmental Protection Act 1990.

[86] s. 23.

[87] s. 9. Sch. 3 deals with requirements relating to the installation and operation of alarms, powers of entry, recovery of expenses and protection of authorised officers from personal liability.

[88] 5th January 1994.

[89] In relation to England and Wales. Control of Pollution Act 1974 in relation to Scotland.

vehicles in the street was outside the scope of the provisions.[90] A requirement in the Road Vehicles (Construction and Use) Regulations 1986 to fit a five minute cut-out device to all vehicle alarms is often ignored and the powers of prosecution vested with the police and Vehicle Inspectorate are seldom used. The Noise and Statutory Nuisance Act 1993 amends the statutory noise nuisance provisions to control noise emitted from or caused by a vehicle, machinery or equipment in a street.[91] The Act defines a musical instrument as equipment; and loudspeakers, tannoys, loud-hailers, radios and "ghetto-blasters" should also be regarded as equipment.

Noise from, or caused by, V.M.E.s in the street used in connection with a political demonstration, or a demonstration supporting or opposing a cause or campaign, is exempted.[92] However, attendance at a place for picketing would not constitute a demonstration and noise or disturbance made by pickets, as opposed to those demonstrating in support of a picket's cause, is not exempted. Noise from traffic, naval, military or air forces of the Crown, or by a visiting force is also exempt.[93]

The abatement procedure of the Environmental Protection Act 1990 is amended to provide the local authority with power to enter or open, if necessary by force, any V.M.E. on the street or to remove it to a secure place if that is necessary to achieve abatement of the nuisance. Such action must be preceded by the service of an abatement notice fixed to the V.M.E.[94] A copy of the notice must be served on the person responsible for the V.M.E., if that person can be found within one hour of fixing the notice to the vehicle, machinery or equipment. No action can be taken to abate the nuisance before that period has expired.

To ensure that the person responsible for the unattended V.M.E. has every opportunity of complying with the notice, it must state that if the person responsible for the V.M.E. is subsequently served with

---

[90] *Tower Hamlets L.B. v Manzoni and Walder* (1983) 148 J.P. 123.
[91] By ss. 2–5. Similar provisions apply to Scotland by virtue of s. 6 and Sch. 1.
[92] Environmental Protection Act 1990, new s. 79(6A), inserted by the Noise and Statutory Nuisance Act 1993.
[93] *Ibid.*
[94] Environmental Protection Act 1990, new s. 80A(2).

a copy notice, the time limit for compliance will be extended by such time as is specified in the notice.[95] This requirement is intended to cater for the situation where the person responsible is only traced just before the expiry of the time limit for compliance. Having entered or opened the V.M.E. for the purpose of abating the nuisance, it must be secured against interference or theft in such manner and as effectively as it was found.[96] In practice, where vehicle alarms are involved, these must be reset if possible. If this requirement cannot be met, then the V.M.E. may be immobilised in some way or removed to a secure place.[97] The costs involved may be recovered from the person responsible for the nuisance. The defence of "best practicable means" exists in relation to a V.M.E. in a street being used for industrial, trade or business purposes.[98] A right of appeal exists within 21 days of service of a notice.

Enforcement/liaison with the police[99]

Unattended commercial vehicles, machinery and equipment may have a name and telephone number displayed. Before enforcing a notice, the investigating officer will attempt to trace the "person responsible".[100] Private vehicles will only have a registration plate and this will be the sole means of tracing that person. The person responsible in the case of a vehicle includes the person in whose name it is registered under the Vehicle (Excise) Act 1971 and any other person who is for the time being the driver. The Association of Chief Police Officers sees no problem in police officers obtaining information from the Police National Computer to pass to local authority investigating officers, providing such information would not contravene the Data Protection Act 1984.[101]

Liaison with the police will be necessary to establish procedures for

---

[95] Environmental Protection Act 1990, new s. 80A(4).
[96] *Ibid*, Sch. 3, para. 2A(2).
[97] *Ibid*, Sch. 3, para. 2A(3).
[98] *Ibid*, s. 82(10)(aa).
[99] See also the very useful *Noise Guide – Good Practice for Police and Local Authority Co-operation*, Chartered Institute of Environmental Health, 1997.
[100] The Noise and Statutory Nuisance Act 1993 amends the definition in s. 79(7) of the Environmental Protection Act 1990.
[101] s. 34(5)(a).

obtaining information on vehicle ownership. The presence of the police may also be necessary if an officer seeks to gain access to a vehicle to disable a noisy alarm. The police must be informed before taking action to secure compliance with an abatement notice or towing a V.M.E. away.[102]

The main types of noise from private vehicles in the street are likely to be continually operating alarms, D.I.Y. repairs and engine tuning. In the latter two cases, the person responsible should be readily identifiable and a notice served requiring immediate cessation or prohibiting the recurrence of the nuisance. In the case of a continually operating alarm causing a statutory nuisance on an unattended vehicle, the procedure outlined above must be used. During the one hour that must elapse between service of notice and taking abatement action, the investigating officer may be able to decide how likely it is that contact will be made with the owner or person responsible. He will also form a view about the ease of access to the vehicle and its alarm. The known availability of a locksmith or alarm specialist should be an element of the procedure established to enforce the statutory powers.

Where a vehicle cannot be disarmed without excessive damage, or it cannot be properly re-secured, towing it away to a secure compound may be necessary. Towing away a vehicle with its alarm ringing may temporarily disturb people on its route but that may be better than continual disturbance at the site of complaint. Care must be taken to ensure that the compound is not in a noise sensitive area.

Shortly after the Noise and Statutory Nuisance Act 1993 came into operation, Westminster L.B.C.'s 24-hour noise team successfully disarmed blaring alarms late at night in two densely populated areas.[103]

Parked heavy goods vehicles can produce noise nuisance due to engines left to "warm up" for long periods, especially in the early morning and noisy refrigerator units are a regular problem. Sophisticated alarms protect valuable cargoes and may be

---

[102] Environmental Protection Act 1990, Sch. 3, para. 2A(1)(a) and (b), (5) and (6).
[103] *Environmental Health News,* 14th January 1994, p. 2.

particularly difficult to disarm. Two particular matters will need to be considered in such cases:

1. The investigating officer may not cause more damage than is necessary.[104] Care must be taken if deactivating a refrigerator motor as this could result in the spoilage of a complete cargo.

2. Having accessed a vehicle, it must be re-secured as effectively as possible. Sophisticated alarms protecting valuable cargoes may be difficult to re-set.

If a successful appeal is to be avoided, one option may be to serve notice specifying compliance within one hour or whatever longer period is considered appropriate, with a further requirement that the nuisance should not recur. Towing away a large H.G.V. may not be a realistic option.

ANTI-SOCIAL BEHAVIOUR

Certain types of noise from human activity might be considered as a consequence of anti-social behaviour, e.g. noise from patrons of entertainment or licensed premises, noise associated with vehicles in streets and noise from neighbours whilst occupying property. Such matters are usually dealt with under quite specific powers.[105] However, there are cases where noise may be just one element of a more serious problem of anti-social behaviour, where an alternative course of action may be required. In such cases, cessation of noise disturbance may be a consequence of resolving a complexity of issues. The Crime and Disorder Act 1998 provides for the issue of Anti-Social Behaviour Orders.[106] Examples of cases where anti-social behaviour orders might be appropriate include:

(a) individuals intimidating neighbours and others through threats of violence;

---

[104] Environmental Protection Act 1990, Sch. 3, para. 2A(4).

[105] e.g. statutory nuisance proceedings under the Environmental Protection Act 1990; night noise offences under the Noise Act 1996; liquor and entertainment licensing controls.

[106] s. 1(4).

(b) persistent unruly behaviour by groups of individuals, possibly at unsocial hours;

(c) families whose anti-social behaviour leads to verbal abuse, vandalism and threats, etc.

Anti-Social Behaviour Orders are intended to deal with this kind of persistent, serious anti-social behaviour. The order is similar to an injunction and can be applied for by the police or local authority[107] against an individual acting in an anti-social manner. Before an application is made[108] for an order, there must be consultation between the police and the local authority.[109] An order can be made against anyone who is at least ten years old. Applications may be made where the police or local authority believe that someone has acted in an anti-social manner and that an order is necessary to protect people in the relevant area from such further behaviour. In considering an application for an order, the magistrates must disregard any act of the defendant which he shows to be reasonable in the circumstances.[110] An Anti-Social Behaviour Order remains in force for at least two years.[111] Breach of an order without reasonable excuse is a criminal offence, subject on summary conviction[112] to a term of imprisonment of up to six months or to a fine not exceeding the statutory maximum, or both; or on conviction on indictment,[113] to a prison term of up to five years or to a fine, or to both. Orders can be applied for and take effect in the local government area in which the anti-social behaviour takes place or the adjoining local government area after consultation with the relevant authority. A court is also able to make an order affecting more than one authority, subject to consultation.[114]

Private disputes between neighbours are not generally issues for this process, and the problems dealt with under this legislation are

---

[107] s. 1(1). These are defined as "relevant authorities" in s. 1(1)(b).
[108] To the local magistrates' court.
[109] s. 1(2).
[110] s. 1(5).
[111] s. 1(7).
[112] s. 1(10)(a).
[113] s. 1(10)(b).
[114] s. 1(6).

likely to require considerable liaison between the police and local authorities. Indeed, the Crime and Disorder Act 1998[115] requires police and local authorities, working with other key partners, to develop and implement a strategy for reducing crime and disorder in each district and unitary local authority in England and Wales. Local authorities, mainly through their Environmental Health and Housing Departments, have a significant role in dealing with anti-social behaviour and may need to decide on the most appropriate legislation in dealing with particular problems in their areas.[116] Up to November 1999, the courts had issued 466 Anti-Social Behaviour Orders.[117]

RECREATION NOISE

The increased interest in different forms of recreational activity has resulted in a range of noise sources that may cause public complaint. These include powerboat racing, model aircraft, motor car and cycle racing, jet-skiing and clay pigeon shooting. Control may be available through local byelaws, planning conditions or the statutory nuisance provisions of the Environmental Protection Act 1990.[118] The risk of hearing damage may be associated with some events. Noise from pop concerts can produce environmental noise problems as well as risk of hearing damage to the participants. Many of the organisations controlling this type of activity have produced their own Codes of Practice to which they expect organisers of events to adhere. Some of these controls are described below.

Model aircraft

A Code of Practice[119] deals with the legal noise control powers available and provides operating guidelines, including the use of

---

[115] ss. 5–7.
[116] See generally Chapter 2.
[117] Reported in *Environmental Health News*, Vol. 16, No. 45, p. 4, 23rd November 2001. The Home Office was reviewing their effectiveness at that time.
[118] s. 80.
[119] *Code of Practice on Noise from Model Aircraft*, 1982, H.M.S.O. Approval to its issue given under the Control of Noise (Code of Practice on Noise from Model Aircraft) Order 1981, made under s. 71, Control of Pollution Act 1974.

mufflers, maximum recommended noise limits, times of operation, the numbers of model aircraft that should be operated simultaneously and the use of noise barriers and separation distances. It also specifies the method of measurement of noise emitted by model aircraft.

Recreational boating and water skiing

Agreement has been reached in principle by the E.U. Council of Ministers on a Directive limiting noise from recreational boats and jet skis. It will impose duties on manufacturers and users to ensure that their craft do not exceed noise limits set by a complex formula.[120] A Code of Practice has also been developed by the British Water Ski Federation[121] which is a good example of the extent to which this and similar bodies associated with water sports seek to improve their environmental acceptability. The code describes the main sources of boat noise and addresses the range of skiing disciplines at club and tournament level. It provides guidelines for avoiding the impact of noise from water skiing on the surrounding community, including factors such as the noise output of the boats, course layout, hours of operation, the number of boats in use at any one time, screening of noise, the siting and use of public address systems, and how to control the effect of cars arriving at and leaving events. The maximum permissible noise levels from individual boats varies from 75 dBL_{Amax} for recreational, tournament and barefoot skiing to 105 dBL_{Amax} for international or world championship water ski racing events under specified noise measurement conditions.

An interesting and relevant common law decision applies to motor-boat races. In the case of *Kennaway v Thompson and Another*,[122] the plaintiff built a house on land she owned near a lake used for motor-boat races and water skiing since the early 1960s. She did not think that the club's activities would materially interfere with the comfort and enjoyment of her new house. However, by the time of its

---

[120] *Environmental Health News*, 23rd November 2001.
[121] *Code of Practice for Water Skiing and Noise*, October 1999.
[122] *Kennaway v Thompson and Another* [1980] All E.R. 329, C.A.

completion more races, using noisier boats, were taking place. By 1977 the club had become a centre for club, national and international races and the number of days used for racing and practising had increased. The plaintiff sought an injunction restraining the club from permitting excessive noise to affect her land and restricting motor-boat racing to certain times. The Judge upheld the claim of nuisance but refused to grant an injunction on the ground that this would be oppressive, having regard to the enjoyment of the activity by large numbers of the public. He awarded £1,000 damages for the nuisance already suffered and £15,000 in respect of future damage likely to be suffered. The plaintiff appealed against the refusal to grant an injunction, contending that having proved the nuisance interfered with her enjoyment of her land in a substantial and intolerant way, she was entitled to an injunction. It was held that although the plaintiff was not entitled to an injunction restraining all of the club's activities, and notwithstanding that an injunction in general terms would be unworkable, she was entitled to an injunction restraining the club from carrying on the activities which caused a nuisance to her enjoyment and use of her land, despite the public interest in such activities. The injunction restricted the club's racing activities in each year and the noise level of boats using the lake at other times. The injunction was granted in lieu of the £15,000 damages award.

Motor sports

Section 13 of the Road Traffic Act 1988 prohibits competitions or trials (other than races or trials of speed) on a public way[123] and involving motor vehicles unless the competition or trial is authorised and conducted in accordance with any conditions imposed by regulations. The Motor Vehicles (Competition and Trials) Regulations 1969[124] contain the relevant conditions. The Regulations specify that the Royal Automobile Club must authorise most events taking place on public roads. Such events must comply with standard conditions contained in the schedules to the Regulations. These include requirements intended to minimise noise nuisance

---

[123] A highway in England and Wales, a public road in Scotland.
[124] S.I. 1969 No. 414 as variously amended.

such as a limit of 120 vehicles driven by competitors in any night events,[125] and the interval between the times of arrival of the first and last competitors at the finish of the event must not exceed two hours in the case of a night event. The Royal Automobile Club can grant or withhold authorisation for any particular event having regard, amongst other things, to the extent to which the amenity or convenience of members of the public may be affected.

Where events do not take place on public roads, these controls do not exist. Although the Motor Sports Association[126] and other organisations such as the Auto-Cycle Union control many off-road events, participation in events under their control is voluntary by both organisers and competitors. It is relatively easy for "pirate" clubs to run an event in fields or other spaces without supervision or rules.

The Motor Sports Association exercises control over most organised car racing in the U.K. through its General Regulations.[127] The majority of car racing clubs are members of the Association and adhere to its rules. The Regulations have no statutory backing, with the Association exercising control by agreement with its members. Vehicles competing in events controlled by the Regulations are subject to mandatory silencing unless a specific waiver is granted.[128] Maximum permitted noise levels are set for car racing and rallycross, hill climbs and sprints, autocross, stage rallies, trials and road rallies. These vary between 98 dB(A) and 110 dB(A) at half a metre from the exhaust outlet, depending on the type of event. For British Formula Three, British GT and British Touring Car Championships, the limit is 118 dB(A).[129] International events such as Formula One (controlled by international rules) are not R.A.C. controlled.

---

[125] Between 10.00 p.m. and 7.00 a.m.

[126] Previously the R.A.C. Motor Sports Association.

[127] Copies of the Regulations and advice can be obtained from the Motor Sports Association, Motor Sports House, Riverside Park, Colnbrook, Slough SL3 0HG.

[128] Usually for specified older cars and for drag race vehicles. This waiver does not apply to events taking place on the public highway, where national legislation will apply.

[129] See paras. 12.17.1–12.17.10 of section E of the 2002 Regulations and para. 5.1 in relation to pre-testing in respect of rallying.

Sound testing requirements are included in the General Regulations and sound tests must be conducted prior to the start of all rallies catering for cars built after 1941 and other events using the public highway. In the case of such events, the organisers have to appoint Environmental Scrutineers to check on sound levels of competitors' and course cars. These officials have "... the power and authority to refuse a start or withhold time cards or route information from competitors deemed to have made excessive sound." The Association publishes a list of trained and accepted Environmental Scrutineers. The officials have to provide reports on their activities to the Clerk of the Course. There is no appeal against the decision of that official.

In the case of off-road motorcycle sport, riders generally have to join a club in order to compete in events. The principal organising bodies of events are the Auto Cycle Union (A.C.U.) and the Amateur Motor Cycle Association (A.M.C.A.). Maximum permitted noise levels are set by the A.C.U. for road racing and T.T. events, moto-cross, trials and Enduro, grass track, long track, beach racing and speedway. These vary from 94 dB(A) to 105 dB(A) at half a metre from the exhaust outlet, depending on the type of event. A Code of Practice[130] advises on noise controls on Enduro, grass track racing, moto-cross, rallycross, sand track, trials, trial cross and beach cross. Legal controls may be available through planning conditions applying to a particular site, the Road Traffic Act 1988,[131] the statutory nuisance provisions of the Environmental Protection Act 1990[132] or local byelaws. The Code of Practice deals with similar noise control principles to those contained in byelaws and also includes different maximum noise limits for machines competing in various types of event. The method of noise

---

[130] *Code of Practice on noise from organised off-road motor-cycle sport*, 1994. Produced by the Noise Council in association with other organisations, including the A.C.U. and A.M.C.A. The Land Access and Recreation Association also publishes guidance notes on sound control through its motorsports facilities unit. Ref. NFU/April 1998.

[131] s. 33 requires local authority authorisation for a motor vehicle trial of any description on a footpath or bridleway, subject to the written consent of the owner of the land over which it runs.

[132] s. 80.

measurement has to comply with the official Federation of International Motor Cyclists' tests. Excessively noisy machines can be excluded from racing by the Clerk of the Course.

Clay target shooting

A *Code of Practice on Noise from Clay Target Shooting*[133] gives valuable practical guidance on the ways in which noise may be controlled, together with a recommended method for noise measurement and its subsequent rating.

Concerts

Proper health and safety provision, including noise control, at large music events is a major consideration for those involved in their organisation. In its comprehensive guide,[134] the Health and Safety Commission provides advice on legal duties, health and safety matters, fire safety, hygiene and many other related issues. Its chapter on planning and organisation is a valuable introduction to the issues to be addressed and the chapter dealing with sound and noise gives helpful advice on the relevant law and ways of controlling employee and audience exposure. A Code of Practice has been published by the Noise Council dealing with environmental noise.[135] The Code recommends music noise levels (M.N.L.) for indoor and outdoor venues and also for controlling noise before and during the event.

Where Codes of Practice are produced by virtue of section 71 of the Control of Pollution Act 1974, they may be taken into account by the courts in the event of legal proceedings. Compliance with the provisions of such Codes must be considered as part of the "best practicable means" defence. Whilst other Codes will not have the

---

[133] Midlands Joint Advisory Committee for Environmental Protection, 3rd revision, March 1993.

[134] *Guide to health, safety and welfare at pop concerts and similar events,* 1993, H.M.S.O.

[135] *Code of Practice on Environmental Noise Control at Concerts,* The Noise Council, 1995. This is not an approved code for the purposes of s. 71 of the Control of Pollution Act 1974, but provides useful guidance as it is based on the considerable experience of the authors.

same standing in the courts, if they have become generally recognised guides to control over the activities to which they relate, in the absence of any better guidance the courts could presumably give them the same kind of consideration.

Bird scarers

The National Farmers' Union *Code of Practice on Bird Scarers* advises on the types of scarers available and alternatives to reduce the need for such devices. Recommended noise controls include use only between sunrise and sunset (not before 6.00 a.m. if sunrise is earlier), firing no more than four times per hour, liaison with other farmers who may also be using them to limit the noise in any one locality, siting as far as possible from noise sensitive buildings and use of noise absorbent shields. The Ministry of Agriculture, Fisheries and Food has also published useful advice.[136]

RECREATIONAL HEARING HAZARDS

Many recreational activities which cause annoyance to people living and working close to them and which may be actionable under the nuisance laws also present a hearing risk to the participants. This fact was recognised by the Noise Advisory Council. The Council said "We usually regard recreational and leisure activities as being beneficial for the body or stimulating or relaxing for the mind – and in most cases they are. But there are leisure pursuits and sports which, if not undertaken sensibly, can result in permanent damage to the hearing of participants and, in extreme cases, of spectators."[137]

The extensive literature on possible hearing hazards from non-occupational noise exposure has been the subject of a detailed review by the M.R.C. Institute of Hearing Research.[138] Despite criticisms of the design, methodology and reporting of some of the

---

[136] *Bird Scaring*, Leaflet 903 public, 1984, M.A.F.F.
[137] *Hearing Hazards and Recreation*, Noise Advisory Council, 1977, H.M.S.O.
[138] *Damage to hearing arising from leisure noise: a review of the literature*, M.R.C. Institute of Hearing Research, 1985, H.M.S.O.

studies undertaken, it was possible to form certain overall conclusions:

(a) the major source of hearing hazard from non-occupational noise exposure is amplified music;

(b) for individuals, the worst cases of discotheque and personal cassette player exposure represent real risks, as do other forms of recreational exposure such as shooting without proper hearing protection;

(c) the number of people exposed to very high levels of leisure noise exposure is not known but those who are regularly exposed to both high levels of leisure noise and occupational noise are exposed to increasing risk of hearing damage.

The literature indicates that the following noise levels might be associated with particular leisure activities:

Discotheques:	120 dB(A)	(Levels above 120 dB(A) are approaching the threshold of pain)
Live pop/rock groups:	119 dB(A)	
Personal cassette players:	128 dB(A)	
Classical music:	100 dB(A)	
Arcade games:	111 dB(A)	
Shotguns:	165 dB(A)	
Military rifles:	173 dB(A)	
Racing cars:	106 dB(A)	
Motor-boats:	99 dB(A)	
Sports stadia:	60-100 dB(A) depending on the sport	
Domestic appliances:	90 dB(A)	

These noise levels are not necessarily typical, merely indicative of maximum levels recorded in some of the literature reviewed. The impact of leisure noise on hearing will depend on the level, duration and frequency of exposure, and the impact of any occupational noise exposure. Although the precise effect of leisure noise on the participants may be uncertain in many cases, regular participants in particularly noisy activities, e.g. shooting and motor racing, should use suitable forms of hearing protection.

Chapter 4

NOISE ABATEMENT ZONES

In its report *Neighbourhood Noise*[1] published in 1971, the Noise Advisory Council criticised the "nuisance" approach to the abatement of excessive neighbourhood noise as it could not prevent a creeping deterioration in the overall noise climate of a neighbourhood and would certainly not secure a positive improvement. It also directed attention to the continuing growth of public sensitivity to noise and to the the greater depth of knowledge and experience that had been gained by local authorities. This increased sensitivity and knowledge accentuated the shortcomings of the Noise Abatement Act 1960,[2] and the Council felt that the opportunity existed to introduce radical new measures to control environmental noise. It was suggested that those measures include the possibility of more comprehensive action, at least in areas experiencing acute neighbourhood noise problems. It has long since been considered that the primary aim of legislation, including that dealing with noise, should be prevention. Both the Noise Advisory Council and the Committee on the Problem of Noise[3] recognised that action needed to be taken to avoid unnecessary noise and prevent further increases in ambient noise levels.

The views of the then Association of Public Health Inspectors (now Chartered Institute of Environmental Health) contained in the *Neighbourhood Noise* report were further endorsed in a subsequent report of the Noise Advisory Council.[4] This latter report also emphasised the value of careful planning to minimise the effects of noise on urban populations. The power to declare Noise Abatement Zones is a potentially useful planning power as it allows control not only of existing noise situations, but also the control of noise from proposed development. The prime purpose of a Noise Abatement

---

[1] *Neighbourhood Noise,* Noise Advisory Council, 1971, H.M.S.O.
[2] Subsequently repealed by the Control of Pollution Act 1974.
[3] *Noise,* Final Report of the Committee on the Problem of Noise, Cmnd. 2056, 1963, H.M.S.O.
[4] *Noise in the Next Ten Years,* Noise Advisory Council, 1974, H.M.S.O.

Zone is to enable the local authority to record existing noise levels from specified classes of premises and to prevent those levels being exceeded without express permission. A Noise Abatement Zone provides a safeguard against the gradual worsening of existing noise levels from premises subject to this form of control and, in appropriate cases where a public benefit would be achieved, notices may be served requiring noise levels to be reduced.

Although the concept of these zones was intended to control the gradual increase in ambient noise levels and maintain controls in designated areas, this has not happened to the extent anticipated. This is probably due to the laborious procedures that must be followed to designate a zone and maintain the necessary registers and noise monitoring regimes. An unpublished study by the Building Research Establishment in 1993 on behalf of the Department of the Environment reported that only 58 zones had been designated since 1976, including just five since 1984. Of the total number, 40 were no longer in operation and it appears that only very limited enforcement action was taken in the others. Monitoring and enforcement was found to be virtually non-existent. The Noise Review Working Party recommended[5] that in the future such zones should be established using procedures issued under a code of practice rather than the present regulations.

LEGAL POWERS – Control of Pollution Act 1974 Part III

In considering implementation of the Noise Abatement Zone powers there are a number of important principles involved. These can be summarised:

(a) initial action on a limited scale is preferable to gain experience of the legal and practical implications. Once initiated, the powers can be extended in the light of experience and local need;

(b) it is important to have regard to the existing legal powers to control noise including the nuisance procedures and Town and

---

[5]   *Report of the Noise Review Working Party,* 1990, p. viii. The Government committed itself to such changes in its White Paper *This Common Inheritance,* Chapter 16, p. 213, 1990.

Country Planning powers, to ensure that the appropriate course of action is taken to deal with noise problems;

(c) guidance issued by the Government[6] together with the relevant statutory instruments[7] and other publications[8] should be considered carefully before implementing the procedures for declaration of zones;

(d) the practical implications associated with measurement as detailed later in this chapter must be carefully considered to ensure correct measurement techniques and therefore adequate subsequent control;

(e) the availability of financial and manpower resources will be significant and where these are at a premium it is likely that the greatest benefit to be achieved by the use of these powers will be:

(i) in areas of new development where factories and other noise producing premises might otherwise become unacceptably intrusive;

(ii) in densely populated areas of mixed residential and industrial property where noise from the fixed premises is a predominant factor in that environment and therefore maintenance of existing levels, and possibly ultimate reduction, is desirable;

(iii)in areas where comprehensive environmental improvement is contemplated. Use of Noise Abatement Zone powers

---

[6] *Control of Pollution Act 1974, Implementation of Part III*, Circ. 2/76 (DoE), 3/76 (Welsh Office), 27th February, 1976. "Noise Abatement Zones: Part 1", *Building Research Establishment Digest No. 203*, July 1977. "Noise Abatement Zones: Part 2", *Building Research Establishment Digest No. 204*, August 1977.

[7] The Control of Noise (Appeals) Regulations 1975, S.I. 1975 No. 2116 and the Control of Noise (Measurement and Registers) Regulations 1976, S.I. 1976 No. 37.

[8] *Noise Levels at the Boundaries of Factories and Commercial Premises*, Jenkins, M.P., Salvidge, A.C. and Utley, W.A., Building Research Station, June 1976.

could be especially valuable where it is proposed to introduce other area improvements under housing, planning or traffic control legislation;

(iv) in cases where noise nuisances have been abated by action under section 80 of the Environmental Protection Act 1990 and it is important to hold the noise climate at the level which results from compliance with the local authority's notice. This is likely to be especially important in the case of extensive premises whose activities affect people in a wide area;

(f) the degree of control to be exercised will remain a matter for local discretion dependent upon individual circumstances and therefore, within the general framework of guidance issued by the Department of the Environment,[9] local authorities will be able to determine the best method of control.

Although the definition of noise includes vibration,[10] no guidance has been given as to how to deal with groundborne vibrations under the Noise Abatement Zone provisions. The complexity of vibration measurement does not readily lend itself to control of this nature and it is probably more appropriate to deal with vibration under the statutory nuisance provisions of the law.

Duty of inspection

Section 57(b) of the Act imposes a duty on local authorities to inspect their areas from time to time to determine how to exercise their powers relating to Noise Abatement Zones. Local authorities are not required to introduce Noise Abatement Zones and may choose to exercise their judgment based upon economic and other considerations. The requirement is to inspect from time to time and therefore any decisions *not* to introduce Noise Abatement Zones can be varied according to changing circumstances. This duty allows local authorities to decide how to exercise their powers under sections 63 to 67 of the Act.

---

[9]   See *Control of Pollution Act 1974, Implementation of Part III*, Circ. 2/76.
[10] s. 73(1), Control of Pollution Act 1974.

Local authorities will not be required to introduce zones by any specified date. The degree of inspection of its area is left to the discretion of the local authority.[11] Criteria are not specified by which local authorities may judge whether it is appropriate to introduce Noise Abatement Zones but factors that may be significant in determining whether the powers should be used may include:

(a) the level of noise from certain types of premises when compared with ambient or background noise relative to existing recommendations on noise levels;[12] and

(b) the volume of public complaint concerning noise so as to determine whether the use of these powers would provide a "public benefit";[13]

(c) the response from social surveys to determine whether local residents consider that the noise climate associated with certain types of premises is acceptable or not;

(d) the need to maintain a reduced noise level achieved as a result of implementing the statutory nuisance powers in the Environmental Protection Act 1990 or Control of Pollution Act 1974.

Noise Abatement Order

Section 63(1) of the Act provides for a local authority to declare by order a "Noise Abatement Order" designating all or any part of its area a Noise Abatement Zone. The Order may not necessarily apply to the whole of the local authority's area or to all premises within a Noise Abatement Zone. However, the Order must specify the

---

[11] See ss. 73(1) and 73(2). "Local Authority" means (a) in England and Wales, the council of a district or a London borough, the Common Council of the City of London, the Sub-Treasurer of the Inner Temple and the Under-Treasurer of the Middle Temple; and (b) in Scotland, an islands or district council.

[12] British Standard 4142:1997 – *Method of Rating Industrial Noise affecting mixed residential and industrial areas*, and the International Standards Organisation recommendation R1996. (This recommendation was not however accepted by the United Kingdom.)

[13] s. 66.

classes of premises to which it applies and which will be subject to the controls under Part III of the Act.[14] The following list of broad classes may be included and there is nothing to prohibit the specification in the Order of individual named premises:

(a) industrial premises – factories, small workshops, etc;

(b) commercial premises – warehouses, offices, shops, hotels, garages;

(c) places of entertainment or assembly – theatres, bingo halls, discotheques, stadia;

(d) agricultural premises – farms, crop drying establishments, grain storage installations;

(e) transport installations – railway stations, bus garages, wharves, locomotive and aircraft repair shops, container bases;

(f) public utility installations – water works, power stations, transformer substations, gas works, coal mines.

The transient noise that tends to be associated with domestic premises and civil engineering works is not intended to be dealt with under the Noise Abatement Zone powers. The statutory nuisance powers and the provisions of sections 60 and 61 dealing with construction works, etc. are more appropriate.

After declaration by a local authority, the Order cannot be confirmed until the authority has considered any objections to its proposals. Schedule 1 of the Act specifies the procedure for notification of making the Order to owners, lessees and occupiers of premises, and to the public. It provides for the consideration of objections by the Secretary of State prior to confirmation of the Order. Orders made and confirmed under section 63 may be revoked or varied in accordance with a subsequent Order made and confirmed.[15]

---

[14] s. 63(2).

[15] s. 63(3). Sch. 1 of the Act is amended by Sch. 2 of the Local Government, Planning and Land Act 1980 in that confirmation of the Order by the Secretary of State is no longer required.

The Act does not state the grounds for objection against the declaration of an Order but the following have been presented at inquiries:[16]

(a) "That confirmation of the Order would involve unnecessary expenditure by the council[17] which, in the prevailing economic climate, would be contrary to Government policy";

(b) that the council might not have adequate numbers of properly qualified staff to administer the Order without taking staff away from other duties;

(c) that the benefits to be obtained from the order were doubtful;[18]

(d) that no one had ever complained about the noise made by the objectors' premises during the 20 years it had operated;[19]

(e) that the small number of complaints about noise from the type of premises operated by the objector (launderettes) adduced by

---

[16] Objections(a)–(g) were particularly related to a launderette but the Secretary of State's decision would seem to apply equally to other premises that may be included in an Order as a class to which the Order applies.

[17] The Secretary of State in his decision considered that it was for the council to decide whether to exercise the discretion given to them under Part III of the Act. It is reasonable to assume that the local authority has had regard to paras. 5 and 6 of Circular 2/76 which refers to "... leaving each authority to decide in the light of local circumstances how far they (the discretionary noise control powers) should be implemented". Circular 2/76 advises (para. 1.5 Appendix 2) that "... Noise Abatement Orders should only be made when adequate resources are available". Local authorities no doubt will therefore have considered the manpower and financial implications of a Noise Abatement Zone programme before embarking on a scheme. As far as Government policy is concerned, the Secretary of State has indicated that it is the total of local authority expenditure which has major relevance to the control of public expenditure and to the Government's economic strategy. Local authorities must make their decisions in the light of local circumstances and determine their own priorities.

[18] In his decision notice, the Secretary of State, whilst accepting the observations of the objector, could see no reason why the Order should not result in an environmental benefit, by preventing or limiting increases in noise emitted from premises. He concluded that confirmation of the Order should not be withheld solely because positive environmental benefit could not be predicted.

[19] *Ibid.*

the council showed that noise nuisance caused by them is negligible;[20]

(f) that specific nuisance from noise can be dealt with under the law as it stands without making the Order;[21]

(g) that confirmation of the Order would entail yet another set of rules and regulations affecting the running of the type of premises operated by the objector which would add to the unfair burden on small businesses;

(h) the establishment of a Noise Abatement Zone could adversely affect the value of the premises subject to control due to specific restrictions being placed on the permitted noise level for those premises and, in addition, deter prospective purchasers or lessees;[22]

(i) the inclusion of premises within a Noise Abatement Zone might adversely affect an application to the local authority for permission to change the use of the premises from, say, "warehousing" to "industrial". It was suggested that such a planning application should be considered by the local authority on its own merits free from any predetermined noise levels.[23]

Measurement of noise

Section 64(1) provides that when a Noise Abatement Order has

---

[20] The Secretary of State referred to Circular 2/76 which states "a wide variety of types of Noise Abatement Zones are possible with purposes ranging from maintaining satisfactory environmental conditions to control of high noise levels in mixed residential and industrial areas" (para. 2.8 of Appendix 2). He concluded that the inclusion of premises producing satisfactory noise levels at the time provided the opportunity to ensure that they remained satisfactory and was therefore consistent with the objective of maintaining satisfactory environmental conditions.

[21] *Ibid.*

[22] An application to the local authority to allow an increase in the registered noise levels can, however, be made under s. 65. This is no more onerous a restriction than most planning conditions and is not accepted by the Secretary of State.

[23] This argument, if accepted, could, because of the nature of the change of use, lead to an increase in noise levels which is precisely the situation the Noise Abatement Zone seeks to avoid unless the local authority consents to an increase.

been confirmed and the zone designated, the local authority is obliged to measure the noise levels from the classes of premises included in the Order. The local authority itself can decide when measurements are to be made and when made these must be recorded in a noise level register[24] and a copy of the record served on the owner and occupier of the premises to which the measurements relate.[25] This section again gives discretion to the local authority as to when measurements are carried out[26] but, if the authority considers it necessary to implement the Noise Abatement Zone provisions, it is sensible to carry out the subsequent measurements as soon as possible after confirmation of the Order so that effective noise control is achieved at the earliest possible date. Section 64 also provides for appeals to the Secretary of State within 28 days of service of the copy of the details in the noise level register.[27] Subsequently, the Secretary of State may direct the local authority, as he considers necessary, as to the record of the measurement of noise and the local authority is obliged to comply with his directions.[28] Presumably, he may accept or reject measurements, order them to be checked or made again and, indeed, require any amendments considered necessary to the register.

It is important for the owner or occupier of premises, if wishing to dispute the measurements, to follow the appeal procedure, as the validity or accuracy of any details in the noise level register cannot be questioned in subsequent proceedings under Part III of the Act.[29] Prior consultation therefore with the enforcing authority is desirable so that the owner or occupier can satisfy himself beforehand of the validity or accuracy of the measurements recorded in the noise level register. The noise level register has to be open to public inspection

---

[24] s. 64(2). The register must contain the particulars specified in the Control of Noise (Measurement and Registers) Regulations 1976, S.I. 1976 No. 37 or the Noise Levels (Measurement and Registers) (Scotland) Regulations 1982, S.I. 1982 No. 600.

[25] s. 64(3). The copy should be served in accordance with s. 233 of the Local Government Act 1972 or s. 192 of the Local Government (Scotland) Act 1973.

[26] s. 64(6).

[27] s. 64(3) and see the Control of Noise (Appeals) Regulations 1975, S.I. 1975 No. 2116.

[28] s. 64(4).

[29] s. 64(5).

and reasonable facilities are to be provided for obtaining copies of entries in the register on payment of reasonable charges.[30]

The intent of the Noise Abatement Zone is to hold steady, if not actually reduce, ambient noise levels. It is therefore provided that the level of noise recorded in the register must not be exceeded in respect of any specified premises except with the written consent of the local authority in accordance with the provisions of section 65. Such consent may be conditional as to the degree by which the noise level may be increased or as to the periods for which, or during which, the levels may be increased. Details of any consent must be recorded in the noise level register.[31] The local authority must determine applications for consent within two months unless a longer period is agreed, on receipt of the application. If notification of the local authority's decision is not given within that period, then the consent is deemed to have been refused.[32] Provision exists for an appeal against the local authority's decision to the Secretary of State within three months of the notification[33] or the expiration of two months (or longer) period where no notification is given.[34] The local authority must act upon the Secretary of State's decision on appeal. *The consent does not in itself constitute a defence against proceedings instituted by an individual on his own account to secure the abatement of a noise nuisance.[35] However, compliance with the terms of any consent would be a defence to an offence of failing to comply with an abatement notice.*

Excess noise
Noise emitted from premises in excess of the noise level recorded in the register, or contravention of a condition attached to a consent under section 65, is an offence under Part III of the Act.[36] On conviction, the court may make an order requiring the execution of

---

[30] s. 64(7).
[31] s. 65(2).
[32] s. 65(3).
[33] s. 65(4).
[34] s. 65(3).
[35] Power of an individual to take proceedings in the Magistrates' Court under s. 82 of the Environmental Protection Act 1990.
[36] s. 65(5).

any necessary works to prevent the offence continuing or recurring.[37] Failure of a person against whom an order is made, *without reasonable excuse,* to comply with the requirements of the order, makes him guilty of an offence under Part III of the Act. In addition, the Magistrates' Court can require the local authority to carry out any requirements that it could make of the convicted person, either instead of, or in addition to, their requirements of that person.[38]

Under the provisions of section 69, the local authority has power to execute any necessary works on its own initiative *and without a Court Order* if the convicted person fails to execute the requirements of the order or notice. In either case, the section allows a local authority to recover its costs in executing works in default, except such of those costs as can be shown to be unnecessary in the circumstances.

NOISE MEASUREMENT

The complexity of noise measurement and the problems affecting the accuracy of recorded results will be well known to those with experience of investigating noise problems. The sound levels being measured may vary substantially. Background noise and noise from other premises in the vicinity, together with different climatic conditions, are all likely to have some effect on the reliability of the results. The Control of Noise (Measurement and Registers) Regulations 1976, together with D.O.E. Circular 2/76, state the requirements placed upon local authorities and also give guidance on the measurement of noise. There are a number of practical implications which need to be considered in implementing these requirements and the following observations relate specifically to the requirements of the Control of Noise (Measurement and Registers) Regulations 1976.[39]

Measurement and calculation of noise level

Until such time as the Secretary of State, in consequence of representations made to him or otherwise, considers it necessary to

---

[37] s. 65(6).
[38] s. 65(7).
[39] S.I. 1976 No. 37.

determine alternative measurement or calculation methods, local authorities must adhere to the requirements of these Regulations. Only experience in the application of the Act and the Regulations will determine whether a more satisfactory method of assessment is available. It should, however, be recognised that the requirements for measurement specified in the Schedule to these Regulations are based upon the field work of the Building Research Establishment and some of the results of that work are contained in a report of a survey of noise levels near the boundaries of some industrial and commercial premises.[40] During the surveys, hand-held meters were used with measurements taken over relatively short periods. That experience and detailed consideration of the problems of measurement were considered in producing the measurement regulations. The lack of any real development of the Noise Abatement Zone powers tends to indicate that, as suggested by the Noise Review Working Party,[41] the measurement requirements are rather complicated. Decisions of the courts will of course be significant in this respect. However, there are so far no reported decisions of the courts to give further guidance.

The noise level to be measured at each measuring position is the equivalent continuous noise level (L_{eq}) measured in dB(A), *over a stated period of time*. L_{eq} is defined as "that level of continuous noise which has, over any defined period, the same energy content as the actual noise during that period". An offence occurs if noise emitted from premises subject to control exceeds the registered noise level. It may be reasonable to assume that if measurements of relatively short duration, say 30 minutes at each measurement point, are recorded in the noise level register, then any subsequent proceedings for contravention can only relate to the period of time recorded in the register and the noise level recorded during that period of time. However, where relatively steady noise exists, it should be possible to agree after discussion with the occupier of the premises subject to control, that short period measurements actually

---

[40] *Noise Levels at the Boundaries of Factories and Commercial Premises,* Jenkins, M.P., Salvidge, A.C. and Utley, W.A., Building Research Station, June 1976.

[41] Page 9, para. 3.15.

represent the normal activity for a greater period. Accordingly, the entry in the register may then be the level assessed as being that equivalent to, say, the whole of the day or night shift as appropriate. Where noise fluctuates significantly, the measurement and calculation procedures of the Regulations should be adhered to.

Absolute attention to detail is essential and must include the details indicated below ("the noise level register"). Adequate staff training on the requirements of the law and the correct use of the equipment required for this exercise will also be essential in order that the correct techniques are used.

The Schedule to the Regulations suggests that, whilst the effects of extraneous noise on measurements must be carefully considered, in certain situations it may be possible temporarily to silence the extraneous noise. Where the silencing involves the cessation of work at adjacent commercial or industrial premises, this suggestion is not likely to be received favourably, particularly where extensive monitoring is required because of a fluctuating pattern of noise.

It is stated that if the sound level averaged visually from a meter over a short period of time (i.e. 30 to 60 seconds) remains substantially unchanged throughout the period of interest, the indicated reading is numerically equal to L_{eq} for that period. The noise is deemed steady if fluctuations of the meter reading do not exceed ± 4 dB(A). To avoid appeals it is extremely important that the agreement of the occupier of the premises being controlled is obtained and that the reading taken in this manner represents the normal noise output and is indeed truly representative.

The noise level register

Section 64(2) requires the local authority to keep a noise level register[42] for the purpose of recording levels of noise from classified premises. In relation to each of the premises in respect of which an entry is required to be made, the following information is necessary:

---

42 See the Control of Noise (Measurement and Registers) Regulations 1976, S.I. 1976 No. 37 and the Noise Levels (Measurement and Registers) (Scotland) Regulations 1982, S.I. 1982 No. 600.

(a) the address, or other sufficient identification, of the premises and the specified class to which they belong or, where section 67(1) applies, will belong;

(b) such other particulars as are appropriate;

(c) any cancellation or alteration of an entry in the register and the reason for the cancellation or alteration;

(d) the date on which each entry, calculation or alteration is made.

The register must contain a record of the noise level and the particulars of the method of measurement or calculation, and must include:

(i) the location (including height) of each point at which the measurements were taken, or for which the calculations were made;

(ii) relevant details of any equipment used for the purpose;

(iii) the dates and times when such measurements were taken and relevant details of the prevailing weather conditions.

The register must include an index which may be in the form of, or incorporate, a map. The use of a map drawn to scale is likely to be essential.

The essence of these requirements is to ensure that detail is provided which is sufficiently accurate to enable the validity and accuracy of the measurements or calculations to be proven and is, of course, essential for subsequent reassessment. If the premise is accepted that most noise problems occur at night-time, and therefore this is a period when control through Noise Abatement Zones is likely to achieve the greatest benefit, then this information is vital if a person carrying out night-time measurements is to find the correct measurement points. This will probably mean the use of detailed plans, drawings and photographs indicating the precise measurement points. Some of the information recorded may also relate to topographical features which it should be recognised will change from winter to summer. Reliance, therefore, on means of identification such as "adjacent to an elm tree" would not be particularly helpful if that tree had been cut down due to Dutch Elm Disease or the person investigating the noise levels could not identify an elm tree in winter without its foliage.

Precision and accuracy in the noise level register is essential as it provides the basis for subsequent statutory control of noise from the premises.

Noise control boundary

Guidance is given on where this should be drawn[43] and the exercise of measurement is easier if this coincides with the site boundary. This is not always the case. In areas where noise is a particular problem, it is likely that premises under control will have contiguous boundaries. In such cases, the noise control boundary could well be in a public highway, on top of a high wall or in privately owned land. These problems are not insurmountable but care is necessary to ensure not only that the measurement points are positioned so as to enable the noise to be properly assessed, but also that they can be relocated for subsequent reassessment of the noise climate.

The "noise control boundary" is that associated with the premises subject to control and will not usually be the boundary of the Noise Abatement Zone unless, for some reason, it is decided that the zone should be the area occupied by one premises. This could occur, for example, in a largely residential area containing one large factory premises with no other noise producing industries and without any areas of land on which noisy activities might be developed. The Regulations and other publications give detailed advice on where to measure. Measurement points should be located on the "noise control boundary" and the basis of locating the measurement points is that the whole face of each of the buildings on the site is regarded as a noise source and is to be contained within a certain angle of the measurement point. This is illustrated overleaf.

---

[43] See memorandum to the Control of Noise (Measurement and Registers) Regulations 1976 and *Building Research Station Digest No. 203*, July 1977, "Noise Abatement Zones: Part 1".

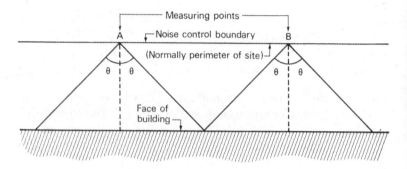

Fig. 9. Geometric basis of measuring points.

Typical plans that might be included in a noise level register showing noise control boundaries and the location of measurement points are also shown.

Guidance is given[44] on how to deal with noise containing noticeable pure tones. The problems associated with measurement where a standing wave pattern exists are indicated. It is likely, however, that noise with a distinguishable pure tone characteristic will also cause complaints of nuisance. In such a case it may well be desirable to act in accordance with the nuisance procedure before carrying out measurements for Noise Abatement Zone purposes.

When to measure

The aim should be to determine typical levels of noise from premises. Measurements should therefore be made when activity is as near normal as possible. Determination of typical noise levels may be difficult and is likely to be influenced by the following factors:

(a) large factories in particular may have to vary their output significantly during any period to meet the variations in trade associated with the national economy, the effects of industrial disputes and changes in production schedules;

---

[44] See memorandum to Control of Noise (Measurement and Registers) Regulations 1976.

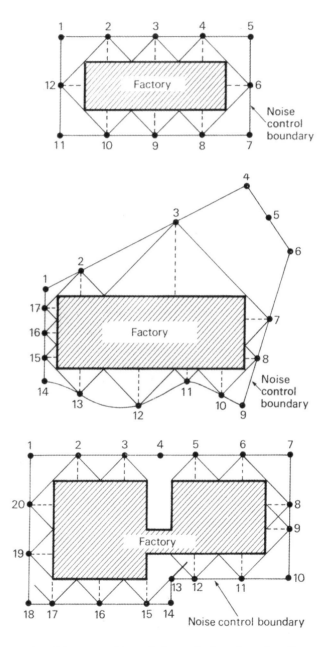

Fig. 10. Noise control boundaries and microphone locations.

(b) noise levels at the perimeter will undoubtedly vary at different times of the year because of different demands for the use of heating or ventilation equipment.

Accordingly, to exercise the full control which is desirable under the Noise Abatement Zone provisions, the detailed control discussed in the Schedule to the Regulations is likely to be desirable.

Meteorological conditions

The Schedule to the Regulations refers to the most suitable conditions for making measurements of noise levels. Adverse weather conditions will obviously make measurements unreliable and attempts at the control under extreme conditions could not be justified. The important factors to take into account are:

(a) *Wind* – the Schedule to the Regulations discusses the desirable conditions but even the conditions suggested to be satisfactory may not always be so, e.g. it is stated "when the noise source is 25 metres from the measuring position, calm or any wind direction is acceptable". The accuracy of measurements, however, even in these circumstances would depend very largely on *wind strength,* the effect of nearby buildings and topographical features and also the level of noise actually being measured;

(b) *Temperature gradient* – this can significantly affect the sound propagation due to the changed behaviour of sound waves when there is a variation of temperature with height. Measurements of noise levels should not, therefore, normally be taken in conditions of temperature inversion (often associated with calm, clear nights and a tendency for the formation of mist or fog);

(c) *Wet weather* – reception of noise can be adversely affected by snow and rain or fog, and normally the measurements should not be taken in adverse conditions such as these.

NOISE REDUCTION NOTICES

The power of the local authority to require the maintenance of existing levels of noise and to give consent to higher levels is further strengthened by section 66 which provides for a reduction in noise levels in certain circumstances. The local authority has power to serve a "noise reduction notice" on the responsible person where it appears that the noise level from any premises is not acceptable, having regard to purposes for which the Order was made.[45] *The local authority must be satisfied that a reduction in level is practicable at reasonable cost and would afford a public benefit.*[46] The requirements of the notice would be to reduce noise to a level specified in the notice, to prevent subsequent increases without the local authority's consent and to take steps specified in the notice.[47] A minimum of six months must be given to carry out the necessary steps[48] and the notice may be more comprehensive by specifying particular times or days during which the noise level is to be reduced and may require the level to be reduced to different levels for different times or days.[49] Relevant details must be recorded in the noise level register.[50] Right of appeal to the Magistrates' Court within three months of the date of service of notice exists.[51] The contravention of the notice without reasonable excuse is an offence under Part III,[52] although the defence of "best practicable means"[53] exists in relation to noise produced in the course of a trade or business. It would seem that there could be no defence that the local authority consented to a higher noise level under s. 65, for a noise reduction notice takes effect whether or not a consent authorises a level higher than specified in the notice.[54] However, compliance with a noise reduction notice is a defence in proceedings for an offence relating to noise nuisance proceedings. Notwithstanding this, a consent given under section 65 must contain a statement that the consent does not of itself constitute any ground of defence against proceedings by an individual in respect of noise nuisance.[55]

---

[45] s. 66(1)(a).
[46] s. 66(1)(b).
[47] s. 66(2).
[48] s. 66(3).
[49] s. 66(4).
[50] s. 66(6).
[51] s. 66(7).
[52] s. 66(8).
[53] See s. 72.
[54] s. 66(5).
[55] Under s. 82 of the Environmental Protection Act 1990.

The question of reasonable cost is a matter which will need to be determined ultimately by the courts but, in the first instance, probably the most important thing to determine is whether a reduction in noise levels would afford a public benefit. No guidance is given as to the degree of noise reduction that should be required or how to determine whether public benefit would be achieved. The assessment of public benefit could involve:

(a) social surveys to determine local opinion as to the acceptability or otherwise of local noise levels from the particular premises subject to a noise reduction notice;

(b) assessment against existing criteria.[56]

Whichever is the case, a most detailed examination of all noise sources in a premises subject to control will be necessary to determine:

(a) the relevance of the contributory noise sources to the overall noise climate;

(b) the degree of sound attenuation that can be achieved within the concept of "best practicable means";[57]

(c) the overall effect of reducing the noise in terms of reasonable expense and the likely response of the local population to the attenuation that it is considered can reasonably be achieved, e.g. would an overall reduction of 3 dB(A), which would barely be noticeable, be justified?

NEW DEVELOPMENTS

Section 67 allows the local authority to determine noise levels in the case of new buildings or premises falling within the classes subject to the Noise Abatement Order. The local authority may determine in advance acceptable noise levels for new buildings which, if in a class included in the relevant Noise Abatement Order, will be the

---

[56] e.g. British Standard 4142:1997 – *Method of Rating Industrial Noise affecting mixed residential and industrial areas.*

[57] s. 66(9) provides a "best practicable means" defence.

subject of control on completion. The local authority may act on its own account in determining such levels, or on the application of the owner or the occupier or a person negotiating to acquire an interest in the premises.[58] The noise level so determined must be recorded in the noise level register[59] and notified to the applicant or, if the local authority has acted on its own account, to the owner or occupier of the premises.[60] Quite clearly a person negotiating to acquire an interest in any premises would be advised to make a search in the noise level register and make enquiries of the owner and occupier as to the intended noise level for those premises. A person served with notice has three months to appeal to the Secretary of State[61] but obviously a person negotiating the acquisition of an interest in premises, if he is not the applicant under section 67, will not receive the notice. In such a case it would probably be necessary to protect his interest in any contract with the building owner. Where an application is made and the local authority decision is not notified to the applicant within two months of its receipt by the local authority, the local authority is deemed to have given notice that it has decided not to determine the application. Section 67 again allows a three month appeal period to the Secretary of State.

It is not a mandatory requirement to apply for determination of the acceptable noise levels in advance. Section 67(5) provides that where a new building or premises, having undergone works, becomes premises to which the Noise Abatement Order applies, and further that no noise level has been determined, then section 66 applies with certain alterations. These are that the authority need not be satisfied that a reduction in the level of noise is practicable at reasonable cost and would afford a public benefit. The noise reduction notice may require the noise level to be reduced and necessary steps taken within three months. In proceedings for an offence under section 66 for contravention of the noise reduction notice, the "best practicable means" would be no defence. There is

---

[58] s. 67(1).
[59] s. 67(2).
[60] s. 67(3).
[61] ss. 67(3) and (4).

therefore an incentive for people proposing to alter or construct premises to apply for a determination of noise levels.

The target levels to be set for new development will be largely dependent upon local circumstances. It would be impracticable, for instance, for industrialists and others to be subjected to the same target levels for new development in predominantly industrial areas as those which might be required in a semi-rural area, although the need to prevent the creeping increase in background noise may justify the determination of noise levels sufficiently below existing ambient levels to avoid any overall increase in the area after the development is completed.

In view of the fact that Noise Abatement Zones are intended to limit increases in ambient noise, ambient levels for an area in which development is to take place should be measured wherever possible and the resultant levels used as a guide to determining target levels. It is difficult to give clear guidance as to the levels that should be set for new development although, as the principle of Noise Abatement Zones is to prevent increases in ambient noise, it could be argued that the target level for new development should be maintenance of the pre-existing ambient levels. Whatever is considered appropriate in individual cases, an exercise is desirable to assess the likely noise levels arising from the completed development at the noise control boundary. Ideally, this could be done by the applicants for planning permission (unless the development does not require planning approval), possibly as an element of a comprehensive environmental assessment submitted as part of a planning application. Alternatively, the local authority may wish to carry out its own assessments based upon the following:

(a) estimated noise from buildings and plant;

(b) noise from circulating traffic.

Such an exercise can involve the provision of details concerning the noise output from items of plant and machinery, details concerning the construction of buildings and additional information such as the anticipated shift pattern and the detailed production programme involved in manufacturing premises. Detailed information on the sound levels of new equipment is not always available and it may often be necessary to make estimates based upon previous experience and measurements under similar conditions. The effects of ground absorption and artificial and natural barriers such as earth mounds should be considered when predicting noise levels at the noise control boundary. Much time and effort can be saved if, during the design of new buildings, detailed consideration can be given with regard to the layout of buildings and machinery, and the method of construction, so as to minimise perimeter noise levels. Recognition of areas of potentially high noise levels by consultation between the developer and the enforcing authorities can do much to ensure that environmental law is adequately met.

APPEALS UNDER SECTIONS 64–67

The Act provides for appeals against an entry in a noise level register,[62] against a refusal to allow a registered noise level to be exceeded,[63] against a noise reduction notice[64] and against a determination of a noise level from a new or altered building.[65]

The reason that an appeal against a noise reduction notice is to the Magistrates' Court is because these appeals are principally about the practicability of achieving the required reduction in noise levels. Appeals in the other three cases lie to the Secretary of State because of the wider range of issues which may be raised. Appeals to the Secretary of State will be dealt with by written representations unless he is of the opinion that a local inquiry should be held. Where the appeal is to be dealt with by written representation, the Secretary of State will suggest a timetable for the exchange of statements which the parties will be asked to meet. Where a local inquiry is to be held, the Secretary of State will decide whether the person appointed by him to hold the inquiry should be an Inspector. Much will depend on the size and complexity of the issues involved.

In both written representations and local inquiry cases, local

---

[62] s. 64(3) – appeal to the Secretary of State.
[63] s. 65(4) – appeal to the Secretary of State.
[64] s. 66(7) – appeal to the Magistrates' Court.
[65] s. 67(4) – appeal to the Secretary of State.

authorities will wish to consider what arrangements should be made for advertising the appeal. Where there is likely to be public interest in appeals which are to be the subject of a local inquiry, the local authority should advertise the appeal and give as much public notice of the inquiry date as possible. For written representation cases, local authorities should notify local residents or others who may be affected as soon as possible and the Secretary of State will take into account any views which are put to him in writing, provided those views are disclosed to the local authority and the appellant. Local authorities should keep a register of all appeals to the Secretary of State available for inspection locally and, in all cases, local authorities should ensure that relevant documents are also made available for inspection, e.g. the local authority's statement of reasons for refusing to allow a registered noise level to be exceeded and the appellant's grounds of appeal.

The grounds for appeals both to Magistrates' Courts and to the Secretary of State are dealt with in the Control of Noise (Appeal) Regulations 1975[66] which also deal with the conditions under which suspension of notices is or is not required.

Insofar as appeals to the Magistrates' Court under section 66(7) are concerned, the grounds for appeal may include the following:[67]

(a) the notice is not justified by the terms of section 66;

(b) there has been some informality, defect or error in, or in connection with, the notice;

(c) the authority have refused unreasonably to accept compliance with alternative requirements, or that the requirements of the notice are otherwise unreasonable in character or extent, or are unnecessary;

(d) the time, or times, for compliance with the notice are insufficient;

---

[66] S.I. 1975 No. 2116.
[67] Regulation 7(2). In Scotland, the Control of Noise (Appeals) (Scotland) Regulations 1983, S.I. 1983 No. 1455 are substantially the same as the Control of Noise (Appeals) Regulations 1975, S.I. 1975 No. 2116.

(e) the noise to which the notice relates is caused in the course of a trade or business and the best practicable means for controlling it have been used;

(f) the notice should have been served on some person instead of the appellant, being the person responsible for the noise;

(g) the notice should have been served on some person in addition to the appellant, being a person also responsible for the noise.

The court shall dismiss the appeal if any informality, defect or error on which the appeal is based, is immaterial.[68] Where the appeal is based on the claim that some person other than the appellant should have been served with the notice, the appellant must serve a copy of his notice of appeal on that person and may serve a copy on any other person with an estate or interest in the premises concerned.[69]

On hearing the appeal, the court may quash the notice, vary it in favour of the appellant in such manner as it thinks fit, or dismiss the appeal.[70]

On hearing the appeal, the court may make an order concerning the person who is to execute any work, the contribution towards the cost of the work and the proportions in which any expenses recoverable under Part III of the Act are to be borne by the appellant and any other person.[71] In exercising this power in the case of a person other than the appellant, the court must be satisfied that that other person has received a copy of the notice of appeal.[72]

Appeals may be made to the Secretary of State under sections 64(3), 65(4) and 67(3). The notice of appeal must state the grounds of appeal and within seven days (or longer if allowed by the Secretary of State) the appellant must send copies of all relevant plans, records and correspondence as specified.[73] The Secretary of State may ask for further particulars and, if he has sufficient information,

---

[68] Regulation 7(3).
[69] Regulation 7(4).
[70] Regulation 7(5).
[71] Regulation 7(6).
[72] Regulation 7(7).
[73] Regulation 9(1).

may decide the appeal on the basis of that information. Otherwise, he must cause a local inquiry to be held.[74] In determining the appeal, the Secretary of State may allow or dismiss the appeal or reverse or vary any part of any record, consent, determination or decision of the local authority to which the appeal relates. In his determination, he can direct the authority as he thinks fit.[75]

An appeal can be abandoned by giving written notice to the Secretary of State at any time before the appeal is determined and a copy of that notice must be sent to the local authority.[76]

SUSPENSION OF NOTICES

The Regulations specify the conditions under which a notice under section 66 (reduction of noise levels) shall or shall not be suspended.[77]

---

[74] Regulation 9(2).
[75] Regulation 9(3).
[76] Regulation 9(4).
[77] See Chapter 2, pp. 65 and 66 *ante* for details of these conditions.

Chapter 5

CONSTRUCTION SITE NOISE

Prior to the Control of Pollution Act 1974, control over statutory noise nuisances did not give adequate control of all common law noise nuisance. Noise associated with construction, demolition and other relatively temporary noises tends to be transient,[1] and therefore the rather slow and cumbersome procedures of the Public Health Act 1936[2], which provided the mechanism for statutory control, were largely unsuccessful as the nuisance had usually ceased by the time the powers could be invoked. Some contractors, being well aware of the weakness in the law, tended to be less receptive to informal requests by the local authority towards noise reduction than the occupiers of permanent premises.[3]

In its *Neighbourhood Noise* report, the Noise Advisory Council stated "The law should be framed so as to provide practical and effective assistance to this end" (i.e. the reduction of noise). The Confederation of British Industry submitted comment with regard to proposals for new legislative powers, being the views of the National Federation of Building Trades Employers and the Federation of Civil Engineering Contractors and Contractors Plant Association. The C.B.I. did not say whether they supported any further control but its statement made reference to certain matters concerning the operations of the building and construction industry.[4] These views were taken into account in framing the noise control

---

[1] See case of *Andreae v Selfridge* [1938] 3 All E.R. 255 in which it was held that temporary or transient noise will not generally be accepted as a nuisance. The case of *De Keyser Royal Hotel v Spicer Bros. and Minter* (1914) 30 T.L.R. 257 did however provide for a common law remedy in respect of building operations carried out at night, which were held to be unreasonable.

[2] The Noise Abatement Act 1960 declared noise or vibration causing a nuisance to be a nuisance for the purposes of the Public Health Act 1936 and subject to action under Parts III and XII of that Act.

[3] *Neighbourhood Noise,* report by the Noise Advisory Council on the workings of the Noise Abatement Act (1971), p.44. The Noise Advisory Council was abolished as a Government quango in the early 1980s. The Noise Council, which comprises a number of professional bodies, subsequently replaced it.

[4] *Neighbourhood Noise,* Appendix F.

legislation in Part III of the Control of Pollution Act 1974.[5] The principal points raised, which are summarised below, are important when considering the application of sections 60 and 61 of the Act, which provide for control of noise from construction, demolition and certain specified engineering activities.

1. The building and construction industry is a special case because of the temporary nature of its activities. It cannot be adapted to fit within the scope of Noise Abatement Zones.

2. A certain amount of noise is inherent in all types of building and construction operations and it can never be completely eliminated. The amount of noise depends on the type of plant and equipment used together with factors such as the sub-strata which could have an effect on the type of plant and equipment used, its manner of operation and accordingly the amount of noise emitted.

3. Many items of plant and equipment can be effectively silenced but there are also many other items of plant and equipment that are not so easily silenced, e.g. pile driving equipment.[6] It was suggested at the time (1971) that no amount of expenditure on silencing would have other than a marginal effect.

4. Builders should have the defence of "best practicable means".

5. Builders should be able to determine in advance that they will be able to carry out their work without unreasonable restrictions.

These matters are clearly important in the effective control of noise from building and construction operations. Equally important, however, is the serious disturbance, even if only for relatively short periods, caused by the very high levels of noise that can occur from this type of activity. The pattern of activity on site often tends to be irregular and according to factors which include the state of site activity (i.e. site clearance, levelling, excavation, concrete mixing, landscaping, etc.), changes in weather conditions causing extension

---

[5] Part III no longer applies to the abatement of statutory nuisances. See generally Chapter 2.

[6] Although quieter types of pile driving equipment are available. See tables in BS5228, Part 4: 1992, *Noise Control on Construction and Open Sites; Code of Practice for Noise and Vibration Control Applicable to Piling Operations.*

of contracts or longer working hours, unforeseen problems with the sub-strata (e.g. presence of shale or rock), and the difficulties of obtaining the appropriate kind of equipment from contractors to carry out different stages of work. This makes prediction of site noise and its control a difficult matter for both contractors and for Environmental Health Departments responsible for implementing the statutory powers of local authorities.

STATUTORY CONTROL – Control of Pollution Act 1974

Sections 60 and 61 of the Control of Pollution Act 1974 provide for control by the local authority. Section 60 provides control over works in progress or any works that are going to be carried out. The works to which the section applies are:

(a) the erection, construction, alteration, repair or maintenance of buildings, structures or roads;

(b) breaking up, opening or boring under any road or adjacent land in connection with the construction, inspection, maintenance or removal of works;

(c) demolition or dredging work;[7] and

(d) (whether or not also comprised in paragraph (a), (b) or (c) above) any work of engineering construction.[8]

The scope of control is therefore very wide and may include large and small works, public and private works, from minor household repairs and improvements to works on the scale of motorway construction, bridge building and massive office development. Contractors and other persons having control over works of this kind such as architects, surveyors and builders should make themselves aware of the legal powers available to local authorities so as to avoid as far as possible the restrictions on their activities and

---

[7] See s. 73(2) – the area of a local authority that includes part of the seashore includes the territorial sea lying seawards from that part of the shore.

[8] See s. 73(1). "Work of engineering construction" means the construction, structural alteration, maintenance or repair of any railway line or siding or any dock, harbour, inland navigation, tunnel, bridge, viaduct, waterworks, reservoir, pipeline, aqueduct, sewer, sewage works or gas holder.

the attendant extra costs that may accrue as a result of action taken under section 60. Consideration of the law and consultation with local authorities before work starts can avoid controls which may involve considerable extra expenditure at a later date.

Notice

Where it appears to a local authority that works are being or are going to be carried out on any premises,[9] the local authority may serve a notice to control the works. The notice *must* be served on the person who appears to be carrying out, or going to carry out, the works *and* on any other persons who appear to be responsible for, or to have control over, the carrying out of the works.[10] The local authority may publish notice of its requirements.

This power is particularly important as notices may place a responsibility on both the developer, main contractor, sub-contractor and their agents. Frequently, architects or surveyors are used by developers not only to draw up plans and secure the necessary planning and Building Regulations approval but also to oversee the site work. It is not sufficient for a person responsible for works falling in the scope of this section to say that he had no representative on site to control work, or that he had delegated on-site control to another person. If he wishes to avoid action under section 60, it is probable that he will have to make his agent solely responsible by way of a written contract. Otherwise he (as well as his agent) must accept legal responsibility for complying with any notice specifying local authority requirements. He may, however, remain liable if a

---

[9]   Premises include land and vessels (s. 105(1) and the occupier of a vessel is the master of the vessel (s. 73(2)).

[10]   s. 60(2) – see Shaws form PA77. Note that it is open to a court to grant an injunction in respect of common law nuisance that is more extensive than the requirements of a section 60 notice that is in force in respect of the same nuisance. *Lloyds Bank v Guardian Assurance plc* (1986) Lexis, 17th October. But a notice in respect of one set of works should not be held to operate in respect of a different set of works on the same site which were not in operation at the time the original notice was served: see *Walter Lilly & Co. Ltd. v Westminster City Council* (1994) K8 J.P. 805, Q.B.D. Crown exemption has not applied to the Control of Pollution Act 1974 since 1998 by virtue of s. 105(3), as amended by the Environment Act 1995. Accordingly, notices can be served on contractors undertaking major highway works.

contract specifies the manner in which work is to be carried out or the type of equipment to be used. Where work is carried out for a local authority either by its own direct works organisation or under contract to an outside contractor, the conditions of contract are extremely important. If the contract requires the contractor to comply fully with any requirements of the Environmental Health Department under the Act, and the department authorising work takes no positive steps to control or direct the activities, then that department may not be liable to the service of notice. If, however, the department issuing the contract retains an element of control or specifies the method of work or equipment, the Head of Department will be responsible under the Act and *must* be served with a notice.[11]

In taking action under this section, the local authority *must* have regard to the following matters:[12]

(a) the relevant provisions of any code of practice;[13]

(b) the need to ensure that the best practicable means[14] are employed;

(c) the desirability in the interests of any recipient of the notice of specifying other methods or plant or machinery which would be substantially as effective;

(d) the need to protect persons in the locality from the effects of noise.

All of these matters have to be considered in respect of any notice served. Contravention of a notice without reasonable excuse is an offence.[15] In proceedings for an offence, however, it is a defence to

---

[11] s. 60(5) requires that a notice *shall* be served "... on such other persons ... responsible for, or to have control over ...".

[12] s. 60(4).

[13] The approved code of practice is currently BS5228:1992/1997 – see pp. 173–192 *post*. The Code of Practice was approved by virtue of S.I. 2002 No. 461.

[14] Defined in s. 72.

[15] s. 60(8). For the purposes of s. 60(8), a notice must be served on the body or person concerned. Service of a notice addressed to the secretary of a company at its registered address did not constitute service upon another, related company at the same address: *AMEC Building Ltd. and Squibb & Davis Ltd. v Camden London Borough Council* [1997] Env L.R. 330. In the same case it was held that a court only has to consider if the notice has been complied with – it does not have to consider if a nuisance has occurred.

prove that the works were being carried out in accordance with a consent under section 61.[16]

There is little reported case law in relation to matters dealt with under section 60, but the following are relevant:

1. A local authority obtained an interlocutory injunction[17] to restrain the construction managers of a development site from breaching a notice served under section 60. The managers submitted that the criminal law provided an adequate remedy and an injunction could not be granted unless it was established that they had deliberately and flagrantly flouted the law. Evidence showed that they had in fact been anxious to comply with the notice but the actual construction work was carried out by contractors. In dismissing the appeal it was held:

    (i) the local authority were not obliged to investigate the specific contractual arrangements on site: the construction managers were in control of the site;[18]

    (ii) the court's discretion to come to the aid of the criminal law by the grant of injunctive relief was exercisable only in exceptional circumstances and with great caution. The basis of that discretion was not that the offender was deliberately and frequently flouting the law but that his unlawful operations would continue unless and until effectively restrained by the law and that nothing short of an injunction would be effective to restrain him;

    (iii) criminal proceedings were a wholly inadequate remedy for securing compliance with the notice, the threat of prosecution having proved ineffective.

2. The London Borough of Camden[19] sought an injunction against

---

[16] s. 61(8).

[17] *City of London Corporation v Bovis Construction Ltd.* [1992] 3 All E.R. 697, C.A.

[18] See also *Wiltshier Construction (London) Ltd. v Westminster C.C.* [1997] J.P.L. B 88, Q.B.D. in which it was held that a notice was valid even though the council did not have knowledge of the contractual arrangements at the time the notice was served.

[19] *London Borough of Camden v Alpenoak Ltd.* (1985) 135 New L.J. 1209.

a company called Alpenoak Ltd., which was renovating one of its hotels. Local residents' complaints of noise caused by builders working early mornings, evenings and weekends led to the service of a notice under section 60. The notice restricted work audible outside the site boundary to the hours of 8.00 a.m. to 6.00 p.m. Monday to Friday, and from 8.00 a.m. to 1.00 p.m. on a Saturday. The company ignored the notice and the local authority obtained an injunction to enforce it. Over the following two months there were 22 infringements. The authority applied for sequestration of all Alpenoak's property. The company denied the infringements when the case went to trial but were found to be in contempt. They were fined £50,000 and around £8,000 costs.

Any contractor preparing to flout the provisions of a notice under section 60 would be advised to have regard to these cases.

Appeals
Right of appeal to the Magistrates' Court exists within 21 days of service of notice under section 60.[20] The procedure for appeal is by way of complaint for an order and the Magistrates' Courts Act 1980 applies to the proceedings.[21] Regulations[22] govern the grounds on which a notice may be subject to appeal. These are:[23]

(a) that the notice is not justified by the terms of section 60;

(b) that there has been some informality, defect or error in, or in connection with, the notice;

(c) that the local authority have refused unreasonably to accept compliance with alternative requirements, or that the requirements are unreasonable in character or extent, or are unnecessary;

(d) that the time or times in which compliance is required is insufficient;

---

[20] s. 60(7).
[21] s. 70(1).
[22] The Control of Noise (Appeals) Regulations 1975, S.I. 1975 No. 2116 (in relation to England and Wales); the Control of Noise (Appeals) (Scotland) Regulations 1983, S.I. 1983 No. 1455, where the appeal is to the Sheriff.
[23] Reg. 5(2).

(e) that the notice should have been served on someone else instead of the appellant, being a person on whom notice could have been served under the section;

(f) that the notice could lawfully have been served on some person in addition to the appellant and it would have been equitable to serve it on that person;

(g) that the authority have not had regard to some or all of the provisions of section 60(4).

An appeal on the grounds of (b) above will fail if the subject of appeal is not material.[24] In relation to any appeal under (e) or (f) the appellant is required to serve a copy of his notice of appeal on any other person referred to and may serve a copy on any other person with an estate or interest in the premises in question.[25] On hearing the appeal, the court may quash the notice, vary the notice in favour of the appellant or dismiss the appeal. Any notice varied by the court is final.

To avoid the necessity for appeals, prior consultation is often desirable for, once a notice is served after work has commenced, contractors are often reluctant to modify their working arrangements because of the disruption and high cost that may result. Certain courses of action may therefore be used to avoid this conflict:

1. Application for prior consent under section 61; or

2. Consultation between the Environmental Health Department and the Planning Authority at the time of planning application or application for Building Regulations consent. This latter procedure will often allow the Environmental Health Department to assess in advance the type of works that are likely to be necessary to carry out a particular project and therefore to determine if the works are likely to fall within the scope of the section. From discussions (and if necessary service of notice can follow), it would be reasonable to expect that agreement on noise control had been obtained, the notice formally indicating

---

[24] Reg. 5(3).
[25] Reg. 5(4).

the authority's need to protect the interest of persons in the locality concerned.

3. Where civil engineering, demolition or other engineering works are involved which are contracted out by the local authority, it is desirable that the Environmental Health Department and the department issuing the contracts liaise on the work and notice control procedures beforehand, if necessary with the contractors.

4. Where the local authority itself carries out its own works through its direct labour force, prior consultation and, if necessary, on-site monitoring will enable effective control and immediate remedial action in the event of any noise problem occurring.

Statutory undertakers

The Wilson Committee[26] recommended that statutory undertakers should not continue to enjoy the exemption from proceedings conferred on them under the Noise Abatement Act 1960.[27] The Scott Report[28] recommended that exemption from legal proceedings should not be granted to statutory undertakers but that consideration be given to any duty imposed on them by law, so far as it related to the need for safety and emergencies. That report also recommended that that saving be universally applicable. This saving is embodied in section 72(4) and (5) of the Act[29] as it applies to the test of "best practicable means" to statutory undertakers.[30]

Where any statutory duty being carried out provides for the "best practicable means" defence, e.g. emergency repair to a burst gas main or water supply pipe, or the sounding of a train whistle as a

---

[26] *Noise,* Final Report, Cmnd. 2056, 1963, para. 397.
[27] Since repealed.
[28] *Neighbourhood Noise,* Noise Advisory Council, 1971, Chapter 12, H.M.S.O.
[29] s. 72(4): "The test of best practicable means is to apply only so far as compatible with any duty imposed by law, and in particular is to apply to statutory undertakers only so far as compatible with the duties imposed on them in their capacity as statutory undertakers." s. 72(5): "The test is to apply only so far as compatible with safety and safe working conditions, and with exigencies of any emergency or unforeseeable circumstances."
[30] Defined in s. 73(1).

warning, then the implied exemption will be reasonably applied. However, where planned work is carried out, e.g. the *programmed*, as opposed to emergency, repair of services, this would not seem to confer this defence unless unforeseen circumstances arose during the course of the work.

Prior consent

Not only does the local authority have the opportunity on its own initiative to take early action in respect of proposed works but any person intending to carry out work controlled under section 60 may wish to ascertain the local authority's requirements in drawing up his proposals to carry out work. Section 61 allows a person intending to carry out works to which section 60 applies to apply formally for a consent.[31] Where works require Building Regulations approval, the application for consent must be made at the same time or later than the request for that approval.[32] The fact that the Building Regulations may not apply to the work in question does not prohibit an application under section 61. In many cases, to aid the process, informal discussions will be desirable before Building Regulations approval is sought.

It may be desirable for the Environmental Health Department's noise control requirements to be sought before tender documents are sent out by developers (either private or the local authority itself). This will make it easier to process formal applications and in addition it will ensure that all contractors tender on the same basis. Two of the main arguments of contractors against submitting applications for prior consent are that:

1. If noise control requirements are sought at the tender stage, they may be the only contractor including them and the costs included in the tender for noise control work may result in the tender being uncompetitive.

2. If an application for prior consent is submitted after a tender has been accepted, any additional costs necessary to meet the local

---

[31] s. 61(1). See also Shaws form PA 80.
[32] s. 61(2) or, in Scotland, a warrant under s. 6 of the Building (Scotland) Act 1959.

authority's requirements are unlikely to be recovered from the developer.

In such circumstances, the safest form of control is probably to specify noise control requirements when inviting tenders or to make it a condition that each person tendering make an application for prior consent so that he may be advised of the local authority's noise control requirements, thereby enabling him to allow for any necessary noise control in his tender price.

The application *must* contain particulars of:[33]

(a) the works *and* the method by which they are to be carried out; and

(b) the steps proposed to be taken to minimise noise resulting from the works.

The local authority *must give its consent* if it is satisfied:

(i) that the application contains sufficient information; and

(ii) if the works were carried out in accordance with the application, it would not serve a notice under section 60.[34] In considering any application, the local authority *must* have regard to the matters in section 60(4) (code of practice, best practicable means, methods, plant or machinery, protection of people in the locality).[35]

Any consent may be subject to conditions and limitation or qualification to allow for changing circumstances, and limitation on the duration of the consent.

The local authority must inform the applicant of its decision within 28 days of receiving the application and it may publish notice of the consent and the works in any way it considers appropriate.[36] If the appropriate committee of the local authority do not give individual

---

[33] s. 61(3).
[34] s. 61(4).
[35] s. 61(5).
[36] s. 61(6).

consideration to applications, they may delegate the power, usually to the Environmental Health Officer.

Major construction projects in residential areas require particular care in planning and execution if disruption from noise is to be avoided over extended time periods. In some cases, planning permission, and possibly environmental impact assessment, will be needed, and the establishment of formal consultation arrangements with local residents will be an essential part of the environmental control strategy.[37]

Appeals

The applicant may appeal to a Magistrates' Court within 21 days after the 28 day period if:

(a) the local authority has not given its consent within the 28 days; or

(b) consent is given but is conditioned, limited or qualified in any way.[38]

No appeal lies where the application is unconditionally approved, the local authority being under an obligation to satisfy itself under section 61(4) that it has sufficient information to determine the application. The grounds of appeal are:[39]

(a) that any condition attached or imposed in relation to the consent (in this regulation referred to as "a relevant condition") is not justified by the terms of section 61;

(b) that there has been some informality, defect or error in, or in connection with, the consent;

(c) that the requirements of any relevant condition are unreasonable in character or extent, or are unnecessary;

---

[37] For a valuable summary of a major project involving railway noise, see "On the right tracks", *Environmental Health Journal*, September 2001.

[38] s. 61(7).

[39] The Control of Noise (Appeals) Regulations 1975, S.I. 1975 No. 2116, Regulation 6(3) in relation to England and Wales; the Control of Noise (Appeals) (Scotland) Regulations 1983, S.I. 1983 No. 1455.

(d) that the time or, where more than one time is specified, any of the times, within which the requirements of any relevant condition are to be complied with, is not reasonably sufficient for the purpose.

If the matter referred to in (b) is not material, the court is required to dismiss the appeal.[40]

Where the appeal relates to a conditional consent, the court may:

(a) vary the consent or any relevant condition in favour of the appellant in such manner as it thinks fit; or

(b) quash any relevant condition; or

(c) dismiss the appeal.[41]

Any consent that is varied becomes final. Where the appeal relates to failure or refusal to give a consent, the court has to give the appellant and the authority an opportunity to make representations and then either adjourn the appeal to enable a fresh application to be made, or make an order giving a conditional or unconditional consent.[42] The court must take into account the same factors that the authority has to consider under section 61[43] and any other matters that appear to be relevant. The consent then becomes final.

A consent given by the local authority or the Magistrates' Court must contain a statement that the consent does not constitute a defence against proceedings taken under section 82 of the Environmental Protection Act 1990[44] (right of an occupier of premises to proceed in respect of a noise nuisance). However, if the authority has acted in accordance with section 61 and considered the "best practicable means", if those means are adopted, proceedings under section 82 would presumably fail.[45]

---

[40] Reg. 6(4).
[41] Reg. 6(5).
[42] Reg. 6(6).
[43] i.e. the provisions of s. 60(4), (5) and (9).
[44] s. 61(9).
[45] See s. 82(9) of the Environmental Protection Act 1990.

Offences

1. An offence is committed if any person knowingly carries out, or permits the carrying out of works in contravention of any conditions attached to a consent.[46]

2. If the applicant for consent fails to take reasonable steps to bring the consent to the notice of any other person who carries out the works subject to the application.[47]

Penalties

The maximum penalty in the case of persons found guilty is a fine not exceeding level 5 on the standard scale and a daily maximum penalty of £50 for offences continuing after conviction.[48]

PRACTICAL IMPLICATIONS OF SITE NOISE AND VIBRATION CONTROL

The problems of site noise control can often be complex and there are a number of practical implications for anyone involved in the works controllable by sections 60 and 61 of the Act. The matters discussed will be of significance to local authorities (in the exercise of their statutory powers or as developers or agents for another authority, e.g. the highway authority), developers, contractors, architects, agents and surveyors. It is probably appropriate to consider the normal process of organising and carrying out work of this kind so that the matters to be considered and the controls that can be used effectively can be assessed at the correct times. In

---

[46]   s. 61(5). In the case of *Tower Hamlets London Borough v London Docklands Development Corporation* (1992) Unreported, Q.B.D., both the Corporation and its contractor, Beattie Balfour Fairclough, had been convicted by magistrates of offences of contravening a consent condition by not using the "best practicable means" to prevent noise. On appeal by the Corporation, it was found that, through information provided by acoustics experts employed by the Corporation, the Corporation knew that its contractors were not using "best practicable means". The Corporation was guilty under s. 60(5) as a person who permits a contravention of a consent condition by a contractor.

[47]   s. 61(10).

[48]   See s. 74(2) – in Scotland consideration must be given to s. 24, Public Health (Scotland) Act 1897 in determining whether an offence is a second or subsequent offence, and in England and Wales see s. 80(4) of the Environmental Protection Act 1990.

considering the different stages in the process, it is essential for all concerned to refer to BS5228,[49] Parts 1–3: 1997, Part 4: 1992, and Part 5: 1997. The Code of Practice is in five parts:

Part 1 – Code of Practice for basic information and procedures for noise and vibration control.[50]

Part 2 – Guide to noise and vibration control legislation for construction and demolition, including road construction and maintenance.

Part 3 – Code of Practice for noise and vibration control applicable to surface coal extraction by opencast methods.

Part 4 – Code of Practice for noise and vibration control applicable to piling operations.

Part 5 – Code of Practice applicable to surface mineral (excluding coal) extraction.

The general guidance in Part 1 is relevant to all those with responsibilities for these activities. It is common to all the types of work covered by all parts of the British Standard.

Planning and design

Planners, developers, architects and engineers will need to be involved if excessive noise and vibration is to be avoided. Careful consideration should be given to the requirements of the local authority so that the project design, equipment to be used and phasing of different operations can be planned to minimise noise and vibration.

---

[49] *Code of Practice for noise and vibration control on construction and open sites.* This is currently the *approved* code for the purposes of this part of the Act. The British Standards Institution revised the earlier (1984) Parts 1–3 (which now include references to vibration) and produced a new Part 5 – *Code of Practice applicable to surface mineral extraction (except coal) sites* (1997). These were submitted for consideration as approved codes of practice by the Government, and were adopted by virtue of S.I. 2002 No. 461, coming into force on 25th March 2002.

[50] Issue 2, April 1999.

It will be necessary to determine the level of noise and vibration likely to be emitted from the site and whether any particular processes or equipment are likely to be prohibited by the local authority. The local authority should ensure that any noise limits are practicable. Consideration should be given to the necessity for alternative measures of controlling noise and vibration, e.g. works under the Noise Insulation Regulations 1975, where applicable.[51]

Careful consideration of site conditions and therefore the type of plant and machinery[52] required for development of the site will be necessary so that the noise and vibration implications can be assessed. The timing of different stages of the work, the siting of noisy equipment, the use of designated site vehicle routes and the location of site entrances away from noise sensitive areas are all necessary considerations.

Tenders

Tender documents should contain details of any noise consent requirements. The tenderer will need to ensure that his selection of plant or machinery and his methods and phasing of work will meet the contract requirements and the consent conditions of the local authority. If he is not clear about any requirements of the local authority, the tenderer would be advised to discuss his proposals with the Environmental Health Department. The developer who grants the contract must also be satisfied that the tenderer's proposals are satisfactory.

Community relations

Much can be done to remove the apprehension of people in the vicinity of a potentially noisy site by the maintenance of good

---

[51] S.I. 1975 No. 1763. Reg. 5 provides a power to insulate certain buildings against construction noise associated with specified highway works. In relation to Scotland, see the Noise Insulation (Scotland) Regulations 1975.

[52] Reference should also be made to the Noise Emission in the Environment by Equipment for Use Outdoors Regulations 2001, S.I. 2001 No. 1701. These specify maximum permissible sound power levels for certain kinds of equipment, much of which are types found on construction and demolition sites. They apply to equipment placed on the market from 3rd July 2001.

public relations between the site developer or contractor and people living and working nearby. It is a factor often forgotten or ignored and the apparent lack of consideration for people resident in an area can result in complaints. It is useful for the developer or contractor to send a circular letter to local residents outlining the nature of the works, their duration, the periods when particular noisy activities are likely to occur, the steps they are taking to minimise inconvenience to residents and the name and telephone number of a person they can contact in the event of complaints. On sites with particular noise problems, or of a long duration, public meetings can be useful both prior to work starting and, if necessary, as work proceeds, to discuss progress and any problems which may adversely affect local people. Noise from blasting operations is a special case and can under some circumstances give rise to concern or even alarm to people unaccustomed to it. The adoption of good blasting practices will reduce the inherent and associated impulsive noise; prior warning to members of the public, individually if necessary, is important.

Training employees

Under Regulation 11 of the Noise at Work Regulations 1989,[53] all employees should be informed about the need to minimise noise and about the health hazards of exposure to excessive noise.

Unnecessary or excessive noise can be avoided by:

(a) training employees in the correct use and maintenance of plant and equipment, e.g. the use of mufflers on pneumatic drills, and the need to report defective machinery or silencing equipment;

(b) giving instructions on the correct equipment for use on a particular task, e.g. a large, noisy generator or compressor may provide sufficient power to carry out works but a smaller, quieter one may do the work equally effectively;

(c) advising on the correct siting of equipment and of noise barriers on the site;

---

[53]   Noise at Work Regulations (Northern Ireland), 1990 Statutory Rules 147.

(d) informing all staff of any noise control measures agreed with the developer or the residents of the area, or specified in any notice or consent issued under sections 60 and 61 respectively;[54]

(e) employees issued with ear protection equipment should be instructed on its use, care and maintenance.

Execution of works

All available techniques should be used to minimise, as far as necessary, the noise to which employees and residents will be exposed. Measures which could be taken into account include:

(a) planning the hours of work and considering the potential effects of noise and vibration on employees[55] and residents;

(b) use of quiet working methods, the most suitable plant, reasonable hours of working for noisy activities and economy and speed of operations. 24 hours a day operations should be programmed to avoid off-site vehicle movements between 7.00 p.m. and 7.00 a.m.;

(c) controlling noise at source and the spread of noise;

(d) regular monitoring of noise levels by a suitably qualified person. It is best to agree a noise monitoring method in advance: a method is described in the Code.

Criteria for setting noise and vibration control targets

It is not possible to set hard and fast criteria for determining whether or not noise or vibration from a site will prove a problem in a particular situation. A number of factors will determine the acceptability of site noise and vibration and the degree of control required.

1. Site location – this will be a major factor. The nearer the site to noise sensitive development, the greater the degree of control required.

---

54 See also generally Chapter 10 re employee protection.
55 See generally Chapter 10. Protection from vibration and in particular "hand-arm vibration syndrome" is important. See also H.S.E. Booklet HS(G) 88.

2. Existing ambient noise levels – the likelihood of complaints will increase as the difference between the site noise and the background noise increases. However, the public response may also be effected by the duration of the noise; greater differences are more likely to be accepted if the operations are of limited duration. There is no known relationship between response and levels when comparing newly intruding and ambient vibrations.

3. Duration of site operations – the longer the duration of noisy activities, the greater the likelihood of complaints. Good public relations are essential. If operations producing noise or vibration are carried out strictly to an agreed schedule, local residents are more likely to accept the intrusion.

4. Hours of work – for noise sensitive buildings some periods of the day will be more sensitive than others, e.g. noise levels likely to cause daytime speech interference in an office would not have that effect outside office hours. In dwellings, work outside normal weekday hours will need special consideration. In such cases, noise control targets for the evening will need to be stricter than any set for daytime, possibly as much as 10 dB(A) less. Any night time noise control targets must be particularly strict. Site noise expressed as L_{Aeq} over 1 hour at the façade of noise sensitive premises may need to be as low as 40 dB(A) to avoid sleep disturbance.[56] Sensitivity to vibration at different times of the day is far more complex than sensitivity to noise. In general, other than at very low frequencies, sensitivity is greater in the head to foot axis of the body. However, in setting vibration control targets, regard should be had to the fact that in general people will be sitting or standing (i.e. vertical) in the day and lying down (i.e. horizontal) at night.

5. Attitude to site operator – site noise and vibration tends to be accepted more readily by residents in cases where the site operator can be seen to be doing all he can to avoid unnecessary emissions.

6. Noise characteristics – in particular cases where an intrusive

---

[56] BS5228, Part 1:1997.

pulse or tone exists, the noise may be less acceptable than might be deduced from the L_{Aeq} level. In some circumstances it may be appropriate to apply a weighting or character correction of 5dB(A) to the source of intermittent, tonal or impulsive noise, as specified in the assessment of industrial noise in BS4142:1997. The use of a short period L_{Aeq}, the maximum sound level, or the one percentile level may also be appropriate. The characteristics of vibration, e.g. whether it is continuous, intermittent or impulsive, may also influence its acceptability.

Maintaining records of situations where noise causes problems will help in deciding when complaints are likely to occur as well as in assessing the impact of specific control measures.

Effect of buildings

The effect of vibration on buildings adjacent to the site should be considered. Guidance on the evaluation of these effects can be found in BS7385: Part 1, and guidance on damage levels from groundborne vibration may be found in Part 2 of that standard or in BS5228, Part 4:1992.

Control of noise levels

Noise emitted from sites can be controlled under sections 60 and 61 of the Act and control may be exercised by:

(a) setting permissible limits (usually by estimating noise likely to be produced or relating to existing background noise); and

(b) monitoring subsequent performance to see if the noise limits are met.

A prediction of anticipated noise levels from sites is useful whether or not noise limits are to be imposed. Before starting work, the following should be considered:

(a) local authorities need to know the expected levels of site noise to decide on any potential problems and controls required. They will want to ensure that any noise limits are achievable and will protect the local community from excessive noise;

(b) developers, architects and engineers will need to know whether noise problems will be caused and whether activities will comply with any specified noise limits;

(c) at the tendering stage, contractors need to select plant and equipment capable of meeting any specified limits.

Different views may exist concerning the best method of expressing noise controls. If control is exercised by setting permissible noise limits, the following alternatives may be considered:

1. Equivalent continuous sound level (L_{Aeq}) for the full working shift(s). This will have the distinct disadvantage of allowing excessively high noise for shorter periods within the shift. It therefore provides only limited control over maximum noise emitted from a site. It will, however, enable the hearing of employees on site to be protected.

2. Period L_{Aeq} for particular noisy activities, restricting them to specific hours, provides a greater degree of control over maximum noise.

3. Maximum or short period noise limits in addition to noise levels expressed as longer period L_{Aeq}. The use of maximum noise limits in this way partly overcomes the disadvantage of only using a longer period L_{Aeq} by restricting the upper limit to which the noise may rise.

4. Setting maximum noise limits only. This may have advantages due to the simplicity of subsequently monitoring the noise but it should be remembered that the degree of annoyance is related not just to the noise level but its frequency characteristics, duration and intermittency. Setting a maximum level alone could result in that level being emitted for long periods and it may therefore not be sufficient to avoid considerable annoyance.

It is important to remember that it is not essential to control noise by setting noise limits alone,[57] although sections 60 and 61 require that consideration be given to any code of practice (BS5228:1992

---

[57] See s. 60(3) concerning matters to be taken into account, and pp. 172–176 *ante*.

and 1997) and, in the case of construction site noise, L_{Aeq} is used as a recognised basis for assessing the likely community response to noise. However, it is not mandatory to use the equivalent continuous sound level as a measure of control and other indices may be used. The methods of control will depend on local circumstances and the powers in sections 60 and 61 to control noise by other means should be used where appropriate.

Estimating noise from sites

The manner in which estimates can be made is contained in BS5228:1992 and 1997[58] and the factors that have to be considered include:

(a) the sound power outputs of processes and plant;

(b) the periods of operation of processes and plant;

(c) the distance from source to receiver;

(d) the presence of screening by barriers;

(e) the reflection of sound;

(f) soft ground attenuation.

It is suggested in the code that the effects of climatic conditions be ignored due to their daily variance.

The expected values of L_{Aeq} should be estimated at the planning stage of the project.[59] This will allow realistic control conditions under section 61 to be set and avoid conflict with local authorities who otherwise choose to impose noise limits based on other factors such as the pre-existing background noise.

The factors in (a)–(f) above can only be properly considered if certain essential information is made available so that accurate calculations can take place.

---

[58] Part 1. See also Parts 3 and 4 in relation to more specific activities controllable under ss. 60 and 61.
[59] See BS5228, Part 1:1997, Appx. A.

1. Accurate information from site machinery or plant manufacturers on the sound power levels of their products. This information is often not known and there is a need for manufacturers to consider carefully this deficiency. The availability of quieter types of equipment should be determined.

2. Manufacturers' sound power levels, where provided, usually relate to brand new equipment. Machinery actually supplied, often from plant hire contractors, may produce higher levels as a result of poor maintenance or when used under difficult ground conditions. It may be desirable, therefore, for the person responsible for a site to specify in a contract for hire the maximum sound power levels he expects from any hired equipment. Whilst this approach may not allow him to avoid his legal obligations under the Act, it will indicate that a certain standard is expected of the equipment supplier who would be advised to ensure that he was able to meet his customer's requirements.

3. Careful consideration should be given to the location of equipment on site, particularly that which may be moved around. If this consideration is given, calculations can be made. If, however, it is not known where equipment is to be sited, accurate prediction of site noise is difficult.

4. The availability of purpose-made noise control screens should be ascertained so that their effect in attenuating site noise can be determined using the manufacturer's noise reduction figures.

5. The possibility of emergency situations occurring should be considered, e.g. flooding requiring the emergency use of pumps. Noise control equipment, where practicable, should be available at short notice to screen machinery such as pumps and generators where emergency use is necessary.[60]

The prediction of equivalent continuous sound levels, except in the case of small sites or those with a limited number of different operations, is likely to be difficult. It will not always be possible to

---

[60] s. 72(5) provides a defence of "best practicable means" only so far as compatible with safety and safe working conditions, and with the exigencies of any emergency or unforeseeable circumstances.

predict precisely when fluctuations in noise will occur. However, as the basis for estimating and controlling noise is the need to avoid unnecessary interference with people living and working outside the site, the control of peak noises is likely to be a particularly important part of the exercise and therefore peak noise prediction, i.e. an understanding of the variation in noise emitted by machines, may have greater benefits than concentrating on controlling relatively quiet noises. *No reliable predictions of noise levels can be made without knowing the noise output of machinery to be used on site.*

Monitoring noise levels

This may take a number of forms.

1. Measuring ambient levels prior to establishing levels for control purposes in any consent issued by the local authority. This is an important part of the planning process and it is suggested[61] that tenderers make themselves aware of any noise limits and the monitoring methods to be used.

2. Regular checks on the noise to ascertain that permitted levels are not exceeded. "On site" measurements may be made by the person responsible for compliance with the noise limits and/or the enforcing authority. The degree of monitoring will depend on the extent of control considered desirable. Noise limits covering the whole work period may require extensive monitoring, whereas noise limits in certain time periods may need a lesser degree of control. Local authority Environmental Health Departments should check on neighbourhood noise resulting from site works. They may, however, choose to follow up consents under section 61 or notices under section 60 only on receipt of complaints. It would be unwise of the person having responsibility for control of noise on site to rely on notification from the local authority that he contravenes any legal requirement, as by that time he could be liable for legal proceedings in contravention of a notice or consent.

3. The locations of measurement points will be those specified in a notice or consent and will generally be at the site boundary or

---

61   BS5228, Part 1:1997, para. 13.

some point close to noise sensitive properties. The type of measurement and duration of measurement periods will depend upon the degree of control required of the person carrying out the work. In general, noise measurements should be made with sound level meters complying with the requirements of BSEN 60804. Detailed guidance is given in Appendix B of British Standard 5228, Part 1:1997.

4. Results of measurements should always be accurately recorded. The information should include:

(i) dates and times of measurements;

(ii) recorded sound levels;

(iii) where appropriate, L_{Aeq} as measured, or calculated from the results of short period measurements;

(iv) items of plant in use, their position on site, and tasks being performed. A dimensional sketch map will be useful;

(v) any significant factors which may increase noise above acceptable levels, e.g. plant breakdown, changes in ground conditions requiring greater power from equipment or use of alternative equipment, any emergency works being carried out;

(vi) location and height of measurement positions;

(vii) weather conditions.

It should be remembered that legal proceedings could be instituted if conditions applicable to a notice or consent are contravened and sufficient information, including statements from persons interviewed, must be obtained to prove a contravention at any subsequent court hearing.

Construction and open sites

All available techniques should be employed to minimise transmission of noise to which workers and people in the area are exposed, considering at the same time the basic requirements of section 60(4).[62] Measures to be taken should include:

1. Programming the various stages of work so as to minimise noise by using soil dumps and intermediate construction work as noise barriers, e.g. it is often desirable to commence building work at or near the site boundary so that the initially completed buildings act as a screen to other operations.

2. The use of specific measures to reduce noise from machines such as exhaust silencers, acoustic screens, mufflers, sheds and barriers. Early consideration should be given to these measures so that any necessary purpose-built noise screens can be obtained.

3. Planning hours of work. The effects on the neighbourhood should be considered, together with the effects on site workers.[63] Account should be taken of the effect of varying hours of work. For example, it may be desirable to lengthen working hours during the colder, wetter months of the year (although this may present difficulties in particularly inclement weather) to avoid the greater complaints that tend to be associated with warmer weather when both noise and dust, particularly in the early stages of construction, tend to occur. Initial site clearance and levelling tends to be concentrated over relatively long hours because of the high cost of hiring the necessary equipment. This may be desirable from the contractor's viewpoint but imposes an unnecessarily high level of noise on nearby residents. A balance must be maintained between the need for speedy completion of this work and the need to minimise local disturbance.

    Noisy work at weekends is likely to cause as many complaints as on weekdays because of the increased amount of leisure time that people expect. Particular care is required to restrict noisy activities at this time. In general it is preferable to prohibit Sunday working.

    In considering working hours or particular equipment, special attention should be given to nearby noise sensitive premises. In

---

[62] See p. 163 *ante.*
[63] See generally Chapter 9.

general, night time activities should not be allowed near hospitals and old people's homes. Strict controls should be exercised during daytime working on sites near these premises together with schools, libraries and similar institutions where low noise levels are essential.

Where work is carried out inside premises, e.g. office and shop alteration, noise and vibration will be transmitted through modern building structures. This may be a particular problem when drills and percussion tools are used. In such cases, normal activities in adjacent premises can become impossible and restrictions on daytime work may be required due to the difficulty of obtaining alternative quieter methods of operation. Contractors should be aware of the high additional cost that may be incurred in carrying out night work and consider their hours of work carefully beforehand. Similarly, airborne noise adjacent to shops and offices may require control over hours of working to avoid disturbance to employees in these premises during the normal working day.

4. The use of quieter methods and types of machinery should be required, particularly where work is carried out during periods sensitive to complaint (i.e. particularly between 10.00 p.m. and 7.00 a.m.) Reasonable hours of work (e.g. 7.00 a.m. to 7.00 p.m.) can be used for the noisier site operations, with a lower level of activity between 7.00 p.m. and 10.00 p.m. Work should be programmed so that off-site vehicles need not visit the site between 7.00 p.m. and 7.00 a.m. This may present difficulties for the following main reasons:

(i) supplies of materials such as bricks and ready-mixed concrete are not usually under the direct control of the site developer or contractor and therefore deliveries may often be made very early in the morning with vehicles queuing in the public highway waiting for the site to open. Control of this practice would seem to require more consultation between contractor and supplier;

(ii) partially completed sites, especially large ones, present problems as it is often difficult to secure them effectively to prevent suppliers delivering goods outside normal site hours. This is an even greater problem when partially completed sites are partly occupied (essential to secure an early financial return) because site roads have to be kept open for occupiers of completed buildings. Co-operation is again an essential part of control.

Parts 3 and 4 of BS5228:1997 and 1992 respectively give more specific guidance on noise control in relation to opencast coal extraction and piling operations.

Control of noise on site

Certain types of equipment and operations on a site are inherently noisy and guidance is given in BS5228, Part 1:1997 on the controls that may be employed to minimise noise. These guidelines are of a general nature and will secure some reduction in the noise from the particular sources mentioned. The overall effect of improvement may depend on the frequency spectrum of the noise, the contribution of that noise to neighbourhood noise levels and also the effect of reducing noise from other equipment on site. Certain basic rules can be applied to the control of noise on sites.

Substitution
Alternative remedies for the most common noise sources are indicated in the table on pages 188 to 191.[64]

Modification and use of equipment
1. Modification may be possible but manufacturers should be consulted to ensure this will not impair the efficiency of machinery.

2. Quieter equipment should be used where possible.

3. Resonance of body panels, a particular problem with low frequency noise output, may produce excessive noise. Stiffening with ribbing or damping using a resonance damping material

---

[64] BS5228, Part 1:1997, *Code of Practice for Noise and Vibration Control on Construction and Open Sites.*

may reduce noise if properly applied over the whole of the vibrating surface.

4. Rattling noises can be reduced by tightening components and fixing resilient material between components.

5. Noise sources should be enclosed as far as practical. This is usually most practicable where stationary equipment is used but extended barriers, particularly at site boundaries, may be effective in reducing noise from a moving source provided the source is operating close to the barrier. The degree of enclosure around a stationary source will depend on how the equipment has to be operated and the safety requirements for the operator and maintenance engineer. If necessary, ear defenders, dust masks and goggles may be required. Noise screens should be properly constructed and maintained in good condition.

6. The correct type of materials should be used for any enclosure. Sound absorbent linings will usually be necessary as a means of reducing the level of reflected noise to which employees are exposed.

7. Equipment should not be misused or overloaded as efficiency will deteriorate and noise increase as a result. Maintenance should be regular and carried out by trained staff.

8. Noisy equipment should be sited away from noise sensitive areas and equipment emitting noise predominantly in one direction should be positioned so that sound is directed away from noise sensitive areas. Care should be taken that equipment is sited so as to avoid sound being reflected from adjacent buildings.

9. Night time working should be minimised as far as possible but, where it is essential, more stringent noise controls should be considered.

10. Machinery operated intermittently should be switched off or, in the case of site vehicles, only allowed to tick over on low idle.

11. Acoustic covers fitted to generators, engines and compressors should be kept in place.

Methods of reducing sound levels from construction plant

Plant	Typical* standard Plant L_{Aeq} sound level at 10 m (dB)	(a) Sound reduction of plant			(b) Alternative plant	
		Source of noise	Possible remedies (to be discussed with machine manufacturers)	Sound reduction (dB)	Plant description	Typical L_{Aeq} sound level at 10 m (dB)
Hammer drive piling equipment	100	Pneumatic/diesel hammer or steam winch vibrator driver	Enclose hammer head and top of pile in acoustic screen	5 to 10	Bored piling using crane or lorry mounted auger or tripod winch	85
		Sheet pile	Acoustically dampen sheet steel piles to reduce levels of resonant vibration		Vibratory system	90
		Impact on pile	Use resilient pad (dolly) between pile and hammer head. Packing should be kept in good condition		Drop hammer completely enclosed in box with opening at top for crane access	75
		Cranes, cables, pile guides and attachments	Careful alignment of pile and rig		Steel jacket completely enclosing drop hammer with dolly and polystyrene chips fed to impact surface to dissipate energy	80
		Power units or base machine	Fit more efficient sound reduction equipment or exhaust. Acoustically dampen panels and covers. When intended by the manufacturer, engine panels should be kept closed. Use acoustic screens when possible		Oil hydraulic pile driver which generates its driving force from the frictional restraint of other piles	70

Plant	Typical* standard Plant L_{Aeq} sound level at 10 m (dB)	(a) Sound reduction of plant			(b) Alternative plant	
		Source of noise	Possible remedies (to be discussed with machine manufacturers)	Sound reduction (dB)	Plant description	Typical L_{Aeq} sound level at 10 m (dB)
Earthmoving plant *Bulldozer/Compactor/Crane/Dump truck/Dumper/Excavator/Grader/Loader/Scraper*	72 to 92	Engine	Fit more efficient exhaust sound reduction equipment Manufacturers' enclosure panels should be kept closed	5 to 10	Alternative super silenced plant may be available. Consult manufacturers for details	–
Compressors and generators	82	Engine	Fit more efficient sound reduction equipment	Up to 10	Super silenced plant is available. Consult manufacturers for details	67
		Compressor or generator body shell	Acoustically dampen metal casing Manufacturers' enclosure panels should be kept closed		Electric powered compressors are available as opposed to diesel or petrol	62
		Total machine	Erect acoustic screen between compressor or generator and noise-sensitive area. When possible line of sight between top of machine and reception point should be obscured	Up to 10	Sound-reduced compressor or generator can be used to supply several pieces of plant. Use centralized generator system	–
			Enclose compressor or generator in ventilated acoustic enclosure	Up to 20		

Plant	Typical* standard Plant L_{Aeq} sound level at 10 m (dB)	(a) Sound reduction of plant			(b) Alternative plant	
		Source of noise	Possible remedies (to be discussed with machine manufacturers)	Sound reduction (dB)	Plant description	Typical L_{Aeq} sound level at 10 m (dB)
Pneumatic concrete breaker, rock drills and tools	102	Tool	Fit suitably designed muffler or sound reduction equipment to reduce noise without impairing machine efficiency. Ensure all leaks in air line are sealed	Up to 15	Hydraulic and electric tools are available	82
					For large areas of concrete, machine designed to break concrete in bending can be used	82
		Bit	Use dampened bit to eliminate ringing		Thermic lance	66
		Total machine	Erect acoustic screen between compressor or generator and noise-sensitive area. When possible line of sight between top of machine and reception point should be obscured	Up to 10		
			Enclose breaker or rock drill in portable or fixed acoustic enclosure with suitable ventilation	Up to 20		
Rotary drills, diamond drilling, boring	78	Drive motor and bit	Use machine inside acoustic shed with adequate ventilation	Up to 15	Thermic lance	66
Riveters	95	Impact on rivet	Enclose work area in acoustic shed	Up to 15	Design for high tensile steel bolts instead of rivets	–

| Plant | Typical* standard Plant L_{Aeq} sound level at 10 m (dB) | (a) Sound reduction of plant | | | (b) Alternative plant | |
		Source of noise	Possible remedies (to be discussed with machine manufacturers)	Sound reduction (dB)	Plant description	Typical L_{Aeq} sound level at 10 m (dB)
Pumps	75	Engine pulsing	Use machine inside acoustic enclosure with allowance for engine cooling and exhaust	Up to 20		
Batching plant	78	Engine	Fit more efficient sound reduction equipment on diesel or petrol engines. Enclose the engine	5 to 10	Use electric motor in preference to diesel or petrol engine	65
		Filling	Do not let aggregate fall from an excessive height			
Concrete mixers	72	Cleaning	Do not hammer the drum			
Materials handling	80	Impact of material	Do not drop materials from excessive heights. Screen dropping zones especially on conveyor systems. Line chutes and dump trucks with a resilient material	Up to 15		

These are typical levels and will vary from plant to plant

12. Care in the handling of materials will avoid unnecessary noise as well as minimising damage to the materials.

13. Materials on site can provide useful noise barriers, for example sheds, building materials, earth mounds constructed of excavated soil and part completed buildings.

Control of vibration at source

Vibration can be more difficult to control than noise. It should be borne in mind that vibration may cause disturbance by causing structures to vibrate and radiate noise in addition to perceptible movement. Where reasonably practicable, plant and/or methods of work causing significant levels of vibration should be replaced by other less intrusive plant and/or other methods of working. Vibration from stationary plant (e.g. generators, pumps, compressors) may, in some cases, cause disturbance when located close to sensitive premises or when operating on connected structures. In these circumstances, equipment should be relocated or isolated using resilient mountings.

NOISE FROM PLANT OR MACHINERY

Section 68 of the Control of Pollution Act 1974 provides the Secretary of State with power to make regulations[65] for:

(a) requiring the use on or in connection with any plant or machinery of devices or arrangements for reducing the noise caused by the plant or machinery;

(b) limiting the noise levels from plant or machinery when used for works to which section 60 of the Act applies or noise caused outside factories[66] by the use of plant or machinery in the factory.

The regulations may apply standards, specifications, descriptions or tests, presumably codes of practice and British Standards. The

---

[65] s. 68(1).
[66] As defined in the Factories Act 1961.

Secretary of State is required to consult persons representing producers and users on the practical and financial implications of any requirements in proposed regulations.[67]

Local authorities will be required to enforce regulations made under this section.[68] An offence will be committed if any person contravenes or causes or permits another person to contravene regulations made under the section.[69] It will be a defence to prove that other no less effective means were taken to reduce the noise in question.

Noise from construction plant is further controlled by the Noise Emission in the Environment by Equipment for Use Outdoors Regulations 2001.[70] These stem from European Parliament and Council Directive 2000/14/EC.[71] This Directive repeals and replaces a series of Directives[72] concerning noise from construction equipment and lawnmowers. The Directive applies to compaction machines; tracked and wheeled dozers and loaders, etc; excavators, etc; concrete breakers and picks; tower cranes; welding and power generators; compressors; and lawnmowers and trimmers.

The purpose of the Directive is to set uniform rules for the use of equipment outdoors in member states in respect of emission levels (Article 12), the noise emission marking of equipment (Article 11), the collection of noise data (Article 16) and conformity assessment procedures (Article 14). Equipment cannot be placed on the market or put into service until the manufacturer ensures that the requirements of the Directive have been met. The Commission is required to report to the European Parliament and the Council on the implementation and administration of the Directive.

---

[67]   s. 68(2)
[68]   Nothing in the section shall be taken to authorise a local authority in Scotland to institute proceedings for any offence (s. 68(4)).
[69]   Subject to a fine not exceeding level 5 on the standard scale, and a further fine not exceeding £50 for each day on which the offence continues after conviction (s. 74).
[70]   S.I. 2001 No. 1701.
[71]   O.J.L. 162, 3.7.2000, p.1.
[72]   There are nine Directives that are repealed.

LAND COMPENSATION ACT 1973[73]

The Noise Insulation Regulations 1975[74] allow a highway authority or its agents (District Councils) to make grants or carry out work to provide sound insulation measures in dwellings where highway works are expected to cause adverse noise for a substantial time period. The Act also contains provision[75] for expenses to be paid to residents who the highway authority have agreed should move during adverse conditions expected to occur during construction, and also to acquire land the enjoyment of which is seriously affected by construction or improvement of a highway. The highway authority may carry out, or make a grant in respect of the cost of carrying out, insulation work to an eligible building which is likely to be seriously affected by highway construction works, even though the use of the highway on completion will not give rise to noise levels which would otherwise make that building eligible for sound insulation works.[76]

There is also power under the Act for the Secretary of State to make regulations concerning payments in respect of caravans and other structures affected by the noise of public works.[77] Regulations[78] provide for noise payments[79] by the appropriate highway authority to people who live in caravans or mobile homes, or other structures that are not buildings, where they are affected by noise during construction work.

Provision is also made for compensation in respect of noise

---

[73]   In Scotland, the Land Compensation (Scotland) Act 1973 applies similar powers.

[74]   S.I. 1975 No. 1763, Reg. 5 (in relation to England and Wales) and the Noise Insulation (Scotland) Regulations 1975, S.I. 1975 No. 460 apply similar provisions. See also the Noise Insulation (Northern Ireland) Regulations 1995.

[75]   s. 28.

[76]   Noise Insulation Regulations 1975, Reg. 5.

[77]   s. 20(a)

[78]   The Highway Noise Payments and Moveable Homes (England) Regulations 2000, S.I. 2000 No. 2887. Similar provision is made for Wales in the Highway Noise Payments (Moveable Homes) (Wales) Regulations 2001, S.I. 2001 No. 604.

[79]   The amount of noise payment shall not exceed £1,650 (Reg. 5).

resulting from the Channel Tunnel development[80] and for the provision of noise insulation of residential properties near to transport systems provided by statute (railways, trams, etc.).[81] The authority responsible for the construction of such a system is required to provide or pay for noise insulation of residential buildings within 300 metres of the works concerned. There is also discretion to make such provision where an existing system is altered.

The Highways Act 1980 and the Land Compensation (Scotland) Act 1973 enable highway authorities to acquire land by agreement when its enjoyment is seriously affected by works of highway construction or improvement. In addition, they give the highway authority power to carry out works, e.g. the installation of noise barriers, to mitigate the adverse effects of works of construction or improvement on the surroundings of the highway.

---

[80] See the Channel Tunnel Act 1987, s. 6(3), Sch. 2, Pt. III, para. 27.
[81] Noise Insulation (Railways and Other Guided Transport Systems) Regulations 1996, S.I. 1996 No. 428 (as amended by S.I. 1998 No. 701). The Regulations apply to operations and also to insulation against construction noise.

Chapter 6

ROAD TRAFFIC NOISE

In 1974 it was reported that road traffic disturbed more people in this country than all other forms of noise nuisance combined.[1] The problem of road traffic noise had previously been recognised by the Wilson Committee and its observations were related to a survey by the London County Council and the Central Office of Information in 1961/62.[2] A subsequent survey in 1972/73[3] on behalf of the Department of Transport revealed that noise levels in London were around 6 dB(A) higher than in other conurbations and areas of high population density. The only explanation for this difference appeared to be the fairly uniform distribution of traffic across the Greater London area in comparison with the less uniform distribution across other conurbations. The Wilson Committee argued for a reduction in traffic noise and said that vehicle noise would have to be reduced to about 80 dB(A) during low speed full power acceleration to be considered to be somewhere between acceptable and noisy. Subsequently, the *Report of the Inquiry into Lorries, People and the Environment*[4] recommended that lorries be manufactured with a maximum noise level of 80 dB(A) by 1990.

The problem of traffic noise was also considered in a 1999/2000 noise attitude survey undertaken by the Building Research Establishment on behalf of the Department for Environment, Food and Rural Affairs.[5] The results revealed that 84% of respondents heard road traffic noise; 40% were bothered, annoyed or disturbed to some extent; 28% said it had got worse and 10% that it had got better over the past five years. The results of a 2000/2001 noise

---

[1] *Noise in the Next Ten Years*, 1974, H.M.S.O., p. 2, para. 7.
[2] *Noise,* Final Report, Cmnd. 2056, 1963, H.M.S.O., p. 22, para. 85.
[3] *Noise and road traffic outside homes in England*, Harland, D.G. and Abbott, P.G., Transport and Road Research Laboratory Digest LR770, 1977.
[4] H.M.S.O. 1980.
[5] *The U.K. National Noise Attitude Survey 1999/2000*, Grimwood, C.J., Skinner, C.J., Raw, G.J., B.R.E. report to C.I.E.H. Noise Forum Conference, May 2002.

incidence study by the Building Research Establishment[6] also reported that significantly more residents in the area of the B.R.E.'s noise measurements thought that the road traffic noise had got worse over the previous five years than thought it had got better. Interestingly, comparing the results in this latter study with a similar one in 1990,[7] it was found that changes in noise levels and noise exposure between 1990 and 2000 were small in magnitude, and the changes were subtle, with different indicators showing different changes. Average noise levels measured by the L_{Aeq} and L_{A10} indicators during the daytime decreased between 1990 and 2000, and the average noise levels measured by the L_{A90} indicator during the night time increased during the same period. Despite the noise measurement results, it is clear that road traffic noise remains a significant source of public dissatisfaction.

The *Report of the Noise Review Working Party 1990* identified road traffic noise as the most serious of all the transportation problems.[8] It made a number of recommendations[9] designed to reduce the impact of traffic noise, including a review of the current standard for noise insulation work, the application of action levels as a basis for planning guidance and the extension of existing rights to compensation against increased traffic noise.

The Royal Commission on Environmental Pollution in its twentieth report[10] indicated that no new noise attitude surveys had been conducted, but that complaints to local authorities in England and Wales rose by 30% to 60 per million people over the period between 1990/91 and 1994/95 (although this figure will not include most traffic related complaints made to highway authorities). As motor vehicle traffic is forecast to increase by between 32% and 73% between 1996 and 2026,[11] the Royal Commission is no doubt

---

6   *The U.K. National Noise Incidence Study 2000/2001*, Skinner, C.J., Grimwood, C.J., B.R.E. report to C.I.E.H. Noise Forum Conference, May 2002.
7   *Effects of environmental noise on people at home*, Grimwood, C.J., B.R.E. Information Paper IP 22/93, December 1993.
8   H.M.S.O. 1990, p. 13, para. 4.2.
9   p. 15, paras. 15–19.
10 *Transport and the Environment – Developments since 1994*, Cmnd. 3752, H.M.S.O., September 1997. But see pp. 197 and 198 *supra* and fn. 5 and 6.
11 National Road Traffic Forecasts (GB), 1997.

correct to conclude that "there is no evidence ... that the problem of transport noise is diminishing, and some suggestion that people are becoming more sensitive to it".[12]

In an E.C. Green Paper published in 1996,[13] the overall success of the legislation on individual vehicles was questioned, suggesting that predicted reductions in noise levels had not been achieved in practice and overall reductions in exposure levels to environmental noise had not been significant. Studies suggested the reductions in actual road traffic noise resulting from legislation had only been 1–2 dB(A). The reasons for this were said to be the slow replacement of older, noisier vehicles; significant growth in traffic; the increased relative contribution of tyre/road noise; and a test procedure which did not reflect realistic driving conditions. It was also felt that regular inspection procedures which ensured the maintenance of acoustic design features were necessary, including a more formal noise test as part of vehicle roadworthiness tests.

The Government in its White Paper, *A New Deal for Transport: Better for Everyone*[14] recognised the adverse impact of traffic noise on health, including sleep disturbance, the performance of school children and the effects of noise-induced stress on the risk of developing heart disease and psychiatric disorders.[15] It also reported[16] that it had work in hand to develop a fuller understanding of the problems associated with traffic noise, including a noise measurement study, an assessment of attitudes to noise, a detailed noise mapping exercise, and a three-year research programme on the health and related effects of noise. The Government also committed itself to the adoption of E.U. standards aimed at reducing noise emissions, developing and introducing quieter road surfaces, and publishing a guide on minimising noise from commercial vehicles.[17] Some noise mitigation measures have been provided on some trunk roads built before the standards in the Noise Insulation Regulations were introduced, and a review of the Planning Guidance

---

[12] Cmnd. 3752, Chapter 3, p. 43.
[13] *Transport: the Way Forward*, Cmnd. 3234, H.M.S.O., April 1996.
[14] Cmnd. 3950, July 1998, p. 23, para. 2.11.
[15] *Ibid*.
[16] *Ibid*, p. 135, para. 4.212.
[17] *Ibid*, p. 136, paras. 4.213–4.216.

Note on noise (P.P.G. 24) is being undertaken. The Government did not accept targets for noise reduction proposed in the Royal Commission for Environment Pollution's eighteenth report on the basis that "targets for noise exposure and reduction cannot be set until an assessment of the current noise climate has been carried out ...", but now that the E.U. Directive will require mapping of ambient noise levels, this issue can be revisited.

THE STRUCTURE OF TRAFFIC NOISE

Traffic noise is not continuous. As a vehicle approaches an observation point, the noise level rises, reaches a peak and then decreases as the vehicle drives away. Traffic is of course made up of a wide variety of vehicle types using the roads at the same time. The noise they collectively produce is complex, irregular and constantly changing. It varies in pitch and loudness and continually fluctuates. On major roads it will, at any one time, be a combination of a number of different noises from different sources. Except where traffic is continuous, high noise levels will be interspersed with periods of relative quiet. At larger distances, the influence of individual vehicles becomes less important compared with the overall effect of traffic distributed along the road.

The sources of noise from individual vehicles include the engine, air inlet and exhaust, cooling fan, transmission, wind noise, tyres, brakes, road surface, body rattles and loads.

In addition to the noise production of individual vehicles and the collective contributions of a large number of vehicles on the roads, the noise level varies with speed and is also dependent on whether the road surface is wet or dry. At low speeds the noise from the engine, gearbox, cooling system and exhaust will generally predominate over the noise associated with the tyre/road surface interaction. On dry roads engine noise generally predominates for speeds up to 50 km/hr for cars and 80 km/hr for lorries. Above those speeds tyre noise becomes the dominant source of noise.[18] Overall

---

[18] *An examination of the relationship between tyre noise and safety performance,*
      Nelson, P.M., Harris, G.J. and Robinson, B.J., Transport Research Laboratory,
      1993.

vehicle noise has fallen as a result of implementing Type Approval requirements arising from the European Community. The tyre/road surface noise has become the dominant source of noise from most high speed traffic. On wet roads, tyre noise is even more important, increasing noise levels by up to 10 dB(A) over dry road conditions.[19]

EFFECTS OF TRAFFIC NOISE

Speech communication

This is one of the most obvious forms of interference, the degree of interference depending on the type of communication taking place, the noise levels, the frequency spectrum of the noise and its time pattern. Traffic noise levels will not normally be intense enough to cause hearing damage but may still disrupt speech communication and interfere with enjoyment of radio, television and use of gardens. It restricts the comfortable use of houses by the need to keep windows closed in warm weather and may require that certain rooms not be used for normal living due to its intrusiveness. The interference with speech may result in a person hearing only a few sounds, making speech unintelligible. It has been stated that a sound level of 48 dB(A) allows normal conversation at four metres.[20] A maximum indoor level of 40–45 dB(A) is necessary if television and radio is to be reasonably understood.[21]

Effects on sleep

Although traffic density tends to die down during the sleeping hours, it can nevertheless cause disturbance particularly in more densely trafficked areas. Experiments have been carried out[22] in which sleeping people were subjected to a recording of noise from a passing lorry. The noise was played at certain peak levels several

[19] *Lorry tyre noise*, Underwood, M.C.P., Transport and Road Research Laboratory Digest LR974, 1981.

[20] *An outline guide to criteria for the limitation of urban noise*, Robinson, D.W., National Physical Laboratory, Aero Report AC 39, 1969.

[21] *Acoustics*, Beraneck, L.L., 1954, McGraw Hill Book Co.

[22] *Effects of noise from passing trucks on sleep*, 1969, Paper QI, 77th meeting of the Acoustical Society of America, also reported in *Urban Traffic Noise – strategy for an improved environment*, O.E.C.D., 1971.

times during the night. At a noise level of 40 dB(A) there was found to be a 5% probability of waking the subject. At a level of 70 dB(A) that probability was increased to 30%. In these experiments the subjects were connected to an electroencephalogram which showed that the probability of a change in the sleep[23] level, including waking, at 40 dB(A) was 10% and at 70 dB(A), 60%.

It has been shown that the level of noise has a bearing on the speed with which people fall asleep and that sensitivity to noise varies with the individual, some being woken by low levels of noise, others not being awoken until a much higher level is reached. The depth of sleep is also less with increasing age.[24]

Physiological effects

There does not appear to be any conclusive evidence that traffic noise exposure results in any harmful effects but physiological effects of exposure to noise levels comparable with those of urban traffic noise include the "startle reaction"[25] when exposed to an unexpected noise.

Effects on buildings[26]

Studies have been conducted into the problems caused by traffic induced vibration on buildings, methods of predicting disturbance to occupants, the effects on buildings and methods of reducing the impact of those effects. The type of soil has a significant impact on the levels of vibration recorded in buildings; low levels of traffic vibration close to the human threshold of perception can have an adverse effect on sensitive equipment but there does not appear to be any firm evidence that significant building damage is directly associated with traffic-induced vibration. It is likely that vibration will assist the development of cracks if the building or its foundations are already under strain. Otherwise, levels of ground-borne vibration

---

23 See also Chapter 1, pp. 11 and 12 *ante*.
24 See *Urban Traffic Noise – strategy for an improved environment,* O.E.C.D., 1971, p. 42, para 2.2.2.
25 See Chapter 1, p. 10 *ante*.
26 *Traffic induced vibrations in buildings,* Watts, G.R., Transport and Road Research Laboratory Digest of Research Report 246, 1990.

would become intolerable a long time before vibration reached levels sufficient to cause structural damage.

TRAFFIC NOISE CONTROL

The sources of traffic noise are indicated above and reduction of noise can be concentrated on the vehicle itself. Effective land use planning, sound insulation of affected buildings and changes in road surfaces can also achieve worthwhile results.

In 1981 the Government established the Quiet Heavy Vehicles for the 1990s Project (QHV90). The object of this project was to help the United Kingdom vehicle and engine industry meet European noise regulations that became operative in 1989/90 and also to provide it with the knowledge and expertise to deal with the even more stringent noise legislation that would follow. The QHV90 project involved the Transport Research Laboratory,[27] other research organisations and industrial companies. Valuable research work has shown that worthwhile reductions in traffic related noise can be achieved.

Reduction of vehicle noise

Engine
The noise of an engine is dependent on its rotational speed, the load on the engine and its cubic capacity. The noise is produced by radiation from the vibrating surfaces and by various individual sources such as exhaust and inlet manifold, transmission and cooling fan. In diesel engines combustion noises are the predominant source caused by the rapid rise in cylinder pressure at combustion; in petrol engines combustion noise is less prominent and mechanical noises make a significant contribution. Turbo-charging a diesel engine smooths out the abrupt pressure rise and generally reduces combustion noise. It is possible to stiffen the structure, thereby reducing vibration, by redesigning the engine block and crankcase. This is, however, a complex task and the subject of continuing research. Improved engine enclosures may achieve worthwhile

---

[27] Previously an executive agency of the Department of Transport but now a limited company.

reductions in noise, although work by Leyland DAF Ltd.[28] resulted in reduction of noise from a 7.5 tonne light goods vehicle to meet the E.C. Directive 84/424/EEC drive-by noise level, mainly by alterations in component design rather than by enclosures or shielding. A drive-by noise level of 78.6 dB(A) was achieved, against a target of 82 dB(A).

Inlet and exhaust noise
The most effective means of controlling inlet and exhaust noise depend on the use of silencers. Without silencers the inlet and exhaust would be the main sources of engine noise. These noise sources increase with engine speed and load. The exhaust noise can be reduced by the design and timing of the exhaust valve. The design of exhaust silencers has seen significant improvements,[29] although further improvements would appear likely to meet possible changes in future legislation. One project forming part of the QHV90 work has resulted in computer programs which enable silencer designers to construct on screen a complete silencer from its basic components and to predict the noise attenuation.[30]

Cooling systems
The cooling fan is a significant noise source. The axial flow type fan is the most common type, usually drawing air through the radiator in water cooled engines. Centrifugal fans may be used with air cooled engines. The rotation of the fan blades close to obstructions in front of the fan causes air turbulence and produces noise with marked tones. Noise also occurs from the vibrating of fan blades. Engine noise may also be transmitted via the fan.

Aerodynamically efficient cooling systems using lower fan speeds have been designed which reduce cooling system noise and control devices which bring the cooling system fan into operation only at certain engine temperatures also help. Noise control of cooling

---

[28] See *QHV90 project: Leyland DAF goods vehicle noise reduction*, Porkess, A.M., T.R.L. Digest of Contractor Report 318, 1992.

[29] See *Designs of silencers for internal combustion engine exhaust systems,* Davies, D.O.A.L. and Alredson, R.J., I. Mech. E./A.S.A.E., Symposium on Vibration and Noise in Motor Vehicles, July 1971.

[30] See *QHV Project: Reduction of noise from lorry exhausts and air intakes*, Callow, G.D. and Peat, K.S., T.R.L. Digest of Contractor Report 226, 1993.

systems has certainly produced reductions in the sound pressure level at one metre distance of 7 dB(A).[31]

Transmission noise
Gearbox and rear axle noise does not appear to contribute as significantly to total vehicle noise as the exhaust and engine but gearbox noise can be reduced by shielding or enclosure, provided cooling problems do not occur. In fact, research conducted for IVECO Ford on one of its medium-sized cargo vehicles showed that it was possible to achieve external noise reductions of up to 8 dB(A) by enclosure of the engine and gearbox and controlling radiation from the external surfaces and pipework of the exhaust system.

Tyre/road surface noise
Considerable research into tyre/road surface noise is being undertaken by the Transport Research Laboratory and similar organisations worldwide. As the relative contribution of tyre/road surface noise increases, the E.C. Directive 92/97/EEC on motor vehicle noise included a commitment to introduce a type approval standard for tyre noise. This might have safety implications as there is, in general, a significant relationship between tyre noise and safety performance, i.e. a decrease in tyre noise is associated with a reduction in tyre safety (adhesion) performance.[32] In general, wider tyres are noisier but less prone to skidding, narrower tyres are quieter but do not have the same resistance to skidding. Higher axle loads and lower tyre inflation pressures increase the amount of tyre tread on the road and the level of tyre vibration, and hence the noise produced. One of the single most significant increases in tyre noise appears to be associated with the increased use of low profile/wide tyres. Increases of up to 10 dB(A) have been associated with increases in the width of tyres in the range 75 mm to 120 mm,[33]

---

[31] See *QHV90 project: Leyland DAF goods vehicle noise reduction*, Porkess, A.M., T.R.L. Digest of Contractor Report 318, 1992.

[32] *An examination of the relationship between tyre noise and safety performance*, Nelson, P.M., Harris, G.J. and Robinson, B.J., Transport Research Laboratory, 1993.

[33] See "Possible methods of reducing external tyre noise", Nilson, N.A., *Proceedings of the International Tyre Noise Conference*, pp. 247–258, Sweden, 1979.

although the Transport Research Laboratory has found[34] that typically car tyre noise levels increase by about 4 dB(A) from the narrowest to widest tyre studied. The corresponding increase for truck tyres was 2 dB(A). Speed is another important factor. Noise generated by tyres increases at rates between 9 and 13 dB(A) for each doubling of speed, depending on the combination of tyre and road surface. Tread pattern and tyre structure, tread materials, tyre wear and temperature also have an impact on noise production.

The tyre noise Directive 2001/43/EC[35] requires member states to implement the Directive by 4th August 2002 and apply its provisions from 4th February 2003 at the latest. The provisions then apply in stages starting with new types of tyres from 4th August 2004. The Directive applies to three classes of tyre: passenger car tyres and two types of commercial vehicle tyres. The limit values for tyre/road noise emissions from passenger car tyres range from 72 dB(A) to 76 dB(A), depending on nominal tyre section width, until 30th June 2007, with the limits ultimately reducing to indicative figures of 70 dB(A) to 75 dB(A). "Extra load" or "special tyres" are subject to increased limit values of 1 dB(A) and 2 dB(A) respectively. The two classes of commercial vehicle tyres are subject to limit values which vary between 75 dB(A) and 79 dB(A). A test method is also specified for the measurement of tyre-sound levels. This is a coast-by method. The test method will not necessarily simulate different types of road surface and will not reflect acceleration or braking conditions. The Transport Research Laboratory has developed a tyre/road noise investigation vehicle which has introduced a new method of determining the *noise influence of road surfaces*. The vehicle is called Triton and is designed to enable testing to be undertaken within normal traffic flows and, where conditions allow, at speeds of up to 70 m.p.h.[36]

The noise generated by vehicle tyres, as a result of their interaction with the road surface, is currently the most important noise source from vehicles operating in excess of 50 km/hr on dry roads. As a

[34] *An examination of the relationship between tyre noise and safety performance*, Nelson, P.M., Harris, G.J. and Robinson, B.J., Transport Research Laboratory, 1993.

[35] Published in *O.J.I.C.*, 4th August 2001.

[36] Described in *TRL News*, September 1999, p. 1.

result, the noise from motorways and other high speed roads is nearly always dominated by tyre noise.[37] The design of a road surface is therefore an important factor in tyre noise production. The development of road surfaces giving good skid resistance at high vehicle speeds has generally led to increased levels of vehicle noise. The peak noise levels from light and heavy vehicles in traffic are dependent on the texture, depth and type of road surface. Open textured and permeable bituminous road surface materials appear to produce the lowest noise level, e.g. it has been reported that the average reduction in free flow traffic noise L_{10} levels produced by surfacing a road with an open graded pervious material, rather than non-porous macadam or concrete with equivalent skid resistance, will vary between 3 and 4 dB(A) depending on the light and heavy vehicle composition of the traffic stream.[38] It has also been found in practice that roads surfaced with 50 mm of porous asphalt (and containing 20 mm maximum aggregate size) have been shown to lower vehicle noise levels by 5–6 dB(A) compared with the noise generated on an equivalent non-porous road surface.[39]

Concrete road surfaces are often textured, producing a highly skid resistant and durable road surface which can also produce excessive noise. The Highways Agency is committed to using quieter road surfaces more widely and, where there is no need to renew a surface for operational reasons, to consider other means of remedying the worst and most pressing cases of traffic noise disturbance.[40] The Ten Year Transport Plan also includes "acceleration of the use of quieter road surfaces on the strategic network. Quieter surfaces will be installed on over 60% of the strategic network, including all concrete stretches, by 2010".[41]

---

[37] *TRL News*, June 1998, p. 5.

[38] See *Noise from vehicles running on open textured road surfaces*, Nelson, P.M. and Ross, N.F., Transport and Road Research Laboratory Digest SR 696, 1981.

[39] "Designing porous road surfaces to reduce traffic noise", Nelson, P.M., *TRL Annual Review*, pp. 33–41. See also "Perception of exterior noise from traffic running on concrete and bituminous road surfacings", Watts, G.R., *TRL Staff Paper*, 1996.

[40] *Towards a National Ambient Noise Strategy*, Department for Environment, Food and Rural Affairs, November 2001, p. 45. In March 1999 an annual budget of £5 million was announced for this work where resurfacing was not expected for some time.

[41] *Ibid*, p. 47.

Legal requirements controlling noise from vehicles

Part II of the Road Traffic Act 1988 deals with the construction and use of vehicles and equipment. Section 41 empowers the Secretary of State to make regulations[42] generally as to the use of motor vehicles and trailers on roads, their construction and equipment and the conditions under which they may be used, and in particular to make regulations with respect to any of the following matters:

"(c) noise;

(g) ... for securing that ... silencers ... shall be efficient and kept in proper working order;

(j) the testing and inspection ... of ... silencers;

(l) for prohibiting the use of appliances fitted to motor vehicles for signalling their approach, being appliances for signalling by sound, at any times, or on or in any roads or localities, specified in the Regulations."

A person contravening or failing to comply with any regulations made under this section or who uses[43] or permits to be used on a road a motor vehicle or trailer which does not comply with the regulations shall be guilty of an offence.[44]

Compliance with these regulations does not exonerate a person from compliance with other legislation. Section 7 of the Road Traffic (Consequential Provisions) Act 1988 specifically provides that nothing in the Road Traffic Acts authorises any person to use on a road a vehicle so constructed or used as to cause a public or private nuisance,[45] or affect the liability, whether under statute or common law, of the driver or owner so using such a vehicle.

---

[42] The primary Regulations are the Road Vehicles (Construction and Use) Regulations 1986, S.I. 1986 No. 1078 (as amended). The standards as to permissible noise levels comply with E.E.C. and E.C.E. instruments.

[43] On "uses" see *James & Son v Smee* [1955] 1 Q.B. 78; *Windle v Dunning & Son Ltd.* [1968] 1 W.L.R. 552; *Crawford v Haughton* [1972] 1 All E.R. 535; and *Garrett v Hooper* [1973] R.T.R.1.

[44] This is a fixed penalty offence for the purposes of the Road Traffic Offenders Act 1988. Also subject to any authorisation by the Secretary of State on the use on roads of vehicles not complying with Regulations made under section 41.

[45] Or in Scotland a nuisance.

CONSTRUCTION AND USE OF MOTOR VEHICLES

The Road Vehicles (Construction and Use) Regulations 1986 apply standards of construction and use to vehicles used after specified dates. They apply noise limits to particular types of vehicles, including motorcycles, and are heavily influenced by Community Directives or E.C.E. Regulations which determine the noise levels to be applied and the methods of noise measurement. Noise testing of vehicles in-use was formerly included in construction and use regulations. However, the procedure was time-consuming and little used by the police. It was found easier to take action under more readily established offences, e.g. relating to excessive noise from defective silencers. The in-use test was therefore removed and has not yet been replaced by a viable testing method.

The Construction and Use Regulations do not deal with off-road uses such as motorcycle scrambling which are considered separately.

Construction, equipment and maintenance

New vehicles
Regulation 55(1) applies to every wheeled motor vehicle as specified, having at least three wheels and first used after 1st October 1983. It provides that every vehicle to which it applies which is first used on or after 1st April 1990 is to be so constructed that the sound level does not exceed the relevant limit specified when measured under the required conditions. Different limits apply to certain vehicles first used on or after 1st October 1996.[46] The maximum levels are contained in items 1–4 of the table in the Regulations. The methods of measurement vary depending on the requirements of the particular E.C. Directive dealing with the various types of vehicle subject to the Regulations. The principle European Directive, Council Directive 70/157/EEC[47] on the approximation of the laws of the member states relating to the permissible sound level and the exhaust system of motor vehicles has been amended or adapted on several occasions. It sets noise levels for several different categories of cars, buses and lorries, and also standards for exhaust systems as

---

46   Reg. 55A and table to this Regulation.
47   6th February 1970, O.J.L. 42, 23.2.1970, p. 16.

Road traffic noise

separate units. At the present time, the limit values vary from 74 dB(A) for passenger cars to 80 dB(A) for the larger heavy goods vehicles. Ultimately, the European Parliament proposes to reduce these limits to 71 dB(A) and 78 dB(A) respectively.

This Regulation does not apply to certain vehicles, including motorcycles with sidecars attached, agricultural motor vehicles first used before 1st June 1986 or which are not driven at more than 20 m.p.h., industrial tractors, road rollers and specially constructed fire engines for use at airports. Instead of complying with the provisions of the Regulation, a vehicle may comply at the time of its first use with certain Community Directives.[48]

Regulation 56 makes similar provision for agricultural motor vehicles and industrial tractors first used on or after 1st June 1986, subject to limited exceptions. The maximum permissible sound levels for vehicles subject to this Regulation vary between 89 dB(A) and 92 dB(A). Sound measurement conditions are again specified in a Community Directive.

Regulation 57, as variously amended, applies noise levels to mopeds and two-wheeled motorcycles (whether or not they have a sidecar attached) which are not mopeds. The Regulation applies to vehicles first used on or after 1st April 1991. The limit applicable to mopeds is 73 dB(A) (a limit of 74 dB(A) applies when a replacement silencer is subsequently used) and that for motorcycles varies depending on the date of the first use and the requirements of the applicable E.C. Directive. Instead of complying with these requirements, a motorcycle or moped may comply at the time of its first use with specified Community Directives.[49]

Vehicles not subject to Regulations 55–57 and which were first used on or after 1st April 1970 have to be constructed, in accordance with Regulation 58, to meet other specified maximum noise limits. These vary between 77 dB(A) for a motorcycle with an engine

[48]   77/212, 81/334, 84/372, 84/424, 92/97 or 96/20 or E.C.E. Regulation 51.02.
[49]   78/1015, 87/56 or 89/235 in the case of vehicles first used before 1st April 1991, or 87/56 or 89/235 in the case of vehicles first used after that date. Moped is defined in paragraph 5 of Schedule 9.

capacity of not more than 50 cc to 89 dB(A) for other vehicles, including agricultural motor vehicles and passenger vehicles constructed to carry more than 12 passengers. A vehicle to which this Regulation applies can, as an alternative, comply with other Community Directives.[50]

The noise limits in the Regulations do not apply to motor vehicles proceeding to, or returning from, a testing place by arrangement for the purpose of noise measurement or alteration to secure compliance with the Regulations,[51] nor do they apply to road rollers and other specified types of vehicle.[52]

Type approval of new vehicles
Section 57 of the Road Traffic Act 1988 allows the Secretary of State to make regulations prescribing "type approval requirements". "Type approval" means that the vehicle involved is of a type conforming to specified requirements relating to design, construction and equipment, etc. including requirements on noise levels and silencers. The type approval requirements are laid down in a number of E.C. Directives,[53] and provision exists under the Motor Vehicles (Type Approval) Regulations 1980[54] and the Motor Vehicles (Type Approval) (Great Britain) Regulations 1984[55] for the issue of type approval certificates in respect of motor vehicles. The 1984 Regulations require[56] that every motor vehicle and its parts first manufactured on or after 1st October 1977 and first used on or after 1st August 1978, which is constructed solely for the carriage of passengers and their effects, or is a dual-purpose vehicle and is adapted to carry not more than eight passengers exclusive of the driver, shall comply with the type approval requirements of the Regulations.[57] The Regulations do not apply to all vehicles and the

---

[50] 70/157, 73/350 or 77/212, or in the case of an agricultural motor vehicle, 74/151.
[51] Reg. 59.
[52] As listed in Regs. 55(2) and 56(1)(a) and (b).
[53] 70/157, 73/350, 77/212, 84/372 and 84/424.
[54] S.I. 1980 No. 1182, as variously amended.
[55] S.I. 1984 No. 981, as variously amended, and see S.I. 1982 No. 1271 in relation to goods vehicles.
[56] Reg. 3.
[57] Reg. 4 and Sch. 1.

exemptions include vehicles temporarily imported by persons resident abroad, vehicles of a visiting force or headquarters, tax exempt vehicles to be exported from Great Britain, and prototypes.[58] In respect of noise and silencers, the type approval requirements are contained in Schedule 1, items 14A to I, and implement Council Directive 70/157/EEC of 6th February 1970 as amended by Directive 73/350/EEC of the 7th November 1973, and various other Directives up to 96/20/EC of 27th March 1996.

On or after the 1st August 1978 it is an offence for any person to use, or to cause or permit to be used, on a road any vehicle subject to type approval requirements, unless it appears from one or more certificates then in force under section 58 of the Road Traffic Act 1988 that the vehicle and those parts of it which are subject to type approval requirements actually comply with them.

The Motor Vehicle (EC Type Approval) Regulations 1998,[59] as amended, empower the Secretary of State to grant, amend, withdraw or suspend E.C. type approval in accordance with the framework directive (Council Directive 70/156/EEC). They also provide for the issuing by the Secretary of State of a first licence or registration to light passenger vehicles in respect of which there is an E.C. certificate of conformity or a Minister's approval certificate under the Road Traffic Act 1988, section 58(1). Such certificates require conformity with specific E.C. pollution standards referred to in Schedule 1 to the Regulations.[60] The Motor Vehicle (Approval) Regulations 2001[61] provide for the approval of single vehicles before entering into service. These are mainly kit cars, amateur built cars, very low volume cars and imported cars not subject to type approval arrangements in the European Union. The Regulations include references to noise and silencers.[62]

---

[58] Reg. 3(2)(a) to (l).
[59] Made under the European Communities Act 1972, s. 2(2), in force from 23rd September 1998. The Regulations apply to the United Kingdom.
[60] Reg. 3(1) and Sch.1, item 1. The principle Directive 70/157/EEC is amended in relation to sound levels by Directives 73/350/EEC and 77/212/EEC.
[61] S.I. 2001 No. 25, in force from 1st February 2001 and applicable to the United Kingdom.
[62] Sch. 4, item 13 and Sch. 6, Part III.

Silencers

Where no silencer is used, inlet and exhaust are the main sources of noise. A silencer reduces exhaust noise by 15–25 dB and inlet noise by 10–15 dB. The Regulation 54 of the Road Vehicles (Construction and Use) Regulations 1986 requires that every vehicle propelled by an internal combustion engine is to be fitted with an exhaust system, including a silencer. The engine exhaust gases are not allowed to escape to the atmosphere without first passing through the silencer.[63] The exhaust system and silencer has to be maintained in good and efficient working order and must not be altered after the date of manufacture so as to increase the noise from the escaping gases. Cars not subject to the primary type approval regulations (i.e. kit cars, low volume cars and amateur built cars) are subject to an exhaust noise limit of 101 dB(A).[64]

The requirements relating to mopeds and motorcycles were amended by the Road Vehicles (Construction and Use) (Amendment) Regulations 1994.[65] Previously, Regulation 57 required original silencers fitted to motorcycles to meet certain requirements in Annex 1 to the 1978 Directive. Regulation 57A(1) requires an original silencer fitted to a motorcycle first used before 1st February 1996 to meet those same requirements. New Regulation 57A(2) requires such a silencer fitted to a motorcycle first used on or after that date to comply with certain requirements of the E.C. Directive 78/1015/EEC as amended by Directives 87/56/EEC and 89/235/EEC. Regulation 57A(4) requires a replacement silencer to meet certain technical and noise requirements. The requirements are based on the above Directives and British Standards B.S. A.U. 193:1983 and B.S. A.U. 193a:1990. The requirements vary according to the date of first use of the motorcycle to which a silencer is fitted. Regulation 57A(13) prohibits the use of a motorcycle on a road if any part of the exhaust system is marked "not for road use" or with similar wording. Regulation 57B prohibits

---

63 Alternatively a vehicle may instead comply with Community Directives 77/212, 81/334, 84/372 or 84/424, 87/56 or 89/235, or in the case of a motorcycle other than a moped, 78/105 or 92/97 or E.C.E. Reg. 51.02.

64 See Motor Vehicles (Approval) Regulations 2001, S.I. 2001 No. 25, Reg. 5 and Sch. 3.

65 S.I. 1994 No. 14.

the use of a motorcycle on a road unless it meets certain requirements and would make materially less noise if it were in good and efficient working order or had not been altered.

The conditions of Regulation 57 have been difficult to enforce. They are complemented by the Motor Cycle Silencer and Exhaust Systems Regulations 1995[66] made under the Motor Cycle Noise Act 1987. They set noise limits for motorcycle silencers and exhaust systems supplied by any person carrying on a business. They also prescribe requirements on packaging and labelling, and instructions on the maintenance of silencers. The Act makes it an offence, in the course of a business, to supply or offer or agree to supply or expose or have in possession for supply, a motorcycle exhaust system, silencer or related component unless it complies with regulations made by the Secretary of State. The Act is enforceable at the point of sale by trading standards officers and carries a penalty of up to three months' imprisonment or a fine up to level 5 on the standard scale.

Noise measurement
In previous construction and use regulations it was an offence to use, cause to be used, or permit to be used, any specified type of vehicle if the noise emitted from it exceeded the statutory noise limits *when measured in accordance with the required noise measurement procedure.* In 1972 the Noise Advisory Council[67] considered the then specified noise measurement procedure to be impracticable and proposed alternatives. The difficulty of applying the criteria in practice meant that very little action was taken and this method of control was subsequently dropped. At the time of writing, no "in-use" noise test is provided for in the Road Vehicles (Construction and Use) Regulations 1986 and the Transport Research Laboratory is conducting research on behalf of the Department of Transport to see if a static test can be produced.[68]

---

[66]   S.I. 1995 No. 2370. The Regulations apply to the United Kingdom.
[67]   *Traffic Noise: the Vehicle Regulations and their Enforcement,* 1972, H.M.S.O.
[68]   In the consultation paper *Towards a National Ambient Noise Strategy* it is indicated that in-use noise testing is likely to be impractical and uneconomic; p. 47, para. 5.2.26.

Other conditions relating to use

Avoidance of excessive noise
Regulation 97 of the 1986 Regulations provides that no motor vehicle shall be used on a road in such a manner as to cause any excessive noise which could have been avoided by the exercise of reasonable care on the part of the driver. It may be a reasonable defence to prove:

1. That the noise or its continuance was due to some temporary or accidental cause and would not have been prevented by the exercise of due diligence and care on the part of the owner or driver of the vehicle.

2. Where proceedings are taken against the driver or person in charge of the vehicle who is not the owner, that the noise arose from a defect in design or construction or through the negligence or fault of another person with a duty to keep it in proper condition, state of repair or adjustment, or to properly pack or adjust the load, and could not have been prevented by the exercise of reasonable diligence and care on the part of the driver.

This Regulation clearly relates to the *manner* in which a vehicle is used, so that excessive noise caused, for example by unnecessary revving of a vehicle engine, could be dealt with under this requirement. However, there is little evidence that much use is made of this provision.

Stopping of engine when stationary
Regulation 98 requires that when a vehicle is stationary, the action of any machinery attached to or forming part of the vehicle must be stopped as far as may be necessary for the prevention of noise. Machinery in this context presumably includes the engine and ancillary equipment such as refrigerator motors on food vehicles. There are exceptions where the vehicle is only stationary because of traffic conditions or the machinery is being examined because of its failure.

Use of audible warning instruments
Regulation 99 prohibits the sounding of any horn, gong, bell or

siren fitted to or carried on a vehicle which is stationary on a road, other than at times of danger to another moving vehicle on or near the road; or when moving on a restricted road[69] between 11.30 p.m. and 7.00 a.m. With the exception of the continuing time restriction, this provision does not apply to the sounding of a reversing alarm when the vehicle to which it is fitted is about to move backwards and its engine is running, or to the sounding of a boarding aid alarm.[70] There are restrictions on the type of vehicle to which a reversing alarm can be fitted.[71] There is a prohibition on sounding any gong, bell, siren or two-tone horn fitted to or carried on a vehicle other than for emergency purposes, or to raise alarm about the theft or attempted theft of the vehicle contents, or to summon help for the driver, conductor or inspector of a bus (even then a two-tone horn is not allowed).[72] Every bell, gong or siren fitted to a vehicle first used after 1st October 1982 and used to prevent theft, or summon help in the case of a bus, must be fitted with a device designed to cut off the noise after five minutes' continuous operation.[73] The provisions of section 62 of the Control of Pollution Act 1974 are also excluded from these requirements.[74]

TRAFFIC MANAGEMENT AND PLANNING FOR NOISE CONTROL

The number of vehicles on the roads continues to increase. In 1990 there were 22 million cars licensed in the United Kingdom. This figure had increased to around 24 million (or about 85% of the total licensed vehicle stock) by the end of 1999.[75] Based on current

---

[69] Defined in section 81 of the Road Traffic Act 1984 as a length of road on which there is a system of street lighting furnished by means of lamps placed not more than 200 yards apart or there is a direction in force under section 82(2)(b).

[70] Reg. 99(2).

[71] Reg. 99(3)

[72] Reg. 99(5). This requirement would appear to indicate that the alarm should be so set that it is not activated merely by someone brushing against the vehicle or leaning on it.

[73] Reg. 37(8). This time limit is likely to be varied following a consultation exercise.

[74] See pp. 114–117 *ante*.

[75] *Transport Trends*, D.E.T.R., March 2001.

national forecasts, motor vehicle traffic is predicted to increase by between 32% and 73% between 1996 and 2026.[76]

The Government's road traffic forecasts in recent years have changed from forecasts based on numbers of vehicles to the distance travelled by different types of vehicle. Whilst it continues to forecast significant increases in the distance travelled by all types of vehicles, the bulk of the increases reflect expansion in the use of motor cars. The rate of change involving freight vehicles is less significant and depends on the type and weight of vehicle, although freight transport continues to have a significant impact on the overall noise from the road network.

Comprehensive planning for traffic noise control incorporates three measures. Reduction at source includes improvements in vehicle noise levels and changes in road surfaces to reduce tyre-road noise. Noise mitigation measures such as improved building insulation and road noise barriers will reduce the impact of noise on the recipient. Traffic management policies may result in a move towards public transport, alter traffic composition towards quieter vehicles, limit traffic in certain areas or at particular times of the day or night, alter vehicle speed, improve driving behaviour and make better use of land use planning options.

The Government recognised the importance of planning new roads to take account of traffic noise over twenty years ago in adopting recommendations of the Urban Motorway Committee.[77] The importance of road planning and design, the separation of noise sensitive development from primary roads and the value of planning conditions to mitigate the effects of noise were reflected in the advice originally contained in the Department of the Environment's Circular 10/73: *Planning and Noise*.

The Government's continuing commitment to reducing traffic

---

[76] National Road Traffic Forecasts (GB), 1997. These figures are also included in the Government's "Integrated Transport White Paper", H. Comm., 31st March 1999, but differ from those in *Transport – The Way Forward*, Cmnd. 3234, April 1996, which quotes increases of between 53% and 83% over the same period.

[77] *New Roads in Towns*, H.M.S.O., July 1972.

noise was stated in a White Paper *This Common Inheritance*.[78] Current guidance on planning and noise builds on the principles contained in Circular 10/73. Advice is contained in Planning Policy Guidance Note 24[79] which includes general principles relating to control through planning. This P.P.G. replaced and cancelled Circular 10/73. The guidance advises that in preparing their local plans or Part II of their Unitary Development Plans, and in exercising their development control functions, local planning authorities should aim to ensure that plans "contain policies designed to ensure, as far as practicable, that noise-sensitive developments are located away from existing sources of significant noise (or programmed development such as new roads) . . ." Noise-sensitive development is considered to include housing, hospitals and schools. The guidance note also suggests the use of traffic management schemes, appropriate planning conditions or planning obligations, and suitable design features.

Properly designed noise surveys are essential in considering the potential impact of proposed traffic management or planning and development control measures on traffic noise levels. The object should be to establish the extent and significance of noise level changes resulting from the nature and variation of traffic flows. Useful guidance is contained in the *Design Manual for Roads and Bridges*,[80] and the technical memorandum on the *Calculation of Road Traffic Noise*.[81]

Noise mitigation on existing roads

The most significant factors affecting noise generated by traffic are the traffic volume and composition of heavy commercial vehicles, the speed and whether the traffic is free-flowing or subject to interruptions, e.g. traffic lights and junctions. Steps that may be taken to reduce the noise from traffic on existing roads include the

---

[78] Cmnd. 1200, H.M.S.O., September 1990. See generally Chapters 8 and 16.
[79] September 1994, England only. For Wales, see Technical Guidance Note (Wales) 11, *Noise* (1997).
[80] Volume 11, section 3, part 7, *Traffic Noise and Vibration,* H.M.S.O., August 1994.
[81] 1988, H.M.S.O.

reduction of traffic volume and the introduction of traffic calming measures, speed restrictions and quieter road surfaces. The highway authority also has a discretionary power under section 282 of the Highways Act 1980 to carry out works for mitigating any adverse effect which the construction, improvement or existence of use of a highway has or will have on the surroundings of the highway. This can include noise barriers, tree or shrub planting and layout of grassland areas.

Reducing traffic volume
Halving the traffic flow will generally produce noise reductions of around 3 dB(A) L_{10} or L_{eq}. This is an extreme traffic reduction and can be difficult to achieve in practice. However, moving large volumes of traffic from noise sensitive areas can have an adverse knock-on effect in other areas. Measures adopted in a number of European cities have included general traffic bans at night, re-routing traffic through shopping streets at night and restricting the numbers of heavy lorries allowed to use certain routes at night. In this context the Road Traffic Regulation Act 1984 provides for the making of traffic regulation orders under section 1(f) "for preserving or improving the amenities[82] of the area through which the road runs". The traffic regulation order may, in particular, specify through-routes for heavy commercial vehicles[83] or prohibit or restrict the use of such vehicles in such zones or on such roads as may be specified. This provision can be used to ban H.G.V.s from noise sensitive areas at night outside Greater London. A similar provision applies to the Greater London area under section 6.

The widespread use of "park and ride" schemes provides for the use of specially designated car parking areas for commuters outside major shopping, tourist and business areas. Users of these schemes then travel, usually by bus, to the town or city centre. The intention is primarily to relieve traffic congestion but there may be some slight reduction in noise where more free flowing traffic results.

---

[82] "Amenity" of land refers to its visual appearance and the pleasure of its enjoyment. See *Cartwright v Post Office* [1968] 2 All E.R. 646; [1968] 2 W.L.R. 63.
[83] Defined in section 138.

Traffic calming/speed restrictions

Section 90A of the Highways Act 1980 provides a discretionary power to the highway authority to construct "road humps in a highway maintainable at the public expense if the highway is subject to a statutory speed limit for motor vehicles of 30 miles per hour or less; or the road humps are specially authorised by the Secretary of State". Such road humps are specifically designed to reduce road traffic speed but a related benefit may be the reduction of noise associated with the resultant lower vehicle speeds. Powers to carry out other "traffic calming" works under section 90G of the Act are subject to the Secretary of State making appropriate regulations. Although these speed limitations may be helpful, the noise of braking and acceleration between the humps may also be significant. In addition, the use of these restrictions may direct more traffic to adjoining roads, causing more noise in those areas.

The use of road humps can affect noise levels in a number of ways,[84] e.g, reducing the speed of vehicles may mean that vehicle noise emission levels are lowered. Additionally, after the measures are installed, traffic flows may be reduced, leading to further reductions in noise levels. However, vehicle noise can also depend on the way vehicles are driven: a passive style of driving at a lower but constant speed helps produce lower levels; aggressive driving, with excessive braking and acceleration between road humps, produces a highly fluctuating noise level which may cause noise disturbance. The use of road humps may also give rise to disturbance from vehicle body noise (rattles, suspension noise, etc.) especially in unladen commercial vehicles.

Similar approaches to speed restriction, apart from mandatory speed limits, have included laying different coloured road surfaces and/or brightly coloured lines across the road, and "rumble strips". These measures are intended to give the motorist a greater awareness

---

[84] For more details on the results of relevant studies see "The effects of traffic calming measures on vehicle and traffic noise", Abbott, P.G., Taylor, M., Layfield, R.E., *Traffic Engineering and Control*, September 1997, and "Vehicle and traffic noise surveys alongside speed control cushions in York", Abbott, P.G., Phillips, S.M. and Layfield, R.E., Transport Research Laboratory, Project Report 103, 1993.

of speed and may have the same effect as road humps without the undesired noise effects.

Planning for reduced traffic noise

The management of existing traffic can have a significant impact on noise levels in some cases. Studies of the impact of future traffic on noise levels must recognise that the measurement of noise levels is logarithmic. The Environmental Foresight Project[85] puts the position clearly "this means, for example, that doubling a noise level of 70 dB(A) results in a 73 dB(A) noise level measurement. More important than this logarithmic relationship, however, is that *perceived* noise levels do not follow a logarithmic progression. Perceived noise impact by the human ear would judge a doubling of sound to occur in 10 dB(A) stages, not 3 dB(A). A 10 dB(A) shift in road traffic noise can correspond to a tenfold increase or decrease in traffic." Accordingly, where traffic noise levels are already high, further traffic increases will not result in a similar increase in traffic noise. However, in quiet areas a relatively small increase in traffic volume can significantly increase noise levels. Conversely, halving traffic levels may only produce a relatively small reduction in noise levels. These are important considerations for traffic planning.

Land availability and use plays an important part in determining the type of sound attenuation measures that may be used to minimise the impact of road traffic noise. It should also be remembered that noise is only one aspect of town planning that has to be considered in formulating detailed proposals. There are few simple solutions to controlling the effect of road traffic noise and many factors have to be taken into account, including the cost of the available alternatives and the availability of land, particularly in built up areas.

Road traffic network

The chosen road pattern for any particular area will have regard to the need to reduce journey times, to the provision of good service

85 *The Environmental Foresight Project Volume 3: The Future Road Transport Noise Agenda in the U.K.,* Mason, K.D., Centre for Exploitation of Science and Technology, 1993, H.M.S.O.

roads for commercial vehicles to supply commercial and industrial areas, road safety and the effects of pollution including noise. The type of road as well as its location will influence the noise produced.

(a) *Motorways* – the construction of motorways, and to a certain extent ring road systems, can reduce the total annoyance from road traffic noise in the following ways:

   (i) by producing free flowing traffic situations which avoid the interruption of traffic lights and intersections which occur on other roads;

   (ii) they are usually constructed with shallow gradients, and traffic produces less noise than on steep inclines where greater engine power is required, and consequently higher noise is produced;

   (iii) coupled with other traffic control measures, motorways draw traffic from other roads. The benefit has been particularly apparent in towns and cities which have previously been used as through routes for heavy vehicles.

(b) *Traffic management schemes* – removal of traffic on to motorways and ring roads allows for the reorganisation of public transport, better use of car parks and improves the possibility of reserving certain streets for authorised vehicles only, pedestrians or buses, and providing one-way systems and culs-de-sac. Traffic management schemes may also increase noise, as they are primarily used to improve traffic flows and safety, by diverting traffic into previously quiet roads. "Rat runs", which are relatively quiet roads remote from any particular traffic scheme, are often used by motorists to avoid rush-hour traffic congestion. These can present problems of safety and noise and traffic management schemes should be designed to avoid this situation as far as possible. The possibility of routes along railway lines or through areas scheduled for early redevelopment may be helpful. In the latter case, the opportunity for incorporating other measures can also be taken.

(c) *Alteration of existing roads* – by widening or the introduction of dual carriageways may bring traffic near to houses and increase its speed and, consequently, the noise. A consequent increase of heavy road traffic, particularly on the slow lanes of improved roads, can result in extra noise and vibration[86] in nearby houses. Coupled with this, the introduction of traffic lights, while generally speeding up traffic flow, can result in more stop-start driving in certain locations. This changing pattern in traffic movement can increase noise levels marginally due to the noise from vehicles accelerating from rest.

Whilst some of these measures may produce improvements it must be recognised that this may not always be the case. In large already well developed conurbations their introduction will have practical limitations.

Design of roads[87]

The most effective means of quietening a road are:

1. *Tunnels* – complete roofing or tunnelling can be particularly effective although the sudden rise in noise as vehicles emerge may be a source of nuisance requiring acoustic treatment at the exit of the tunnel. Exhaust ventilation plant may also produce noise from the fan itself and the transmitted traffic noise from inside the tunnel. This will be a problem primarily at night but noise can be reduced by acoustic treatment of the ventilation shafts and/or reducing the rotational speeds of the fans (in this latter case it may be necessary to increase the number of fans to maintain the desired rate of ventilation). Underpasses are more frequently used in towns than tunnels and speed (and therefore noise) tends to increase at their entrance due to their downward gradient. Heavy vehicles may have to change to a lower gear and use more power as they emerge on the upward gradient and

---

[86] The law of traffic noise does not specifically deal with traffic induced vibration. Generally, however, road traffic does not cause structural damage although it will cause annoyance. Low frequency airborne sound is primarily responsible for vibration in buildings adjacent to roads.

[87] See also "Design Manual for Roads and Bridges, Vol. II Environmental Assessment", s. 3, Part 7, *Traffic Noise and Vibration*, Dept. of Transport, August 1994 and *Transportation Noise Reference Book*, Ed. Nelson, P., Chap. 11, Butterworth.

again noise may be increased. Dwellings near to the entrances and exits may therefore be adversely affected.

2. *Open or vertically retained cuttings* – one advantage of a road being placed in a retained cutting is that the amount of land required is reduced. A cutting results in the motor vehicle (provided the cutting is of sufficient depth) being below the level of the adjacent ground. This results in an "acoustic shadow", the adjacent land being subject to lower noise levels than if the road and adjoining land were on the same level. This can result in a significant reduction in noise levels. Vertically retained cuttings are useful in areas of low-rise development. In some cases the effect of noise shielding can be reduced by reflection of noise from the vertical walls of a cutting but, in certain circumstances, the adverse effect can be reduced by having the vertical cut closest to the most sensitive side of the road and an open cut on the opposite side. This allows the noise to spread out of the cutting into the least noise sensitive area, thereby removing the reflected noise from the most sensitive area. Whether a road should be constructed in a cutting will depend on a variety of factors, the primary one being cost. Construction costs are lowest with level roads and open cuttings, retained cuttings and tunnels costing substantially more. On the other hand land acquisition costs are cheaper for tunnels and most expensive for open cuttings. Developers need to consider carefully the relative costs.

3. *Barriers* – the use of barriers can be very effective, especially when there is low rise housing close to an elevated road. To be effective a barrier should be close to the source or receiver and be as high as practicable. The height and length should be sufficient to cast a big sound shadow while the noise passing through it must be substantially less than that passing over the top and round the ends. There should be no gaps in or beneath the barrier through which sound can pass, and a historic rule of thumb has been that the thickness of barrier should ensure it weighs at least 10 kg/m². The effectiveness of a barrier will depend on a variety of factors in addition to its height, length and weight, including the road level relative to the adjacent

ground, type of ground cover, distance of exposed houses from the road, traffic flow (and accordingly the noise from the road) and the height of the affected buildings. In general, the noise reduction will vary from as little as 4/5 dB(A) at the edge of the barrier sound shadow, to a maximum of 20 dB(A) close to the barrier. Beyond the sound shadow there is a rapid decrease in noise attenuation.[88]

4. *Buffer zones* – these are areas, often of undeveloped land, running parallel and adjacent to major roads. They may be designed for safety and future expansion purposes but the nature of the ground and its treatment, and the distance of noise sensitive development from the road, can play an important part in reducing road traffic noise. The degree of noise attenuation by vegetative barriers in buffer zones is likely to be negligible except in the case of a barrier of dense evergreen trees.[89] The desirable width of land, subject to its availability, will depend on the traffic noise, the nature of the ground surface and the type and extent of vegetative cover. In field trials a dense spruce plantation gave the greatest attenuation, at about 6 dB(A)L_{10} more than grass, over 30 metres.[90] The provision of buildings

---

[88] See *Designing against Road Traffic Noise,* Scholes, W.E. and Sargent, J.W., Building Research Station Current Paper CP 20/71, May 1971. See also "Performance of a Motorway Noise Barrier – Heston", Scholes, W.E., Mackie, A.M., Vulcan, G.H. and Horland D.G., *Applied Acoustics (7)*, 1974; "Acoustic performance of the M6 noise barriers," Nelson, P.M. and Abbott, P.G. (Transport and Road Research Laboratory) and Salvidge, A.C. (Building Research Establishment), *T.R.R.L. Digest LR731,* 1976; "Improving the performance of traffic noise barriers," Watts, G., T.R.L. Published Article 1995; "Traffic Noise Barriers", Watts, G., *T.R.L. Annual Review,* 1995. See also the "Design Guide for Environmental Barriers", published in two parts as Vol. 10.5 of the *Design Manual for Roads and Bridges,* and Kotzen, B. and English, C., *Environmental Noise Barriers – A guide to their acoustics and visual design,* E. & F.N. Spon.

[89] "Highway Noise and Acoustical Buffer Zones", Zulfacor, A. and Scott Clark, C., *Transportation Engineering Journal,* May 1974, pp. 389–401 provides useful references to work done in connection with attenuation associated with vegetation.

[90] See *The use of vegetation for traffic noise screening,* Huddart, L., Transport and Road Research Laboratory Digest of Research Report 238, 1990. See also "The effects of vegetation on the perception of traffic noise", Watts, G., Chinn, L., Godfrey, N., *Applied Acoustics* 1999, vol. 56, pp. 39–56.

in a buffer zone of a type less sensitive to traffic noise can be of value as a screen to residential properties, provided their size, location and construction will achieve worthwhile sound reduction. These may include warehouses and factories. Care should be taken in such cases to ensure that the intervening development does not itself create a worse environment by increasing the noise from its activities and from service traffic.

COMPENSATION AND NOISE INSULATION

The Land Compensation Act 1973 incorporates the principles and recommendations contained in two reports.[91] These reports recognised that the advantages to communities as a whole from certain types of development put many people at a disadvantage environmentally. Accordingly, the Act does two main things:

(a) it allows for improved planning and design of new development to minimise the disturbance that may occur; and

(b) where disturbance cannot be avoided it provides for compensation to alleviate the disturbance.

The law relating to compensation for depreciation, the purchase of land to provide "buffer zones" and expenses payable for temporary removals is outlined in Chapter 9.[92]

INSULATION AGAINST ROAD TRAFFIC NOISE

The Secretary of State is given powers in the Land Compensation Act 1973 to make regulations imposing a duty or conferring a power on responsible authorities to insulate buildings against noise caused or expected to be caused by the construction or use of public works, or to make grants in respect of the cost of such insulation.[93] The Noise Insulation Regulations

---

[91] *New Roads in Towns*, July 1972, H.M.S.O. and *Development and Compensation – Putting People First*, 1972, H.M.S.O.

[92] pp. 368–371 *post*.

[93] s. 20. For the special provisions for compensation for noise resulting from the Channel Tunnel development, see the Channel Tunnel Act 1987, s. 6(3) and Sch. 2, part III.

1975[94] give effect to this power.

Duty and power to provide sound insulation

Highway authorities are required to carry out, or make grants for the cost of, work to insulate certain residential properties. There is a mandatory duty on the highway authorities in the case of:[95]

(a) a new highway;[96]

(b) a highway for which an additional carriageway has been or is to be constructed;

(c) a highway or additional carriageway first opened to public traffic after 16th October 1972.

A discretionary power exists[97] to provide grants or to carry out work in respect of dwellings similarly affected by noise from new or improved roads which were first opened to traffic between 16th October 1969 and 17th October 1972.

In either case, the entitlement to sound insulation works depends on compliance with certain qualifying conditions. These qualifying conditions are:

(a) the use of the highway to which the regulations apply must cause or be expected to cause noise at a level not less than 68 dBL_{A10} (18 hour)[98] when measured one metre in front of the most exposed of any windows and doors in the façade of a building. Living rooms and bedrooms are eligible for treatment;

---

[94] S.I. 1975 No. 1763 as amended by the Noise Insulation (Amendment) Regulations 1988, S.I. 1988 No. 2000. In Scotland, the Land Compensation (Scotland) Act 1973, s. 18 provides corresponding powers. The Noise Insulation (Scotland) Regulations 1975, S.I. 1975 No. 460 are also similar. See pp. 236–237 in respect of noise insulation associated with railways.
[95] Reg. 3.
[96] Defined in Reg. 2 – includes part of a highway and means a highway or part of a highway maintainable at the public expense as defined in s. 329(1) of the Highways Act 1980, as amended by S.I. 1988 No. 2000.
[97] Reg. 4.
[98] L_{10} is the level of noise which is exceeded for 10% of the measurement period, and the 18-hour period is from 06.00 hours to 24.00 hours.

(b) the noise levels referred to above must exceed the noise level attributable to traffic at the same measurement points immediately before commencement of the highway works by at least 1 dB(A);

(c) the noise caused or expected to be caused by traffic using or expected to use the highway must make an effective contribution to the noise measured in front of the building façade of at least 1 dB(A).

The duty and power apply to dwellings and other buildings used for residential purposes which will be not more than 300 metres from the nearest point on the carriageway of the highway after the construction, alteration or addition.[99] Certain buildings subject to compulsory purchase orders under the Acquisition of Land Act 1981 or local legislation, etc., closing or demolition orders or undertakings under the Housing Act 1985, or clearance under the provisions of the Housing Act 1957, and buildings occupied after the relevant dates referred to above, are ineligible for sound insulation under the regulations.[100]

Following the London Noise Survey of 1961[101] which showed that the main source of noise in towns was road traffic, a further study was carried out in 1968 to assess the subjective effects of traffic noise[102] at a number of sites exposed to free flowing traffic. At each site residents were interviewed to assess factors which included sleep interference, dirt and general dissatisfaction. Assessment of the results produced a complex noise unit called the Traffic Noise Index. The survey results were analysed in further detail to find a simpler noise unit. It was found that the L_{A10} (18 hour) index could be usefully related to the survey results. The survey indicated that

---

[99] Reg. 7(1).

[100] Reg. 7(2) – this does not, however, prohibit the owners or occupiers carrying out similar works of sound insulation at their own expense.

[101] *London Noise Survey,* 1968, H.M.S.O.

[102] "Subjective response to road traffic noise", Building Research Station Current Paper 37/68, *Journal of Sound & Vibration Vol. 8(II),* 1968. See also *An examination of the relationship between noise measures and perceived noisiness,* Watts, G.R. and Nelson, P., T.R.R.L. Digest of Research Report 318, 1991.

a noise level of 70 dB on the L_{A10} (18 hour) index represented the maximum acceptable limit of road traffic noise for the majority of people and its use was recommended by the Noise Advisory Council.[103] The qualifying noise level of 68 dB(A) was selected as it appeared to provide sufficient tolerance to ensure that people exposed to noise at or above 70 dB(A) would be provided with sound insulation. The Report of the Noise Review Working Party 1990[104] recommended further research to assess whether the current standard of 68 dBL_{A10} (18 hour) for noise insulation work remained appropriate having regard to the changes in social attitudes that have occurred since 1973.

Determining level of noise[105]

In order to determine whether a duty under Regulation 3, or a power under Regulation 4, has arisen with respect to an eligible building, the noise levels must be ascertained in accordance with the advice and instruction contained in a technical memorandum *Calculation of Road Traffic Noise.*[106] This memorandum requires the highway authority to predict the noise levels likely to exist 15 years after the opening of the new or altered highway and therefore takes into account the predicted traffic flows over this period. The procedure detailed in the memorandum for the prediction of noise at the reception point in front of the eligible building is firstly to predict the noise 10 metres away from the nearside edge of the road using the traffic data-flow, speed and percentage of heavy vehicles, allowing for the road gradient and surface where necessary. A series of corrections to this 10 metre level have to be applied to allow for propagation-distance of the reception point from the road, nature of the intervening ground and screening – and for complexities such as non-uniformity of the road, partial screening, angle of view from the reception point, multiple sources and reflective effects, all appropriate to the particular situation. The guidance is detailed and takes account of the screening effects of different types of road

---

[103] See *Noise in the Next Ten Years,* Noise Advisory Council, 1974, H.M.S.O.
[104] p. 15.
[105] Reg. 6(1).
[106] H.M.S.O. 1988.

cuttings, the impact of two or more roads and road junctions, and the effects of side roads.

Where a highway authority has a mandatory duty under Regulation 3 it must ascertain every eligible building in respect of which that duty has arisen. It must prepare a map or list, or both, identifying those buildings.[107] The preparation of a map and lists must be carried out by the highway authority alone unless they have appointed a local authority to act as their agents in the construction or alteration of the highway or carriageway.[108] The highway authority will often use the services of consultants to determine the eligible buildings. The determination of those buildings and building façades which are likely to be exposed to the relevant noise level is frequently carried out using computer programs into which is fed the relevant information required for the purposes of the memorandum *Calculation of Road Traffic Noise.*

The map or list produced must be deposited at the highway authority's office or their agent authority's nearest office to the eligible buildings identified in the list. This enables public inspection. The map or list must be made available for public inspection not later than six months after the new or altered highway or carriageway is first open to public traffic.[109]

Offers and acceptance of insulation work or grant

As soon as the highway authority has deposited its map or list, it must make a written offer[110] to carry out work of sound insulation

---

[107] Reg. 6(2).

[108] Reg. 14(2).

[109] Reg. 6(3). Contractors interested in carrying out sound insulation work may approach the agent authority before maps are available, expressing their interest in carrying out sound insulation work. In such cases, notification of when the lists of eligible properties are available may prompt a sales drive. Early consultation with contractors is desirable to ensure (a) their products meet the specifications in the Regulations, and (b) that their sales approach is satisfactory, i.e. that they do not imply they are "approved" by the local authority, that they are the "official contractors" or that they are otherwise working on behalf of the local authority.

[110] Reg. 8.

or to pay a grant in respect of the cost of the insulation. The offer must be made to the occupier of the building or, if unoccupied, to the person entitled to occupy it; or to the immediate landlord or his licensor. The offer must describe the work required and set out the conditions subject to which the offer is made.[111] The person receiving the offer, if he is the landlord or his licensor, must notify the occupier or person entitled to occupy it of the terms of the offer. If an offer has not been accepted after three months, it may be accepted by any other person to whom it could have been made in accordance with Regulation 8.[112] In practice the highway authority or their agents will monitor progress and notify the other persons of their right to accept the offer after the expiration of the three month period.

An acceptance of the offer must be in writing[113] and may be acceptance of the offer in respect of one or more of the eligible rooms but no offer of a grant can be accepted in respect of any room if an offer to carry out insulation work has been accepted in respect of that room.[114] A person accepting an offer of grant must complete the necessary work within 12 months of the date of acceptance.[115] Insulation work can be carried out in respect of an eligible building which is tenanted notwithstanding the withholding of any consent required by the tenant or landlord.[116]

Nature and extent of sound insulation work

Work carried out pursuant to the Regulations must be in accordance with the specification in Schedule 1.[117] Notwithstanding anything in the Regulations, where an eligible room contains a flueless

---

[111] Contained in Reg. 10 and Reg. 8(4)–(7).
[112] Reg. 8(4).
[113] Usually by completion of a pre-printed form attached to the offer – this will indicate the rooms subject to the offer in respect of which the offer is accepted, whether the acceptance is in respect of the offer of grant or work, and leave space for the signature and address of the person accepting the offer.
[114] Reg. 8(5).
[115] Reg. 10(1)(c).
[116] Reg. 12.
[117] Reg. 9(1).

combustion appliance other than a gas cooker, after completion of the insulation work there must remain an uninsulated window capable of being opened.[118] No authority is required to carry out work or make a grant in respect of defects in a building or the maintenance or repair of any apparatus or equipment installed in accordance with the Regulations.[119]

The specification of work contained in Schedule 1 to the Regulations concentrates on the acoustically weak parts of any building structure, i.e. windows and doors, and specifies works to reduce solar gain (build up of heat in a room) and maintain satisfactory means of ventilation. Noise insulation requires that windows be kept closed and the best results are obtained using double windows with a wide cavity between the inner and outer panes of glass. Closed windows, however, cause high temperatures to build up in summer time. Shading is therefore required to limit this build up. White Venetian blinds are used between the panes. Ventilation must be maintained and this is done by using a fan which draws external air into the insulated room. A second, permanent air-vent is also required. The ventilation system is sound attenuated to minimise the ingress of external noise.

Windows – the specification for windows[120] details the requirements for double windows, including the type of material to be used – wood, metal or plastic for the inner window; the sealing of gaps; the openability of windows for direct ventilation when required and cleaning; the lining of the reveals between the inner and outer windows; and the distance between, and the thickness of, the glass in the inner and outer windows. In this latter case the minimum distance related to glass thickness is as follows:

Less than 4 mm. and not less than 3 mm. thick – 200 mm.

Less than 6 mm. and not less than 4 mm. thick – 150 mm.

6 mm. thick or more   – 100-150 mm.

---

[118] Reg. 9(2). This requirement is for safety reasons to avoid the build-up of harmful gases and the reduction of oxygen which could cause suffocation.

[119] Reg. 9(3).

[120] Sch. 1, part III(4).

Where it is not practicable to comply with any of the specifications, the most practicable alternative solution can be used subject in every case to the windows being adequately openable for direct ventilation.

Venetian blinds – these have to be fitted between the inner and outer panes of glass and the slats must be white or near white. The width and spacing of the slats is controlled, as is the method of fixing. The controls, when practicable, must be operative from inside the insulated rooms. If compliance with the detailed specification cannot be achieved, the most practicable alternative can be used.

Ventilator systems – a detailed specification exists relating to weather and vermin resistance, fixing, electrical and fire safety, ventilation rates and sound levels. Permanent ventilators are constrained to specified ventilation areas and their sound attenuation performance.

Gas cookers – the Regulations require that a gas cooker in an eligible room where all the windows are double glazed be fitted with a fan failure valve designed to cut off the gas supply if the ventilation fan is not providing an adequate output for the room.[121]

A person accepting an offer under the Regulations may decide to accept it in respect of only some of the eligible rooms. All work carried out must comply with the requirements in the Regulations, i.e. means of double glazing, solar control and ventilation must be provided in each of those rooms, according to the specifications, but including alternative means as allowed by the Regulations.

Amount of grant

The amount of grant must be equal to the actual cost incurred in carrying out work in accordance with the relevant specifications, or

---

[121] At the time the Regulations were introduced it was anticipated that a fan failure device would be available. Technical difficulties have prevented its production and accordingly the highway authorities have to recommend that, in rooms containing gas cookers, a window remains uninsulated or kept open when the cooker is in use. It will presumably be necessary to amend the Regulations if a suitable fan failure valve cannot be developed.

to the reasonable cost, whichever is the less.[122]

Local authorities as agents of highway authorities

A local authority may act as agent for the appropriate highway authority in the discharge of its duties and powers under the Regulations,[123] except for determining eligible buildings or applications made to the effect that a duty under Regulation 3 exists where no offer has been made.[124] The agency arrangements will usually arise from a request to the local authority by the highway authority. It is necessary for the agency to be approved by the appropriate committees and council. The highway authority must reimburse its agents the amounts paid by them in respect of work carried out under the Regulations together with reasonable costs in respect of the agent authority's services. To avoid the agent authority having to raise finance and incur debt charges pending the reimbursement of their expenditure by the highway authority, it is advisable to make arrangements for payments in advance of anticipated expenditure, perhaps on a quarterly basis.

---

[122] Reg. 11. The Department of Environment specifies "maximum cost limits" which it considers should be applied to work carried out to meet the specifications in the Regulations. These are reviewed from time to time. The costs in respect of double glazing and Venetian blinds are quoted per square metre of area to be treated and unit cost is quoted for ventilation systems. These include fixing. In general the highway authorities request their agent authorities to submit for approval any costs quoted by a contractor which exceed the overall cost calculated as the maximum permissible for individual dwellings. In practice, cost limits have fallen into disuse because of wide variations in costs across the U.K. Current advice is to obtain best value by competitive quotations from local suppliers. In addition, some discretion is allowed for grants to the value of the secondary glazing to be paid to home owners who wish to fit double glazing instead.

[123] Reg. 14(1).

[124] Reg. 13 entitles a person who would be eligible to receive an offer under Reg. 3 to make written application to the highway authority requesting that that authority makes an offer under that Regulation. The highway authority must then review or carry out calculations in accordance with Reg. 6. If it finds that a duty has arisen it must make an offer. If it refuses it, it must give a written statement of its reasons. The agent authority can only determine eligible buildings or applications under Reg. 13 if it is also acting as agent in respect of the construction or alteration of the highway or carriageway.

Operational railway environmental noise[125]

Railway noise is an increasingly significant issue. The main source of noise is that of wheel/rail interaction, more particularly the excitation of the wheel and track by the combined roughness of the surface at the contact patch between wheel and rail. This leads to vibration, predominantly in wheels, rails and sleepers which results in the radiation of sound from those areas. For this reason, wheels with smoother rolling surfaces produce lower wheel/rail noise. A good example of this is the reduction of 8 to 10 dB(A) in rolling noise found when disc-braked wheels are substituted for cast iron tread-braked vehicles.

Rails that have a higher level of head roughness also result in higher levels of rolling noise. One extreme example of this is the effect of rail head corrugation. This is a cyclic wear phenomenon and, in the presence of severe corrugation, which occurs fairly widely throughout the U.K. rail network, rolling noise from disc-braked wheels can increase by as much as 20 dB(A).

Rolling noise predominates at higher speeds, and at lower speeds the main source of running noise is traction. In diesel locomotives this is a combination of exhaust noise and noise from cooling fans for the engine and traction motors. Electric locomotives can also be relatively noisy, especially those with high power ratings which require a significant amount of cooling for transformers and motors. Diesel multiple units and electric multiple units have some of the traction equipment noise problems of locomotives, and older stock can exhibit marked tonal characteristics due to the drive train gearing. Idling diesel locomotives or multiple units cause complaint, particularly at night or standing at signals.

Aerodynamic noise from the body of a train tends to have an impact on overall levels only at speeds above 300 k.p.h., although it may occur at lower speeds.

Another noise problem associated with wheel/track interaction is curve squeal. This is a consequence of incompatibility between the

---

[125] Taken from private communication from A.E.A. Technology-Rail, 14th May 2002.

suspension characteristics of the train and the curve geometry. This is a particular problem with more modern vehicles with bodies that are stiff in yaw for high speed stability. The squeal results from stick/slip effects at the contact patch between wheel and rail, or through flange contact with the running rail or check rail. In its extreme form noise levels of around 130 dB(A) are generated at high frequencies close to the train, leading to extreme discomfort and annoyance for trackside residents and passengers.

The type of track and its supporting structure can affect its noise emission, e.g. in elevated structures vibration in the structure can lead to the radiation of additional noise. Slab track, jointed track, and switches and crossings will also affect the noise characteristics of train movements. Other mechanisms associated with train noise include wheel flats, couplings and suspensions, compressors, track warning horns, and public address systems on stations.

There is not a great deal of legislation specifically controlling noise and vibration from railways, but that relating to environmental assessment, planning policy guidance, construction noise and statutory nuisance is all relevant.[126] Additionally, the Rail Regulator has issued *Railway Operations and the Environment – Environmental Guidance*[127] in which the Regulator advises that operators are expected "to take their environmental responsibilities seriously; to achieve all statutory requirements; to make improvements in those and other areas wherever practicable; and to have appropriate management and monitoring in place".

The Noise Insulation (Railways and Other Guided Transport Systems) Regulations 1996[128] provide for similar duties and powers in respect of noise insulation to those dealing with road traffic noise. They apply[129] to railways, tramways and systems using

---

[126] Variously dealt with in other chapters.

[127] Office of the Rail Regulator, *Railway Operations and the Environment – Environmental Guidance*, O.R.R., 1996.

[128] S.I. 1996 No. 428, in force from 1st March 1996 and made under the powers in s. 20 of the Land Compensation Act 1973 and as amended by S.I. 1998 No. 1701.

[129] Reg. 3(1)(c) and Sch. 2, Part I – magnetic levitation, monorail, road-based with cable, rail or side guidance, and track-based with side guidance.

specified modes of guided transport.[130] The Regulations do not apply in respect of noise from ground-borne vibration.[131] The powers and duties to make noise insulation grants virtually mirror those relating to road traffic noise and the specifications for insulation work[132] are very similar. The method of determining[133] whether a duty or power has arisen under the Regulations is by employing the calculation specified in a technical memorandum of 1995 entitled *Calculation of Railway Noise*.[134]

---

[130] Sch. 2.
[131] Reg. 3(2).
[132] Sch. 1.
[133] Reg. 9.
[134] H.M.S.O.

Chapter 7

INTEGRATED POLLUTION
PREVENTION AND CONTROL (I.P.P.C.)

WHAT IS INTEGRATED POLLUTION PREVENTION AND CONTROL?

The Department of the Environment, Transport and the Regions[1] described I.P.P.C. as follows:

> "The system of Integrated Pollution Prevention and Control (I.P.P.C.) applies an integrated environmental approach to the regulation of certain industrial activities. This means that emissions to air, water (including discharges to sewer) and land, plus a range of other environmental effects, must be considered together. It also means that regulators must set permit conditions so as to achieve a high level of protection for the environment as a whole. These conditions are based on the use of the "Best Available Techniques" (B.A.T.), which balances the costs to the operator against the benefits to the environment. I.P.P.C. aims to prevent emissions and waste production and where that is not practicable, reduce them to acceptable levels. I.P.P.C. also takes the integrated approach beyond the initial task of permitting, through to the restoration of sites when industrial activities cease.[2]

> "It aims to achieve a high level of protection of the environment as a whole by, in particular, preventing or, where that is not practicable, reducing emissions into the air, water and land."[3]

I.P.P.C. applies primarily to those more heavily polluting or complex industrial processes, with enforcement being divided between the Environment Agency and local authorities. The I.P.P.C. regime

---

[1] Functions in relation to I.P.P.C. are now the responsibility of the Department for Environment, Food and Rural Affairs.

[2] *Integrated Pollution Prevention and Control, A Practical Guide*, Edition 1, para. 1.1, DETR, August 2000.

[3] *Ibid*, para. 2.1. Emissions include noise and vibration.

will eventually replace that under Part I of the Environmental Protection Act 1990 which first introduced the systems of integrated pollution control into the U.K. The operation of I.P.P.C. falls under the Pollution Prevention and Control (England and Wales) Regulations 2000[4] (P.P.C. Regulations). The Regulations implement European Community Directive 96/61/EC (the I.P.P.C. Directive) in relation to installations in England and Wales.[5]

Prior to the P.P.C. Regulations, many industrial sectors covered by the I.P.P.C. Directive were regulated under Part I of the Environmental Protection Act 1990 (and some will continue to be so under transitional arrangements). This introduced the systems of:

(a) Integrated Pollution Control (I.P.C.), which controlled releases to all environmental media; and

(b) Local Air Pollution Control (L.A.P.C.), which only controlled releases to air.

The P.P.C. Regulations create a coherent new framework to prevent and control pollution with two closely aligned systems similar to I.P.C. and L.A.P.C. These are:

1. The Part A regime of I.P.P.C. – this is a similar integrated approach to I.P.C. which includes the additional requirements of the I.P.P.C. Directive. There are two classifications of installation, viz:

   (i) Part A(1) installations – regulated by the Environment Agency; and

   (ii) Part A(2) installations – regulated by the relevant local authorities, usually the district, London or metropolitan

---

[4]   S.I. 2000 No. 1973, made under s. 2 of the Pollution Prevention and Control Act 1999, and as amended by S.I. 2001 No. 503.

[5]   In Scotland, the I.P.P.C. regime is implemented by the Pollution Prevention and Control (Scotland) Regulations 2000, S.S.I. 2000 No. 323. They provide similar control to the England and Wales Regulations and the timetable for their introduction is in Sch. 3 to the Scottish Regulations. In Scotland, the Scottish Environmental Protection Agency (S.E.P.A.) is the sole regulator.

borough councils in England, and the county or county borough councils in Wales. The "emissions" controlled in relation to Part A installations (and mobile plant)[6] mean "... the direct or indirect release of substances, *vibrations*, heat or *noise* from individual or diffuse sources in an installation into the air ..."

2. Part B installations – dealing with emissions to air only and controlled by local authorities. Noise control in relation to these installations is not subject to the I.P.P.C. regime but is controllable by local authorities under the relevant provisions of the Control of Pollution Act 1974 or the Environmental Protection Act 1990.[7]

ENFORCEMENT RESPONSIBILITY

Regulation 8 of the P.P.C. Regulations specifies that Part A(1) installations or mobile plant are controlled by the Environment Agency and Part A(2) installations by the local authority in whose area the installation or mobile plant is (or will be) situated.[8] Determination of whether an activity falls under Part A(1) or A(2) is by reference to Part 1 of Schedule 1 to the Regulations which lists the activities falling within these two categories. In some cases, the production capacity[9] of the installation will determine the category and therefore the regulator responsible for its control. Schedule 1 to the Regulations comprises six chapters, each containing a number of types of activity falling within the scope of I.P.P.C. They are:

1. Energy industries.

2. Production and processing of metals.

---

[6] Pollution Prevention and Control (England and Wales) Regulations 2000, S.I. 2000 No. 1973, Reg. 2(1)(i)–(iii).

[7] See generally Chapters 2–5.

[8] The Secretary of State may direct that a specified local authority's functions be transferred to the Environment Agency – Reg. 8(6) and *vice versa* – Reg. 8(8).

[9] See Part 2 of Sch. 2 to the Regulations and p. 71 of *Integrated Pollution Prevention and Control, A Practical Guide*, Edition 1, D.E.T.R., August 2000.

3. Mineral industries.

4. The chemical industry.

5. Waste management.

6. Other activities.

The Environment Agency also regulates the operation of waste management facilities under its powers in the Environmental Protection Act 1990 and the Waste Management Licensing Regulations 1994, and by using related technical guidance (Waste Management Papers) on the effective control of such activities. Many of those facilities will fall *outside* the scope of I.P.P.C. In such cases, the Agency will consider noise controls as part of its licensing conditions, in consultation with the planning authority, local environmental health officer, and Health and Safety Executive. It will seek to ensure the compatibility of any noise controls it may include as a licence condition with any statutory controls and conditions imposed by those other regulatory bodies.[10]

Relationship between the Environment Agency and local authorities

Prior to I.P.P.C., environmental noise from installations and mobile plant, now controlled by the Regulations, was the sole responsibility of local authorities, with action in respect of noise nuisance taken under the Environmental Protection Act 1990. Local authorities were accountable to the general public via their local elected representatives. This public accountability also served as a check against any failures by local authorities in enforcing noise control legislation. As the Environment Agency is a central government organisation, the same level of accountability through elected members and local authority committees does not exist in relation to Part A(1) installations. However, to try and ensure both uniformity of approach to enforcement of the P.P.C. Regulations and I.P.P.C.

---

[10]   For further information, see *Environment Agency Noise Guidance – internal guidance for the regulation of noise at waste management facilities under waste management licensing regulations*, May 2000, version 2.0, draft for external consultation.

in general, the Agency has produced a protocol[11] intended "... to set out the high level principles to ensure that the operations work in the most effective way possible to secure the highest level of environmental improvement under the legislation." The shared aims are reflected in the following extracts:

"Aims and objectives

1. Ensure that A(1) and A(2) installations are operated in such a way that all the preventative measures are taken against pollution, in particular through the application of the best available techniques ...

2. Enhance the environment by reducing emissions (including noise and vibration) to the environment ...

Co-operation

For effective implementation and on-going regulation of I.P.P.C. there is a requirement for close co-operation and working between the two parties at all levels. Both agree to use best efforts to develop and maintain an effective partnership arrangement. Areas where liaison is particularly important include:

● planning issues[12] relating to noise for specific installations

● local initiatives for noise control

---

[11] A draft document as at 12th November 2001, *Protocol agreed by local government association and the agency on arrangements to implement the requirements of the I.P.P.C. Directive.*

[12] The relationship between I.P.C., now I.P.P.C., and planning permission was considered in *Gateshead Metropolitan Borough Council v Secretary of State for the Environment and Northumbrian Water Group* [1995] J.P.L. 432 in which the Court of Appeal stated that the two systems overlapped but that H.M.I.P. (now the Environment Agency) should "not consider that the grant of planning permission inhibits them from refusing authorisation if they decided in their discretion that this is the proper course". However, the same case suggested that it was proper for the planning authority to take into account that, where a relevant statutory regime, such as I.P.C., applies, that regime can be expected to take the primary role in controlling pollution.

... both the Agency and local authorities will need to rely upon information from each other to discharge their responsibilities.

Co-operation is expected to include as a minimum:

4. Liaison on procedural and technical guidance, in particular ... matters relating to noise and vibration.

Relevant information which may be exchanged includes:

1. Monitoring data.

...

(b) Information relating to noise and vibration.

... local authorities will assist Agency officers by providing information relating to ... noise and vibration arising from permitted installations.

5. Handling of complaints.

It is expected that suitable arrangements for re-direction to the lead regulator of complaints ... will be made at local level."[13]

THE I.P.P.C. REGULATORY PROCESS

The regulatory process for I.P.P.C. consists of three main elements: the issue of permits, operations, and closure.

Stage 1 – Permitting

No person can operate an installation or mobile plant[14] after the prescribed date[15] without a permit granted by the regulator. An application for a permit has to be made to the regulator[16] in accordance with specified details.[17] In relation to Part A(1) and (2) installations and mobile plant, the information required includes:

---

[13] Essential, as some installations may have been subject to many years of local authority control over noise and vibration.
[14] Reg. 9.
[15] As determined in accordance with Sch. 3.
[16] Reg. 10.
[17] Sch. 4, Part 1, paras. 1–3.

(g) the nature, quantities and sources of foreseeable emissions[18] ... and a description of any foreseeable significant effects ...;

(h) the proposed technology and other techniques for preventing or ... reducing emissions ...;

(i) the proposed measures ... to monitor the emissions;

(k) ... any proposed additional measures to be taken to comply with the general principles set out in Regulation 11;[19]

(o) any additional information ... the applicant wishes the regulator to take into account ...;

(p) a non-technical summary of the information.

The Agency provides detailed and comprehensive guidance for applicants, consideration of which is essential reading for anyone contemplating a permit application.[20] The above conditions demand that an applicant for a permit will have to give very detailed consideration to the potential for noise emissions associated with his activities. One of the primary considerations in an application will be that of demonstrating compliance with "best available techniques".[21]

Best available techniques (B.A.T.)
The Environment Agency in its own guidance[22] states "in determining B.A.T. across an installation, noise will have to be considered and balanced within the wider context of other releases to different media (air, land and water) and taking issues such as usage of energy and raw materials into account. Noise cannot,

---

[18] Including noise and vibration.
[19] i.e. that installations and mobile plant are operated in such a way that:
  (a) all the appropriate measures are taken against pollution, in particular through application of the best available techniques; and
  (b) no significant pollution is caused.
[20] Integrated Pollution Prevention and Control (I.P.P.C.), *Part A(1) Installations: Guide for Applicants*, Version 2 – December 2000.
[21] See footnote 19 and defined in Reg. 3.
[22] IPPC H3 Final draft version 1, Integrated Pollution Prevention and Control (I.P.P.C.), *Horizontal Guidance for Noise, Part 1 – Regulation and Permitting*, Environment Agency, December 2001.

therefore, be considered in isolation from other impacts on the environment." As the Regulations require all installations to be operated in such a way that "all appropriate preventative measures are taken against pollution ... through the application of best available techniques",[23] and the definition of pollution[24] clearly relates to "emissions which may be harmful to health ... cause offence to human senses or interfere with amenities ...", then the minimum aim of B.A.T. must be to avoid nuisance beyond the site boundary. Equally, it is arguable that the noise level from an installation, whether from specific sources or generally, should not be allowed to increase.[25] Where noise from an installation or mobile plant regulated under I.P.P.C. is considered to be a statutory nuisance, a local authority cannot initiate summary proceedings without the consent of the Secretary of State.[26]

The Environment Agency suggests[27] that the aim of B.A.T. should be to achieve the following:

(a) underpinning of good practice, e.g. plant maintenance;

(b) noise levels should not be loud enough to give reasonable cause for annoyance to persons in the vicinity; and

(c) prevention of creeping ambient noise, i.e. gradual increase in ambient sound levels as industry expands and areas develop.

The Agency has produced a series of "sector guidance notes" which contain indicative standards at a sector or national level for determining noise issues under I.P.P.C. These apply to new and existing plant but may in individual circumstances require modification to reflect local conditions and circumstances. For existing plant, the Agency will concentrate on applying good practice (B.A.T.) and minimising the likelihood of annoyance. For new plant, it will consider noise targets to prevent creeping ambient sound levels. In considering permit applications, the Agency,

---

[23] See footnote 19.
[24] Reg. 2(1).
[25] There is no case law on this issue.
[26] This emphasises the need for the close co-operation referred to on p. 243–244 and fn. 11 above.
[27] Horizontal Guidance Note IPPC H3, p. 2.

through its consultation process, will take account of other, related, statutory controls that may already be in place to control noise at a particular installation.[28]

The Regulations[29] set out what information an applicant has to provide and the Agency will expect the level of detail in the application to be commensurate with the level of risk[30] of causing annoyance or other environmental impact. The potential risk is most likely to be determined from consultation with the relevant local authority, which may have records of past involvement in noise issues, and also from the information provided in the application. It is quite possible that, in assessing the extent of the installation, there will be elements of the activities not included as part of the I.P.P.C. installation, e.g.

(a) intruder alarms on buildings;

(b) guard dogs;

(c) transport on access roads;

(d) construction work.

The Agency and the local authority will need, at the time of permit application, to agree what particular aspects of an installation's activities will fall within the I.P.P.C. regime and what will remain outside that control to be dealt with under other statutory means of noise control.[31] A useful indication of the level of detail required in connection with noise and vibration when submitting a permit application can be obtained from the following extract from the Environment Agency's Technical Guidance Note IPPC S2.03.[32]

2.9   Noise and vibration

Within this section "noise" should be taken to refer to "noise and/or vibration" as appropriate, detectable beyond the site boundary.

---

[28]   e.g. via planning conditions, abatement notices and noise abatement zones.
[29]   Reg. 10 and Sch. 4, Part 1.
[30]   Horizontal Guidance Note IPPC H3, para. 2.2.
[31]   *Ibid.*
[32]   IPPC S2.03 Integrated Pollution Prevention and Control (I.P.P.C.), *Technical Guidance for Non-ferrous Metals*, Draft 1, April 2001.

The PPC Regulations require installations to be operated in such a way that "all the appropriate preventative measures are taken against pollution, in particular through the application of BAT". The definition of pollution includes "emissions that may be harmful to human health or the quality of the environment, cause offence to human senses or impair or interfere with amenities and other legitimate uses of the environment". BAT is therefore likely to be similar, in practice, to the requirements of the statutory nuisance legislation, which requires the use of "best practicable means" to prevent or minimise noise nuisance.

In the case of noise, "offence to any human senses" can normally be judged by the likelihood of complaints, but in some cases it may be possible to reduce noise emissions still further at reasonable costs, and this may exceptionally therefore be BAT for noise emissions.

For advice on how noise and/or vibration-related limits and conditions will be determined see "IPPC Horizontal Guidance for Noise – Part 1 Regulation and Permitting" (see Reference 21).

Information needed to determine BAT for noise and vibration

Application form Question 2.9
Identify the main sources of noise and vibration (including infrequent sources); the nearest noise-sensitive locations and relevant environmental surveys that have been undertaken; and the proposed techniques and measures for the control of noise.

With the Application the Operator should:
1. Provide the following information for each main source of noise and vibration that falls within the IPPC installation:

    ● the source and its location on a scaled plan of the site;

    ● whether continuous/intermittent, fixed or mobile;

    ● the hours of operation;

    ● its description (for example, clatter, whine, hiss, screech, hum, bangs, clicks, thumps or tonal elements);

    ● its contribution to overall site noise emission (categorise each as high, medium or low unless supporting data is available).

A common-sense approach needs to be adopted in determining which sources to include. The ones that need to be considered are those that may have environmental nuisance impact; for example, a small unit could cause an occupational noise issue in an enclosed space, but would be unlikely to cause an environmental issue. Conversely a large unit or a number of smaller units enclosed within a building could, for example, cause a nuisance if doors are left open. Remember that noise, which is not particularly noticeable during the day, may become more noticeable at night.

2. Provide the information required in 1 for each source plus its times of operation. For *infrequent sources of noise and vibration,* not listed above that fall within the IPPC installation (such as infrequently operated/seasonal operations, cleaning/maintenance activities, on-site deliveries/collections/transport or out-of-hours activities/emergency generators/pumps/alarm testing).

3. Identify the nearest noise-sensitive sites and receptors (typically dwellings, parkland and open spaces – schools hospitals and commercial premises may be considered noise sensitive, depending upon the activities undertaken there) and any other points/boundary where conditions have been applied by local authority officers or as part of a planning consent, relating to:

    (a) the local environment:

    ● provide an accurate map or scaled plan showing grid reference, nature of the receiving site, distance and direction from site boundary;

    (b) conditions/limits imposed that relate to other locations (that is, boundary fence or surrogate for nearest sensitive receptor):

    ● any planning conditions imposed by the local authority (day/evening/night*);

    ● other conditions imposed by agreements, for example, limits on operating times, technologies and the like;

    ● any requirements of legal notices and the like;

    ● any complaints received within the last three years and outcome of any investigations.

    (c) the noise environment:

    ● background noise level, if known (day/evening/night) $L_{A,90,T}$;

    ● specific noise level (day/evening/night) $L_{Aeq,T}$; and/or

    ● ambient noise level (day/evening/night) $L_{Aeq,T}$, as appropriate;

    ● vibration data that may be expressed in terms of the peak particle velocity (ppv) in mm s^{-1} or the vibration dose value (VDV) in m s$^{-1.75}$.

For noise these are given the meaning as defined in BS4142:1997 *Method for rating industrial noise affecting mixed residential and industrial areas*, and to which reference should be made for a full description. For vibration, the appropriate standard is BS6472:1992

Evaluation of human exposure to vibration in buildings "1 to 80 Hz". In very general terms "background" is taken to be the A-weighted sound pressure level of the residual noise at the assessment position that is exceeded for 90% of a given time interval, T, measured using time weighting, F, and quoted to the nearest whole number of decibels. The "ambient" level is the equivalent continuous A-weighted combination of all noise sources far and distant, including the source under investigation. And "specific noise" is the equivalent continuous A-weighted noise level produced by the source under investigation as measured at a selected assessment point. Both are averaged over a time period, T. BS4142 gives advice on the appropriate reference periods. "Worst case" situations and impulsive or tonal noise should be accounted for separately and not "averaged out" over the measurement period.

4. Provide details of any environmental noise measurement surveys, modelling or any other noise measurements undertaken relevant to the environmental impact of the site, identifying:

   ● the purpose/context of the survey;

   ● the locations where measurements were taken;

   ● the source(s) investigated or identified;

   ● the outcomes.

5. Identify any specific local issues and proposals for improvements.

6. Describe the current or proposed position with regard to the techniques below, any in Reference 21 or any others that are pertinent to the installation.

7. Demonstrate that the proposals are BAT by confirming compliance with the indicative requirements, by justifying departures (as described in Section 1.2 and in the *Guide for Applicants*) or alternative measures.

Indicative B.A.T. requirements
1. The Operator should employ basic good practice measures for the control of noise, including adequate maintenance of any parts of plant or equipment whose deterioration may give rise to increases in noise (for example, maintenance of bearings, air handling plant, the building fabric as well as specific noise attenuation measures associated with plant, equipment or machinery).

2. The Operator should also employ such other noise control techniques to ensure that the noise from the installation does not give rise to reasonable cause for annoyance, in the view of the Regulator and, in particular, should justify where either Rating Levels ($L_{Aeq,T}$) from the installation exceed the numerical value of the Background Sound Level ($L_{A90,T}$), or the absolute levels of 50 dBL_{Aeq} by day or 45 by night

are exceeded. Reasons why these levels may be exceeded in certain circumstances are given in Reference 21.

3. In some circumstances "creeping background" (see Reference 21) may be an issue. Where this has been identified in pre-application discussions or in previous discussions with the local authority, the Operator should employ such noise control techniques as are considered appropriate to minimise problems to an acceptable level within the BAT criteria.

4. Noise surveys, measurement, investigation (which can involve detailed assessment of sound power levels for individual items of plant) or modelling may be necessary for either new or existing installations depending upon the potential for noise problems. Operators may have a noise management plan as part of their management system. More information on such techniques is given in Part 2 of Reference 21.

Determination of B.A.T.

The Agency will compare an applicant's submission and the consultation responses with the noise-related aspects of its sector-specific and other[33] guidance notes to:

(a) confirm there is sufficient information in the application;

(b) assess the risk and therefore the appropriate conditions to be applied;

(c) determine the B.A.T. for the installation in respect of noise;

(d) have regard to both noise and other environmental impacts.[34]

Permit conditions

Regulation 11 sets out general principles to be taken into account in conditioning a permit.[35] The Secretary of State expects regulators

---

[33] Horizontal Guidance Note IPPC H3, para. 2.2.

[34] By reference to I.P.P.C. Guidance Note H1 – *Environmental Assessment and Appraisal of BAT*, Environment Agency, 2001. This provides a tool for undertaking an assessment of the environmental impact of an activity or a whole installation for the purposes of a P.P.C. permit. IPPC H3 Integrated Pollution Prevention and Control (I.P.P.C.), *Horizontal Guidance for Noise, Part 1 – Regulating and Permitting* sets out in more detail how the Agency assesses B.A.T.

[35] e.g. taking appropriate preventative measures including B.A.T. and ensuring that no significant pollution is caused. Reg. 12(9) sets out more specific requirements concerning the monitoring and reporting of emissions.

to apply the P.P.C. Regulations proportionately, i.e. "the regulatory effort needed to determine an application and any permit conditions should be appropriate for the complexity of an installation and its environmental effects".[36]

I.P.P.C. requires emission limit values and other permit conditions to take account of the technical characteristics of the installation concerned, its geographical location and the local environmental conditions. The regulator must take account of whether the applicant will operate the installation or mobile plant in accordance with the permit and any associated conditions. An application for a permit will be refused[37] if the regulator is of the opinion that:

(a) the installation will have an unacceptable environmental impact;

(b) poor management systems, or lack of technical competence, will result in non-compliance with the permit or its conditions.

In most cases, permits are likely to be site-specific and based on the application details and the regulator's assessment. However, Regulation 14 enables the Secretary of State to make "general binding rules" (G.B.R.s) for certain types of installation. These rules can be used instead of site-specific conditions to permit certain types of installation and mobile plant which share a number of similar characteristics, so long as he is satisfied that this will result in the operation of an installation to the same high level of environmental protection and integrated prevention and control of pollution as if it were permitted using specific conditions.

In its guidance document,[38] the Agency suggests that conditions which could be applied to the control of noise and/or vibration could take the form of:

---

[36] *Integrated Pollution Prevention and Control, A Practical Guide*, Edition 1, p. 23, para. 7.1, D.E.T.R., August 2000.

[37] Reg. 10(3). An application will also be refused if a requisite planning permission has not been granted under the Town and Country Planning Act 1990.

[38] IPPC H3 Integrated Pollution Prevention and Control (I.P.P.C.), *Horizontal Guidance for Noise, Part 1 – Regulating and Permitting*, version 1, December 2001, p. 14, para. 2.5.1.

(a) descriptive/qualitative – e.g. relating to specific equipment or containment requirements, or timing of certain operations or other management issues;

(b) numerical[39] – e.g. specifying noise levels at the installation boundary or other suitable point.

Conditions must pass the five key tests of being reasonable, necessary, precise, relevant and enforceable. Existing planning conditions or other relevant conditions which meet these tests can be replicated in the permit. If necessary, the operator could be required to produce a "noise management plan" in complex situations. Where a permit application sets out acceptable techniques for managing noise, it may be appropriate to include specific reference to these in the permit. Even where specific noise-related conditions have not been written into a permit, there remains an obligation on the operator to use B.A.T. to provide and maintain measures to prevent annoyance by noise. In using descriptive conditions to control noise, the Agency warns of the need to exercise care in their wording. It gives advice under the following headings:[40]

(i) Restrictions on noise characteristics.

(ii) Restrictions on activities (timing, location).

(iii) Conditions relating to the source or its containment.

(iv) Other conditions.

In discussing the application of numerical noise conditions, the Agency draws attention[41] to the use of BS4142:1997 *Method of Rating Noise Affecting Mixed Residential and Industrial Areas*, as a guide to setting external levels. In doing so, however, it recognises the British Standards limitations in quantitatively assessing general

---

[39] Descriptive/qualitative conditions are given first priority; numerical conditions will only be used where there is a demonstrable need.

[40] IPPC H3 Integrated Pollution Prevention and Control (I.P.P.C.), *Horizontal Guidance for Noise, Part 1 – Regulating and Permitting*, version 1, December 2001, p. 15, para. 2.5.4.

[41] *Ibid*, pp. 16–19.

community annoyance and nuisance. It also indicates the value of seeking the advice and experience of relevant local authority departments, e.g. Environmental Health and Planning, in arriving at noise control conditions. Additionally, the improvement section of the permit can be used to require changes in techniques or other appropriate actions, including monitoring, and to apply appropriate upgrading timescales, as long as the requirements can be justified within the B.A.T. criteria. This would apply in particular to indicative B.A.T. techniques laid down in the relevant sector guidance.

Stage 2 – Operation

Monitoring and enforcement
The general public has traditionally expected local authorities to deal with environmental noise issues. It is, therefore, important for the Environment Agency and local authorities "to reach a clear understanding with respect to:

(a) any split of sources between regulators and regulatory regimes on an installation; and

(b) the arrangements for on-going monitoring and compliance assessment."[42]

It is particularly important that suitable arrangements are made to re-direct complaints to the appropriate regulator.[43] This will involve clear guidelines for officers of the Agency and local authorities, and the provision of appropriate information to local elected representatives, ratepayer and related organisations, local area committees (in some authorities) and specific environmental action groups. The Agency identifies a number of monitoring activities that might be undertaken:[44]

---

[42] IPPC H3 Integrated Pollution Prevention and Control (I.P.P.C.), *Horizontal Guidance for Noise, Part 1 – Regulating and Permitting*, version 1, December 2001, p. 20, para 2.6.

[43] *Ibid*, p. 20, para. 2.6.1 and see also *Protocol agreed by local government association and the agency on arrangements to implement the requirements of the I.P.P.C. Directive*, p. 8.

[44] *Ibid*, p. 20, para. 2.6.2.

1. Spot measurements by Agency staff (to check for compliance or in response to complaints).

2. Operator spot check (for the same purposes as above).

3. Operator monitoring (surveys) to check compliance.

4. Operator monitoring for planning or noise prediction purposes.

5. Check monitoring by the Agency.

In relation to noise monitoring, the Agency has produced a comprehensive guide dealing with the measurement and evaluation of noise, and the techniques and technology for control.[45] The Agency will regulate installations according to the IPPC permit conditions and it suggests a number of possible compliance/enforcement issues:

1. Planning conditions are breached – a noisy operation is conducted during hours in which it is prohibited. If the planning conditions are not also included as part of the I.P.P.C. permit, the local authority will consider taking planning enforcement action. Otherwise, if the installation is controlled by similar noise conditions in both the I.P.P.C. permit and a planning consent, the two organisations will presumably decide which is the most appropriate course of action.[46]

2. The installation operator fails to meet an I.P.P.C. improvement condition relating to noise and the Agency advises the local authority of its intention to serve an enforcement notice.

3. There are no planning conditions controlling noise and an operator fails to comply with noise control conditions in his permit, resulting in public complaints. In this case, the Agency will discuss action with the local authority. If the authority disagrees with the proposed action, it or a third party may challenge the action by application for judicial review, or a

---

[45] IPPC H3 Integrated Pollution Prevention and Control (I.P.P.C.), draft *Horizontal Guidance for Noise, Part 2 – Noise Assessment and Control*, version 1, October 2001.

[46] They may, of course, decide to proceed under each of their respective powers. In relation to this matter, see also fn. 12.

private individual may bring a nuisance action under Part III of the Environmental Protection Act 1990.[47]

Review and variations

Regulators are required periodically to review permit conditions and may do so at any time.[48] They must review a permit where:

(a) the pollution caused by the installation or mobile plant ... is of such significance that the existing emission limit values ... need to be revised or new emission limit values need to be included ...;

(b) substantial changes in the best available techniques make it possible to reduce the emissions ... significantly without imposing excessive costs; or

(c) the operational safety ... requires other techniques to be used.

The operator of a permitted installation must give at least 14 days' notice to the regulator if he proposes to make a change in the operation of the installation.[49] A regulator may at any time vary the conditions of a permit[50] and an operator may also apply for a variation.[51] If the regulator decides to vary the permit conditions, he must serve a "variation notice" on the operator[52] specifying the variations of the conditions and the date(s) they become effective.

Transfer of permits

If the operator of an installation or mobile plant wishes to transfer all or part of a permit to someone else, he must make a joint application to the regulator and pay a fee.[53] The regulator must decide whether to allow the transfer, and must allow it unless he

---

[47] The local authority is barred from such action by virtue of the Environmental Protection Act 1990, s. 79(10), but no such restriction appears to apply if an individual takes proceedings under s. 82.

[48] Reg. 15(1).

[49] Reg. 16.

[50] Reg. 17(1).

[51] Reg. 17(2).

[52] Reg. 17(5). The determination of applications under this Regulation is subject to the conditions of Sch. 7.

[53] Reg. 18(1) and (2).

considers that the proposed transferee will not be the person who will have control over the operation or will not comply with the permit conditions.[54] There is also provision for partial transfers[55] and, if transfer applications are not determined within two months or such longer period as agreed by the regulator and the applicant, the application is deemed to be refused.[56]

Enforcement notices
Regulation 23 requires the regulator to take such action as is necessary for ensuring that permit conditions are complied with. If an operator has contravened, is contravening or in the opinion of the regulator is likely to contravene the conditions of a permit, an enforcement notice may be served.[57] This will specify the steps needed to remedy the problem and the time period allowed to undertake those steps.

Suspension notices may be served where the regulator considers that the operation of an installation or mobile plant involves an imminent risk of serious pollution.[58] This applies whether or not a breach of permit conditions has occurred. In such cases, the regulator has the power to remedy the matter.[59]

The regulator may, at any time, revoke a permit, in whole or in part, by serving a revocation notice.[60] The notice must allow at least 28 days after service for the revocation to come into effect and it then ceases to authorise the operation or activity in the manner specified in the notice. Revocation is probably most likely where other enforcement action has failed to produce the required response.

Stage 3 – Closure

Where the operator of a Part A installation or mobile plant ceases or intends to cease operations, either in whole or in part, he may

---

[54] Reg. 18(4).
[55] Reg. 18(5)–(7).
[56] Reg. 18(8) and (9).
[57] Reg. 24.
[58] Reg. 25.
[59] Reg. 26.
[60] Reg. 21.

apply to surrender his permit or the relevant part of it.[61] The application must include a site report identifying, in particular, any changes in the condition of the site as contained in the site report submitted with the application for the permit. The operator must identify any steps taken to avoid any pollution risk resulting from the operation of the installation or return it to a satisfactory state. If the regulator is satisfied, the surrender will be accepted and notice of determination given,[62] the permit then ceasing to have effect on the specified date. In the case of a partial surrender, the regulator may serve a variation notice to take account of the surrender.[63] If he is not satisfied that sufficient steps are being taken to avoid any pollution risk arising from the proposals, he can refuse the application.[64] If the application is not determined within three months, or such longer period as agreed between the regulator and the operator, the application is deemed to be refused.[65]

Appeals
Regulation 27 provides for appeals to the Secretary of State in respect of the refusal to grant a permit, a variation of permit conditions, transfer of a permit, application to surrender a permit, or conditions attached to any permit.

Fees and charges
Fees and charges are levied for Part A(1) installations under a scheme made under section 41 of the Environment Act 1995. The charges are intended to reflect the activities associated with the issue of permits, monitoring and enforcement, sampling, operation of public registers of information, and general administrative costs. The fees and charges for A(2) installations are subject to an alternative scheme.[66]

---

[61] Reg. 19(1) and (2).
[62] Reg. 19(4).
[63] Reg. 19(5).
[64] Reg. 19(6).
[65] Reg. 19(7) and (8).
[66] The Local Authority Permits for Part A Installations and Mobile Plant (England and Wales) Fees and Charges Scheme 2000, made under Reg. 22(2).

Prosecutions

For offences under the Regulations, conviction in a magistrates' court carries a fine of up to £20,000 and six months' imprisonment.[67] Conviction on indictment in the Crown Court may lead to an unlimited fine and up to five years' imprisonment. Where an I.P.P.C. regulator and another enforcement authority, e.g. a planning authority, both have the power to prosecute, they should liaise to agree on the most appropriate course of action.

Information and publicity

Regulators have a duty to maintain public registers[68] on the installations for which they are responsible. The registers must contain specified information, subject to conditions relating to national security and commercial confidentiality. The registers must be available for inspection by the public at all reasonable times, free of charge.

---

[67] Reg. 32(2)(a).
[68] Regs. 29–31 and Sch. 9.

Chapter 8

AIRCRAFT NOISE

Heathrow and Gatwick are two of the world's busiest airports. In 2001, over 64 million people used Heathrow and over 32 million used Gatwick. These and other major international airports in the United Kingdom are continually expanding their activities to cope with the increasing demand for air travel, both passenger and commercial. Over 7,000 British registered general aviation aircraft, mostly used for private flying, now operate from about 280 airfields. These factors have resulted in a vast increase in the total number of air traffic movements since aircraft noise was addressed in the Air Navigation Act 1920. United Kingdom air traffic is predicted to grow at an average of 4.25% per year, from around 160 million passengers in 1998 to 401 million by 2020.[1] Boeing predicts that world-wide increases in air traffic may result in the size of the world's commercial fleet increasing from 13,670 aircraft at the end of 1999 to almost 32,000 by 2019.[2]

Aircraft noise mainly affects people living near airports.[3] There are several ways of reducing this noise; by making aircraft quieter, operating them in a manner which reduces or controls the noise heard at ground level, providing noise insulation in appropriate cases, imposing local restrictions on types of aircraft or their activities, or on hours of operation. Significant progress has also been made in the design and manufacture of aircraft engines and their associated casings and structures to produce successive generations of less noisy aircraft. The Government's 1998 transport

---

[1] Department of the Environment, Transport and the Regions, *Air Traffic Forecasts 2000*, May 2000. This is a mid-point forecast; the range of forecasts is between 3.6% and 4.9%.

[2] *Current Market Outlook 2000: Into the New Century*, Boeing Commercial Airplanes Group, August 2000.

[3] Although socio-economic factors influence complaints, e.g. Hounslow is closer to Heathrow than Richmond but there are fewer complaints from the Hounslow area. The different socio-economic characteristics of these areas are suggested to be a factor. (Private communication from BAA.)

White Paper[4] proposed to introduce statutory powers to enable airports to enforce noise mitigation measures, e.g. by taking action against non-compliant airlines, and to enable local authorities to enforce noise mitigation agreements. A subsequent consultation paper[5] sought comment on various Government proposals, including the regulation of flying behaviour on non-designated aerodromes; local noise amelioration schemes, with infringements dealt with on a civil basis; noise related airport charges; and maintenance of the statutory restrictions on actions for nuisance in respect of aircraft noise.[6]

The most logical answer to the problem of aircraft noise might appear to be to build new airports away from populated areas but this is clearly impracticable in countries with high population densities where it is almost certain that aircraft flight paths will produce some interference. Indeed, the Government decision to approve a fifth terminal at Heathrow Airport may well reflect not only the need for additional facilities to cope with increasing demand but also the difficulty in finding suitable alternative, environmentally acceptable facilities. It may also be found that, in the future, U.K. controls could be influenced by decisions of the European Court of Human Rights.[7]

---

[4] *A New Deal for Transport: Better for Everyone*, Cmnd. 3950, July 1998, p.137.

[5] *Control of Noise from Civil Aircraft*, A consultation paper from the Department of the Environment, Transport and the Regions, July 2000.

[6] The Government has recently published a statement of responses, *Summary of responses to control of noise from civil aircraft*, D.T.L.R., March 2002, and any policy proposals will be included in the forthcoming aviation White Paper due in Spring 2003.

[7] See *Hatton and Others v The United Kingdom* (application no. 36022/97), Judgment of the European Court of Human Rights, Strasbourg, 2nd October 2001. The court ruled that the U.K. Government had infringed the basic human rights of residents living near Heathrow Airport by failing to protect them adequately from night-time aircraft noise. The judges decided that in setting night-time noise restrictions for Heathrow in 1993, the Government had failed to strike a fair balance between the U.K.'s economic well-being and the applicants' right to enjoy their homes, and their private and family lives. At the time of writing, the Government has a right of appeal against this judgment. Under the Human Rights Act 1988, British courts are not strictly bound by European Court decisions but are obliged to take account of them. See also an analysis of this case in *Human Rights and Aircraft Noise*, ENDS Report 321, pp. 53/54, October 2001.

SOURCE OF AIRCRAFT NOISE

Aircraft noise is primarily a problem which occurs during take-off and landing, although ground running of engines can also cause annoyance. The thrust required to get an airliner off the ground is enormous and the huge mass of air moved by the engine is a vast source of sound energy. In earlier jets, noise was first reduced by using fluted nozzles which rapidly mixed the jet stream with the outside air and by fitting modified air intakes with sound absorbent linings. The noise from the older generation of jet engines can be further reduced by fitting them with "hush-kits". Quieter and more efficient engines were produced through by-passing air from the compressor stage around the outside of the combustion and turbine stages. The slower, cooler, by-passed air acts as a cushion between the main jet and surrounding air, reducing engine noise. The proportion of this by-passed air (the by-pass ratio) has increased and now the modern, large fan engines, with by-pass ratios of around 8:1[8] make much less noise than earlier designs.

The U.K. has actively participated in the establishment of international standards for aircraft noise through the International Civil Aviation Organisation (ICAO). The standards for civil jet aircraft are known as "Chapter 2" and "Chapter 3" of the relevant international document. This is Annex 16 of the "Chicago Convention".[9] Flights in this country and the rest of the European Union by jet aircraft which do not meet the requirements of Chapter 2 are banned.[10]

EFFECTS OF AIRCRAFT NOISE ON HEALTH

The effects of aircraft noise on health have been variously reported. German research[11] indicated that 600 people exposed to noise at Munich and Hamburg airports were examined and the study found that even if aircraft noise causes no major illness, such as heart

---

[8]   e.g. B777 Rolls Royce Trent engine.
[9]   Signed 7th December 1944 at the International Civil Aviation Conference in Chicago. Cmnd. 8742, 6th edition 1980, International Civil Aviation Organisation, Doc. 73006.
[10]   See p. 295 regarding new proposals.
[11]   Reported in *New Scientist,* 1st May 1975.

circulatory disease or diabetes, it does cause nervousness and changes in "vegetative functions", especially blood pressure. Perhaps most importantly, 95% of the people observed in the study who were disturbed or annoyed by the sound of an aircraft landing did not ever get used to it. The idea of "conditioning" to aircraft noise was rejected in the report. The results confirmed for the most part research done in the United Kingdom and the research also found that people who believed noise to be detrimental to health suffer far more from aircraft noise than those who believe aviation is significant for other reasons.

In a population near Zurich airport it was found that the consumption of sleeping pills correlated with aircraft noise and psychological performance was below par the next day.[12]

The effects of aircraft noise on the sleep of babies has also been examined.[13] It was shown that the reactions of babies examined varied according to the length of stay of mothers in the noisy area. Babies born of mothers who came to the noisy area before or during the first five months of pregnancy showed little or no particular response to the noise. On the other hand, those babies whose mothers came to the area in the later part of pregnancy, or who arrived in the area after birth, showed a significantly greater reaction. It was concluded that the difference in reaction was due to a pre-natal difference in the time of exposure to the noise.

Other effects of aircraft noise on sleep are summarised in a paper published by the Civil Aviation Authority.[14] The older an individual, the more likely they are to be awakened or to have their sleep stage changed. People are less likely to be disturbed during the deepest sleep stages, which usually occur during the initial hours of sleep. A given noise is, therefore, more likely to wake people towards the end of a night's sleep. In 1977, a three year research programme was commissioned to study the relationship between aircraft noise and sleep disturbance around Heathrow and Gatwick airports. The

---

[12] Reported in *The Lancet,* 21st May 1977.
[13] "Effects of noise on sleep of babies," Ando, Y. and Hattori, H., *Journal of Acoustical Society of America,* Vol. 62, No. 1, July 1977, pp. 199–204.
[14] *Noise and Sleep,* C.A.A. Paper 78011, June 1978, Civil Aviation Authority.

research was commissioned to provide a scientific basis for future policy decisions on aircraft movements at night from these airports.

A subsequent major study[15] was undertaken in 1991 to determine the relationship between outdoor aircraft noise levels and the probability of sleep disturbance, and the variation of these relationships with time of night. 400 people were monitored for 15 nights in eight study areas around four major U.K. airports – Heathrow, Gatwick, Stansted and Manchester. Outdoor aircraft noise levels were measured at up to three positions at each site using noise monitors set to record all levels in excess of 60 dB(A). Some of the main findings can be summarised as follows:

(a) once asleep, very few people living near airports are at risk of any substantial sleep disturbance due to aircraft noise, even at the highest event noise levels;[16]

(b) below outdoor event levels of 90 dB(A) on the Sound Exposure Level scale (80 dB(A) L_{max}), aircraft noise events (noise experienced when a single aircraft passes by) are most unlikely to cause any measurable increase in the overall rates of sleep disturbance experienced during normal sleep. For outdoor event levels of 90–100 dB(A) on the Sound Exposure Level (80–95 dB(A) L_{max}) the chance of the average person being wakened is about 1 in 75. Based on expert opinion on the consequences of sleep disturbance, the results of the study provide no evidence to suggest that aircraft noise is likely to cause harmful after-effects;

(c) there may be particular times of night, perhaps when sleep is not so deep, when individuals could be more sensitive to noise. People appear more resistant to disturbance after first falling asleep and less resistant at the end of the night;

---

[15] *Report of a field study of aircraft noise and sleep disturbance,* December 1992, Department of Transport.

[16] There was some criticism of this study in that no reference appeared to be made to the difficulty of getting back to sleep once woken, and that not enough attention was given to noise events during the "shoulder periods", especially 6.00 a.m–7.00 a.m. when there may be a lot of early morning arrivals.

(d) the data indicates that aircraft events with noise levels greater than 100 dB(A) on the Sound Exposure Level scale (95 dB(A) L_{max}) outdoors, will have a greater chance of disturbing sleep.

The effect that aircraft noise has on the person on the ground who is exposed to it depends on a number of factors:

1. *The noise level at source* – this is associated primarily with the level of noise from the engines and the airframe, although the latter is only relatively significant during the final phase of landing.

2. *The distance between the noise and the receiver* – this is affected by the take-off and approach paths and by flight control procedures, aircraft with a steeper climb and approach gradient generally producing less noise at a given point.

3. *Frequency of occurrence of noise events.*

4. *Planning* – the effective use of land in noise sensitive areas and the sound insulation of exposed properties where noise is at an unacceptable level will help alleviate noise.

Some investigations have suggested that minor neurotic conditions are related to high noise levels. A study of schools near to London Heathrow airport indicated symptoms of mild affective illness amongst teachers.[17] There is also evidence suggesting that exposure to aircraft noise in particular may be associated with an increase in psychiatric illness. A survey of admissions from the Borough of Hounslow to a local mental hospital during the period 1966–1968 showed a significant excess of admissions from areas of high aircraft noise exposure over those from a relatively less noisy area.[18]

The Government continues to support research into the effects of

---

[17] "The effects of aircraft noise in schools around London Airport", Crook, M.A. and Langdon, F.J., *Journal of Sound and Vibration*, 1974, Vol. 34, p. 221.

[18] "Mental Hospital Admissions and Aircraft Noise", Abey-Wickrama, I., a'Brook, M.F., Gattoni, F.E.E. and Herridge, C.F., *The Lancet*, 13th December 1969.

aircraft noise. A recent study[19] considered the potentially adverse effects of night-time aircraft noise on people and identified a number of issues for further research. In reviewing international studies into the subject, including the most extensive of those,[20] it was acknowledged that environmental noise adversely affects health by causing chronic subjective reactions but also suggested that there appeared to be no hard scientific evidence of clinically significant health impairment, i.e. chronic objective effects. It suggested a number of further research options and, on receipt of the results, the Department of Transport, Local Government and the Regions will decide whether there is a case for a full scale study on the effects of night-time aircraft noise.[21]

In a ministerial statement,[22] the Government has announced new research. It has concluded that it has no reason to doubt the validity of studies on the relationship between annoyance and aircraft noise over 24 hours carried out in the 1980s (including the Aircraft Noise Index Study). However, in light of its commitment to developing a new air transport policy, of changes in air traffic patterns, and the general noise reduction of individual aircraft, it proposes a fresh study, concentrating on subjective responses to night and day-time annoyance. The study is expected to last three years.[23]

GENERAL CONTROL OF AIRCRAFT NOISE

Most of the earlier enactments relating to aircraft noise were repealed and replaced by the Civil Aviation Act 1982. Some of the requirements derive from international law. Section 60 of the Civil Aviation Act 1982 allows the Crown through Order in Council (referred to as an "Air Navigation Order") to give effect to the "Chicago Convention" and regulate, amongst other things, the licensing and operation of aerodromes, operational safety, the

---

[19] *Adverse effects of night-time aircraft noise*, R. & D. Report 9964, Porter, N. D., Kershaw, A. D., Ollerhead, J. B., prepared by D.O.R.A. on behalf of the Department of the Environment, Transport and the Regions, March 2000.

[20] *Report of a field study of aircraft noise and sleep disturbance*, Department of Transport, December 1992.

[21] R. & D. Report 9964, p. 32, para. 4.20.

[22] Statement of the Aviation Minister, 8th May 2001.

[23] Until 2004.

prohibition of aircraft from flying over specified areas of the United Kingdom and the prohibition of landing and taking off unless there are in force certificates of compliance with noise standards as specified in the Order and those conditions are complied with. Section 77 of the Act states that an Air Navigation Order may provide for regulating the conditions under which noise and vibration may be caused by aircraft *on* aerodromes. The order *may* provide that no action shall lie in respect of nuisance by aircraft noise and vibration *on* an aerodrome so long as the provisions of the Order are complied with.

There is also a power under section 5 of the Act which permits the Secretary of State to require the Civil Aviation Authority to consider environmental matters, including noise and vibration attributable to the use of aircraft for civil aviation, when licensing or re-licensing an aerodrome. This power has never been used. The Government proposes[24] to repeal this section as it believes that licensing does not necessarily offer the best way of resolving environmental problems. It believes environmental matters should be looked at separately using alternative powers proposed in its consultation paper.[25] An additional power under section 6 enables the Secretary of State, after consultation with the Civil Aviation Authority, to direct the Authority where it already has powers to act, to take action to prevent or deal with noise or vibration attributable to aircraft used for the purpose of civil aviation.[26]

The Air Navigation Order 2000[27], made under section 77 of the Act, gives the Secretary of State power to prescribe the conditions under which noise and vibration may be caused by aircraft (including military aircraft) on Government aerodromes, aerodromes owned or managed by the Civil Aviation Authority, licensed aerodromes (licensed by the Civil Aviation Authority under the Order for the landing and taking-off of aircraft engaged in public transport of

---

[24] Consultation paper *Control of noise from civil aircraft*, para. 25, D.E.T.R., July 2000.
[25] Referred to in the appropriate parts of this chapter.
[26] This power was used to end the Heathrow-Gatwick helicopter link on environmental grounds.
[27] S.I. 2000 No. 1562, Art. 108.

passengers or for the purpose of instruction in flying or of any classes of such aircraft) or on aerodromes at which the manufacture, repair or maintenance of aircraft is carried out by persons carrying on business as manufacturers or repairers of aircraft. The Order also states that no action shall lie in respect of nuisance caused by noise and vibration from aircraft.[28] The *Report of the Noise Review Working Party* 1990 recommended that the Air Navigation Order made under section 77 should no longer exclude the ground activities of aircraft from the statutory nuisance procedures (of the Environmental Protection Act 1990) because of the serious nuisance these activities could cause.[29] However, in its *Review of Aircraft Noise Legislation,* the Government said[30] that no evidence of significant ground noise problems was presented in response to its consultation paper. It proposed that a new power of designation (to replace sections 5 and 78–80 of the Civil Aviation Act 1982) would cover the issue of ground noise.[31]

Although the power in relation to ground noise has not been used, this is one of many issues considered by the Government.[32] However, a night-time ground noise study was undertaken at Heathrow, Gatwick and Stansted airports on behalf of the Aircraft Noise Monitoring Advisory Committee in 1996.[33] Its aim was to develop an understanding of the sources of ground noise at night and to consider possible ways of minimising the impact on local communities. It found that there were a number of issues involved, including the effect of wind direction on the propagation of ground

---

[28] See Civil Aviation Act 1982, s. 77(2).

[29] *Report of the Noise Review Working Party 1990*, page 17, H.M.S.O.

[30] Published March 1993, paragraph 18.

[31] The Government consultation paper *Control of Noise from Civil Aircraft*, D.E.T.R., July 2000, proposes no change in the controls over ground noise. Ground noise includes noise from aircraft and aircraft servicing activities on the ground, e.g. aircraft taxiing, engine testing, aircraft auxiliary power units and other mobile power equipment.

[32] *Control of Noise from Civil Aircraft*, D.E.T.R., July 2000. In its response, the Aviation Environment Federation urged the Government to strengthen the law on aircraft noise, including a duty on airport operators to produce noise amelioration schemes, with legal sanctions if they were not produced or not complied with.

[33] *Night-time ground noise*, R. & D. Report 9850, Jopson, I., Jones, C., Porter, N., White, S., National Air Traffic Services Ltd., London, August 1998.

noise, the impact of road traffic, taxiing aircraft, ground noise from airport service vehicles and sirens, the audibility of auxiliary power units and the ground running of aircraft engines. Noise mitigation measures were suggested, many of which were adopted by the airports. The statutory limitation on actions in respect of nuisance[34] is only applicable to aircraft, and other ground noise such as that from heat and power generating plant or maintenance facilities may still be actionable under the statutory nuisance provisions of the Environmental Protection Act 1990.

The Air Navigation (General) Regulations 1993[35] implement the Secretary of States' power in the Order by specifying the conditions under which noise or vibration may be caused by aircraft (including military aircraft), on the aerodromes referred to in the Order, whether in the course of manufacture or otherwise as being when

"(a) the aircraft is taking off or landing, or

(b) the aircraft is moving on the ground or water, or

(c) the engines are being operated in the aircraft—

(i) for the purpose of ensuring their satisfactory performance,

(ii) for the purpose of bringing them to a proper temperature in preparation for, or at the end of, a flight, or

(iii) for the purpose of ensuring that the instruments, accessories or other components of the aircraft are in a satisfactory condition."

This does not mean that unlimited noise is permissible and noise can be regulated by statutory and bye-law control. Section 63 of the Airports Act 1986 provides that, where an airport is either designated for the purposes of the section by order or managed by the Secretary of State, the airport operator can make bye-laws regulating the use and operation of the airport, including controlling the operation of aircraft, within, or directly above, the airport for the purpose of

---

[34] Civil Aviation Act 1982, s. 76(1).
[35] S.I. 1993 No. 1622, Reg. 13.

limiting or mitigating the effect of noise and vibration caused by aircraft using the airport.

Section 78 of the Civil Aviation Act 1982 gives power to the Secretary of State to require aircraft operators at designated aerodromes to comply with any specified requirements to limit or mitigate the effects of noise and vibration connected with the landing or taking off of aircraft at the aerodrome. The Government's Consultation Paper[36] proposes a new power to designate an aerodrome, provided it is not already designated for the purposes of section 78. The new power would give the Secretary of State discretion to direct an aerodrome to prepare a compulsory noise amelioration scheme.

AIRPORT MANAGEMENT

Airports may be managed by one of the following organisations:

(a) Civil Aviation Authority;

(b) B.A.A. plc;

(c) local authorities;

(d) private owners;

Civil Aviation Authority

The Civil Aviation Act 1982[37] prohibits the Authority from establishing or acquiring any aerodrome in addition to those already owned by it.[38] It can, however, with the written consent of the Secretary of State, undertake the management of any specified aerodrome which it does not own.

B.A.A. plc

The Airports Act 1986 provided for the dissolution of the British Airports Authority and the vesting of its property rights and

---

[36] *Control of Noise from Civil Aircraft*, D.E.T.R., July 2000, para. 15.
[37] s. 28.
[38] By virtue of the Civil Aviation Act 1971, Sch. 2, para. 1.

liabilities in a company nominated by the Secretary of State. B.A.A. plc was formed and it owns and operates seven airports in the U.K. – Heathrow, Gatwick, Stansted, Glasgow, Edinburgh, Aberdeen and Southampton.

Local authorities

Section 30 of the Civil Aviation Act 1982 allows local authorities, subject to the consent of the Secretary of State, to establish and maintain aerodromes. Under section 13 of the Airports Act 1986, the Secretary of State can also give to any principal council[39] who control an airport to which the section applies, a direction requiring the council to form a company for the purpose of carrying on the business of operating the airport as a commercial undertaking.[40]

STATUTORY CONTROL OF AIRCRAFT NOISE

The Civil Aviation Act 1982, Air Navigation Order 2000[41] and Air Navigation (Noise Certification) Order 1990[42] provide the principle means of control over aircraft noise. There are various detailed ways in which the control is exercised.

Take-off and landing noise

The characteristic of jet noise most distinguishable at take-off is the terrific roar associated with the operation of the engines at high thrust. This rises quickly and then falls as the aircraft passes overhead, and extends over a wide area during climb. During landing and throttling back the whine of the compressor is the dominant sound. Apart from very close to the airport, the rise and fall of aircraft noise as it passes overhead during landing is quicker

---

[39] In relation to England and Wales, this means the council of a non-metropolitan county, of a district or of a London Borough.

[40] The section applies to an airport with an annual turnover in excess of £1 million.

[41] S.I. 2000 No. 1562.

[42] S.I. 1990 No. 1514. See also the Aeroplane Noise Regulations 1999, S.I. 1999 No. 1452 which make provision for implementing the European Community obligations of the U.K. under Directives relating to aircraft noise.

than during take-off. This is due to the landing approach being closer to the ground for a longer distance than during take-off and the fact that the engines are operating at much reduced power. For this reason and the straight path of the aircraft's landing approach, landing noise does not extend over as wide an area as that during take-off. However, incoming aircraft become established on Instrument Landing System (I.L.S.) beams from 10–12 nautical miles from the airport runways, thereby following consistent flight paths.[43] Accordingly, although noise levels may be lower, the frequency of over-flying aircraft is greater and more constant than that of departing aircraft.

The Civil Aviation Act 1982, section 78(1) provides:

> "The Secretary of State may by a notice published in the prescribed manner provide that it shall be the duty of the person who is the operator of an aircraft which is to take off or land at a designated aerodrome to secure that, after the aircraft takes off, or, as the case may be, before it lands at the aerodrome, such requirements as are specified in the notice are complied with in relation to the aircraft, being requirements appearing to the Secretary of State to be appropriate for the purpose of limiting or of mitigating the effect of noise and vibration connected with the taking off or landing of aircraft at the aerodrome."

Three airports are designated for the purposes of this section.[44] The powers in section 78 do not apply to noise from sources on the ground. The notice[45] in respect of Heathrow Airport[46] is typical of the kind of requirements imposed at the designated airports and includes the following:

---

[43] In good weather conditions, an aircraft can intercept the ILS as far out as 20+ nautical miles.

[44] For the purpose of section 78, Heathrow, Gatwick and Stansted airports are designated, by virtue of the Interpretation Act 1978 and the Civil Aviation (Designation of Aerodromes) Order 1981, S.I. 1981 No. 651.

[45] Published in the manner prescribed by the Civil Aviation (Notices) Regulations 1978.

[46] Heathrow Airport–London (Noise Abatement Requirements) Notice (2) 2001. These requirements are regularly revoked and replaced to take account of changing needs.

"3. It shall be the duty of every person who is the operator of any aircraft which is to take off or land ... to secure that ... the following requirements are complied with –

(1) After take-off the aircraft shall be operated in such a way that it is at a height of not less than 1,000 feet above ground level at 6.5 km from start of roll as measured along the departure track of that aircraft.

...

(3) ... any aircraft other than Concorde and those specified in sub-paragraph (4) shall, after take-off, be operated in such a way that it will not cause more than 94 dB(A) L_{max} by day (from 0700 hours to 2300 hours local time) as measured at any noise monitoring terminal ...

(4) ...

    (b) ... any aircraft (specified by their registration marks) shall, after take-off, be operated in such a way that it will not cause more than 97 dB(A) L_{max} by day (0700 hours to 2300 hours local time) as measured at any noise monitoring terminal ...

(5) ... any aircraft other than Concorde shall, after take-off, be operated in such a way that it will not cause more than 89 dB(A) L_{max} by night (from 2300 hours to 0700 hours local time) *and* that it will not cause more than 87 dB(A) L_{max} during the night quota period (from 2330 to 0600 hours local time) ...

(6) The limits specified ... shall be adjusted ... in respect of any noise monitoring terminal ... to take account of the location of that terminal and its ground elevation relative to the aerodrome elevation.

(7) For the purpose of determining an infringement of the limits specified ... if the aircraft was required to take off with a tailwind, an amount of up to 2 dB of the noise recorded at the noise monitor should be disregarded.

(8) Where the aircraft is a jet aircraft, after passing the point referred to in sub-paragraph (1) above, it shall maintain a gradient of climb not less than 4% to an altitude of not less than 4,000 ft. The aircraft shall be operated in such a way that progressively reducing noise levels at points on the ground under the flight path beyond that point are achieved.

(9) After the aircraft takes off ... the aircraft shall follow the Noise Preferential Routing Procedure ...[47]

This latter requirement does not apply to propeller drive aircraft whose maximum total weight authorised (MTWA) does not exceed 5,700 kg, or during 0600 and 2330 hours local time to any propeller driven aircraft whose MTWA does not exceed 17,000 kg, or to any Dash 7 aircraft.

(10) Where the aircraft is approaching the aerodrome to land it shall, commensurate with its ATC clearance, minimise noise disturbance by the use of continuous descent and low power, low drag operating procedures ... Where the use of these procedures is not practicable, the aircraft shall maintain as high an altitude as possible.

(13) ... the aircraft shall at all times be operated in a manner which is calculated to cause the least disturbance practicable in areas surrounding the aerodrome."

These rules are to be followed by aircraft pilots and are contained in the Aeronautical Information Publication (Air Pilot) entries for B.A.A. airports. These rules are subject to safety requirements which must always be paramount.

Reduction in power after take-off[48] reduces disturbance in residential

---

[47] The aircraft is required to follow the Noise Preferential Routes to specified heights which vary with the airport and time of day in some cases.

[48] It has been found that the flight procedures for take-off and climb (including those relating to noise abatement) have been implicated in an aircraft accident. In this case, the immediate causes of the accident included "a failure by the handling pilot to achieve and maintain adequate speed after noise-abatement procedures", *Report of the public inquiry into the causes and circumstances of the accident near Staines on 18th June 1972*, Aircraft

areas crossed during the first few miles of a route but the reduction in the rate of climb aggravates the conditions for people living further away from the airport who would obviously be happier for aircraft to pass as high as possible over their houses. The layout of housing beneath a route has to be considered before a suitable compromise can be obtained between these conflicting interests, and identical procedures may not be equally applicable to all airports.

If any requirements of a notice issued under section 78(1) are not complied with, the Secretary of State may, after considering any representations made by the aircraft operator, direct the aerodrome manager to withhold facilities for using the aerodrome from the aircraft operator until such time as the direction is revoked.[49] Compliance with noise abatement requirements is, however, generally good. The aerodrome manager has a duty to comply with the direction.

Additionally, if the Secretary of State decides it is necessary for the purpose of avoiding, limiting or mitigating the effect of noise and vibration connected with the take-off or landing of aircraft at a designated aerodrome, he can prohibit aircraft from taking off or landing or limit the number of take-offs and landings during certain periods. He can specify the maximum number of occasions on which aircraft of certain specified descriptions can take off or land, subject to any specified types of emergency.[50] He can also decide those operators whose aircraft may take off and land during those specified periods and the number of occasions on which aircraft of a particular description may take off or land at the aerodrome during those periods.[51] On safety grounds, however, an aerodrome manager is not required to prevent an aircraft from landing.[52]

Accident Report No. 4/73, United Kingdom Air Investigation Branch. See also "Pilots link jumbo near-disaster to noise lobby", *The Guardian*, 21st May 2000. This article related to a near disaster when a Boeing 747 skidded off a runway in wet, windy conditions allegedly due to the inflexibility of Heathrow Airport management in how two runways were used as a means of minimising aircraft noise.

[49] s. 78(2).
[50] s. 78(3)(a) and (b).
[51] s. 78(3)(c).
[52] s. 78(5)(e).

Where it appears that an aircraft is about to take off in contravention of the Secretary of State's limitations, a person authorised by him may detain the aircraft for such a period as is considered necessary for preventing the contravention.[53]

It is possible for the Secretary of State, by written notice, to disregard any particular take-off or landing.[54] The aerodrome manager is responsible, in relation to designated aerodromes, for complying with any directions of the Secretary of State requiring him to take steps to limit or mitigate the effect of noise and vibration associated with aircraft take-offs and landings.[55] In its consultation paper, the Government proposed that aerodromes not designated for the purposes of section 78 of the 1982 Act be given greater power to regulate flying behaviour, as it affects noise, within certain surrounding areas; and that they also be given discretion to limit the frequency of take-offs and landings in 24-hour periods or between certain times.

Noise monitoring

After consultation with the manager of a designated aerodrome, the Secretary of State may require him by order to provide, maintain and operate at his own expense, specified noise measuring equipment,[56] and to provide the Secretary of State with reports of the noise measurements.[57] The aerodrome manager has a duty to comply with the order.

Noise monitoring on a continuous 24 hour basis by permanent equipment is increasing throughout the world. Its value can be summarised:

1. Evaluation of alternative flight procedures for noise control.

2. Assisting in investigation of specific complaints and enquiries.

---

[53] s. 78(5)(d).
[54] s. 78(5)(f).
[55] s. 78(6).
[56] s. 78(8)(a).
[57] s. 78(8)(b).

3. Demonstrating to the public that their interests are being properly considered.

4. Validating noise modelling methods over a period of time.

5. Helping to address land-use planning and the effects of aircraft noise.

6. Monitoring compliance with local aircraft noise abatement schemes.

7. Educating and advising pilots and the public about airport noise and its characteristics.

8. Research purposes.

Airport noise monitoring schemes consist basically of four components – a series of remote monitoring stations for each departure route, central processing facilities, computer software and graphic map terminals. A number of airports maintain an electronic map at the terminal building, which produces a graphic display of the monitored noise levels. In some cases, these monitored levels may be shown with coloured lights indicating the degree of compliance with noise restrictions, e.g. green light indicating compliance, a flashing red light showing permissible take-off noise exceeded.

A number of major international airports have now introduced Noise and Track Keeping Systems (NTK) and these include Heathrow,[58] Gatwick, Stansted, Manchester and Birmingham. The airport noise and operations monitoring system (ANOMS) at Birmingham International Airport is a good example. AIRVIRON is a complementary system using complex geographical information software to support community complaints management, flight track analysis and population and housing analysis for noise contours and Noise Preferential Routes. Seven continuous noise monitoring terminals[59] feed noise data into a central computer.

---

[58]   Heathrow uses G.E.M.S. (Global Environmental Management System), and
       Stansted, Gatwick and Manchester all use versions of G.E.M.S.
[59]   One of which is not fixed.

Fig. 11. Airport noise and operations monitoring system (ANOMS)

Continuous flight track information on all incoming and departing aircraft is also fed into the computer from remote radar stations. Combined with other details such as aircraft identification numbers and aircraft height, the system enables accurate detection of any aircraft exceeding permitted noise levels, departing from predetermined flight routes, and low-flying incidents. Public complaints can be rapidly investigated, computer print-outs of relevant information produced and explanations sought from airline flight managers and aircraft pilots. The diagram on the previous page demonstrates how the system works and is typical of all NTK systems.

Birmingham International Airport also operates a "flight operations forum" which is a means of communication similar to those used at other airports in the United Kingdom. Pilots, air traffic controllers and airport operations managers have built up communications procedures to produce rapid responses to local complaints, and use the forum to consult on proposed development and operational changes.

The noise controls exercised at Birmingham International Airport, coupled with a reduction in the numbers of Chapter 2 aircraft, have resulted in the number of people exposed to noise in the noise contour bands 57–69 dB(A) 16 hour L_{Aeq} falling from nearly 90,000 in 1993 to less than 35,000 in 2000.[60] A night noise violation level of 87 dB(A) also exists and 99.1% of night-time movements fell below this level in 2000/01.[61]

Once airborne, pilots must, subject to safety considerations, continue to climb at power settings which ensure a progressive reduction in the noise level along their route. Infringements of the noise limits are taken up with the airlines concerned. Because of noise restrictions, some of the larger and noisier aircraft cannot use certain runways and some long range aircraft required to carry large supplies of fuel cannot comply with these limits when fully loaded. Reduction in fuel load may therefore be necessary, resulting in the need for a refuelling stop at a later stage. These stops can be expensive because of the airport landing charges incurred, in addition to delays in schedules, general inconvenience, additional fuel consumption and environmental pollution.

---

[60] *Birmingham International Airport Environment and Community Report 2000/2001.*
[61] *Ibid.*

Noise Preferential Routes

The Noise Advisory Council defined Minimum Noise Routes[62] as "predetermined routes ... designed to direct departing aircraft, within their performance limitations, over such sparsely populated local areas as may exist." These routes were not designed solely to meet amenity considerations but were designed to enable aircraft, within their performance characteristics, to climb safely and in a controlled manner from the departure runway to the appropriate airways. As the noise problem developed, modifications were made to routes to take advantage of open areas of ground and to avoid areas of high population density.

In their report on the review of aircraft departure routing policy, the Working Group of the Noise Advisory Council reported that the minimum noise routing policy had been the subject of considerable criticism on the grounds that it was neither fair nor reasonable to expose even a relatively small community under a concentrated route to high noise levels in order to reduce the disturbance to a larger number of people elsewhere. They concluded, however, that there was insufficient justification for changing the policy of concentrating traffic on Noise Preferential Routes and expressed the view that any limited dispersion outside these routes which could bring relief to those people beneath them would be outweighed by the disturbance imposed on the large number of people living underneath the new routes. They recommended, therefore, that the policy of concentrating traffic on Noise Preferential Routes be continued but accepted that there could be situations where noise disturbance was so high as to justify further examination of that rule.

For airports next to built up areas, Noise Preferential Routes have been defined and pilots taking off from these aerodromes are normally required to follow them. The Noise Preferential Routes have "swathes" within which aircraft are expected to stay. At Heathrow, these are 3 km wide (1.5 km either side of the route

---

[62] *Aircraft Noise: Review of Aircraft Departure Routeing Policy*, 1974, H.M.S.O., para. 2, page 1. These routes are now known as Noise Preferential Routes and are referred to as such in the text.

centreline) and continue to a height of 4,000 feet, at which point aircraft may be directed to a more direct heading. The corresponding height at Gatwick is 3,000 feet.

The routes are not the shortest flying distances but they are designed to ensure minimum flying over residential areas and lead from the take-off runways to the airways which link the major airports. An airway is an air corridor approximately 10 miles wide, the centre line being marked by navigational aids. Unfortunately, with Noise Preferential Routes, it is not always possible to achieve the ideal. These routes are set for perfect conditions but these do not always exist. In reality the path flown by an aircraft is affected by the wind strength and direction, types of navigation equipment and normal flying variations. These factors are taken into account in producing the routes. Safety must be paramount and therefore the air traffic controllers, being responsible for the safety and effectiveness of flights in their controlled airspace, retain the right to take aircraft away from these routes where safety or operational requirements demand. Noise Preferential Routes and additional information concerning the height aircraft must achieve at specified points on the route are published as Standard Instrument Departures for the relevant airports.

Controlling landing noise

The landing of aircraft is a complicated matter and aircraft, it will be seen, fly at what appears to be a relatively low height for a long time before they land. The reason for this is that aircraft have to follow radio beams and need to be stabilised during the process of landing. A long straight approach (the Continuous Descent Approach) is essential for this[63] and the internationally recommended minimum descent angle is 2.5°. However, an approach angle of 3° has been widely used in the United Kingdom and other countries for many years. Notices issued under section 78(1) of the Civil Aviation Act 1982 may impose specific restrictions on aircraft operation to reduce landing noise, for example:

---

[63] Although CDA does not only apply to the straight approaches; the ground track can be curved. The emphasis of a CDA is avoiding periods of level flight.

"Whenever practicable, where the aircraft is approaching the aerodrome to land it shall minimise noise disturbance by the use of ... continuous descent approach and low power/low drag ... where the use of these procedures is not practicable, the aircraft shall maintain as high an attitude as possible."[64]

This requirement is waived if necessary to avoid immediate danger or to comply with the instructions of Air Traffic Control.

A technical working group has sought to describe the sources of noise from arriving aircraft[65] and to consider possible means of control. The noise of arriving aircraft is affected by the constraints of the 3° standard descent angle and the continuous descent approach, but also by:

(a) the position of an airport and the orientation of its runways;[66]

(b) the design and use of airspace, and the location of aircraft holding stacks;[67]

(c) missed final approaches to an airport that do not follow normal departure Noise Preferential Routes, with annoyance occurring in areas less frequently exposed to aircraft noise;[68]

(d) reduced flap settings that create less noise on approach but increase landing speed and require more use of reverse thrust.[69]

The working group produced some initial proposals for a "minimum noise arrivals code",[70] including:

---

[64] Article 3(5) of the Heathrow–London (Noise Abatement Requirements) Notice 1993. In practice the Continuous Descent Approach is more effective than low power/low drag as it keeps the aircraft higher for longer, keeping the receiver further from the noise source.

[65] *Noise from Arriving Aircraft: final report of the ANMAC technical working group*, D.E.T.R., 13th March 2000. The report dealt with arrivals at Heathrow, Gatwick and Stansted.

[66] *Ibid*, para. 3.1.1.

[67] *Ibid*, paras. 3.2.1 and 3.2.2. At Heathrow, approximately 45% of traffic is already stacked for at least one circuit through a typical 24-hour day.

[68] *Ibid*, para. 4.3.5.

[69] *Ibid*, para. 4.3.8.

[70] *Ibid*, Appx. E.

1. Airline procedures – guidelines on speed, use of flap, undercarriage deployment, use of reverse thrust, calculations to help achieve continuous descent approaches, and special night-time arrangements.

2. Air traffic control procedures – timing and accuracy of information to flight crews, special night-time procedures to help achieve continuous descent approaches, and publication of continuous descent policy.

3. Airport procedures and implementation of the code – runway maintenance, provision of immediate feedback to flight crews and air traffic controllers, compliance auditing, analysis and open communication of results, and appropriate contractual arrangements. An early morning landing trial[71] at Heathrow Airport was also used to try and reduce noise over parts of Central London between 4.00 a.m. and 6.00 a.m. This involved increasing the height and changing the distance at which aircraft joined the Instrument Landing System. The result was a reduction in noise levels which varied according to the distance from touchdown.

A proposal in the Government's consultation paper[72] would, if adopted, also place a duty on air traffic controllers and information services to take account of the need to minimise disturbance caused by noise and vibration, and to consult the managers of substantial aerodromes over proposals to change standard procedures for the control or direction of aircraft close to those aerodromes. At present, section 70(2)(d) of the Transport Act 2000 requires the Civil Aviation Authority, in carrying out its air navigation functions, to take account of any guidance on environmental objectives given by the Secretary of State. Guidance has been published[73] requiring

---

[71] See *Assessment of revised Heathrow early mornings approach procedures trial*, R. & D. Report 9823, Cadoux, R. E., White, S., Critchley, J. B., National Air Traffic Services Ltd./Department of Environment, Transport and the Regions, 1998.

[72] Consultation Paper, *Control of Noise from Civil Aircraft*, D.E.T.R., July 2000, para. 23.

[73] *Guidance to the Civil Aviation Authority or environmental objectives relating to the exercise of its air navigation functions*, D.T.L.R., January 2002. The guidance sets out detailed arrangements for compliance.

that, in performing its air navigation functions, the Civil Aviation Authority takes account of "... the need to reduce, control and mitigate as far as possible ... the annoyance and disturbance caused to the general public arising from aircraft noise and vibration." It also requires that where any changes in the "airspace arrangements, or to the use made of them, are proposed, including changes to air traffic control procedures", the Civil Aviation Authority must consult with the relevant aerodrome managers and local authorities in areas likely to be significantly affected by noise under the arrival tracks and departure routes.

Runway usage

The direction of aircraft take-off or landing is governed by the speed and direction of the wind at ground level. In the case of most aircraft, depending on the aircraft type and runway length, it is not safe to take off or land with a tail wind exceeding five knots. In any case, it is not operationally advisable to land with a tail wind component if an alternative exists. Within the limits of this constraint, a preferential runway system is adopted at many airports so that aircraft take off as far as possible over areas less likely to be affected by noise. At Heathrow, most of the aircraft have traditionally taken off and landed to the west, wind permitting. Other airports operate in a similar manner, with aircraft taking off and landing in the same direction.

However, in 2001, the westerly preference at night was replaced by a weekly rotation between westerly and easterly operations whenever weather conditions permit.[74] This was intended to allow a fairer and more equitable distribution of aircraft noise. A system of "runway alternation" also applies at Heathrow to westerly operations only and applies to day and night operations, e.g. one runway is used for landings between 7.00 a.m. and 3.00 p.m. and the parallel runway used from 3.00 p.m. to 11.00 p.m. The order is reversed weekly. The arrangement gives the population of people affected by noise defined, quieter periods of activity.

---

[74] D.E.T.R. News Release No. 2835, 21st December 2000. Full implementation of the system will be completed on resurfacing of the runways in 2002/2003.

Aircraft stacking

When air traffic is light, aircraft are brought by the shortest route to line up with the runway approximately eight miles from touch-down. On occasions, however, air traffic may build up and aircraft have to be directed to a greater height and distance from the airport. Landing may have to be delayed in the case of heavy traffic and the aircraft have to circle around at different levels in what is known as a "stack" around a radio beacon at the exits from the airway. The aircraft are separated vertically at 1,000 feet intervals. This can produce a significant number of aircraft circling in the same area which may occasionally be the subject of complaints of noise. This is, however, only done on safety grounds.

Night flights

Night flying restrictions are needed to protect local communities from excessive aircraft noise levels but without unnecessarily restricting the aviation industry and the travelling public. The demand for night flights reflects passenger traffic needs, aircraft positioning and servicing, and the requirement to carry time-sensitive cargoes, e.g. mail and perishable goods.

In relation to the designated airports of Heathrow, Gatwick and Stansted, from time to time the Government publishes proposals for night flight restrictions. Following on extensive review of the then restrictions, a consultation paper was issued in January 1993 and new arrangements from mid-summer of that year were based on the following criteria:

(a) the quota-system – the noisier the Certified Noise Level of the different types of aircraft, the fewer that were allowed to land at night;

(b) Night Quota Period – quota restrictions would apply to movements between 2330 and 0600 hours;

(c) quotas for the three designated airports – these varied for each airport;

(d) only aircraft that were quieter than those specified in the quota system would be unrestricted as to the number of movements;

(e) end of season flexibility – several factors cause air traffic movements to fluctuate between equivalent seasons in succeeding years. Some of these are outside the airlines' control, including:

(i) winter and summer seasons are not exactly the same length every year;

(ii) Easter, a period of very heavy traffic, may occur towards the end of the winter season, or in the summer season;

(f) introduction of financial penalties for breaches of the night time noise limits;

(g) noise monitoring – the Department of Transport's Noise Monitoring Advisory Committee would review noise levels and the monitoring arrangements.

These arrangements were the subject of challenge and judicial review. In September 1993 the grounds of objection were rejected except that it was ruled that the policy of setting quotas was contrary to the provision in section 78 of the Civil Aviation Act 1982 which limits the power of the Secretary of State to "(3)(b) specifying the maximum number of occasions on which aircraft ... may be permitted to take off and land".

In its subsequent decisions on night flight restrictions, the Government took account of the court's decision by basing its policy on limits to the number of permitted movements during the night quota period. However, it retained the quota count system as a supplementary measure to discourage airlines from using noisier aircraft at night, as well as retaining the other elements indicated above.

The most recent restrictions were introduced in 1999[75] and cover

---

[75] Night restrictions at Heathrow, Gatwick and Stansted: revised restrictions with effect from 31st October 1999. The current detailed requirements are contained in the London Heathrow, London Gatwick and London Stansted Airports Noise Restrictions (No. 2) Notice 2001 published in the supplements to the United Kingdom A.I.P. (Air Information Pilot). But see also the case of *Hatton and Others v United Kingdom* (application No. 36022/97), European Court of Human Rights which challenges the Government's position on night-time aircraft noise – see fn. 7 on p. 262.

the period from 31st October 1999 to the summer of 2004. The three London airports are controlled through movement limits supplemented by quotas. The Transport Minister stated "The underlying principle of the restrictions is to preserve a balance between the need to protect local communities from excessive aircraft noise at night and the operation of services where they provide economic benefits." The restrictions comprise three main elements:

1. A maximum number of flights during the "night quota period" (i.e. 11.30 p.m. – 6.00 a.m.). These numbers vary between each airport and are higher in summer than in winter.

2. The supplementary quota system. Aircraft types are given a "quota count" (QC) value depending on their noise levels at take-off and landing. The lowest quota count of QC/0.5 reflects a certified noise level (EPNdB) of less than 90. The highest quota count of QC/16 reflects a certified noise level (EPNdB) of more than 101.9. Aircraft movements score these QC values against maximum allowance quotas for the winter and summer seasons.

3. Aircraft of QC/8 and QC/16 (the noisiest) cannot be scheduled to operate between 11.00 p.m. and 7.00 a.m.[76] There is a 5% seasonal flexibility margin to the movements limits and exemption for certain smaller jet and propeller aircraft.[77] Monitoring of noise performance of aircraft in relation to their QC classification is the responsibility of the D.L.T.R. Aircraft Noise Monitoring Advisory Committee.

Engine ground running

Piston engined aircraft need to warm up before taking off. This is not necessary for jet aircraft, although it is customary to run up to full power before releasing the brakes. After routine maintenance or repair longer running is necessary and to minimise disturbance

---

[76] But may be allowed to take off and land outside these times in exceptional circumstances.

[77] Jet aircraft with a maximum certificated weight not exceeding 11,600 kg, and propeller aircraft if certified noise levels are less than 87 EPNdB.

the running up of jets takes place wherever possible using special mufflers. These are massive silencers placed very close to the engines. The control of noise from ground running is the responsibility of the aerodrome owner and there are usually restrictions on the times and locations at which engines can be tested, with severe restrictions at night time. At some airports, ground running in the maintenance areas is screened from neighbouring houses either by airport buildings or by earth banks and other noise shields specially constructed by the operating airlines.

Airport operational instructions used by Birmingham International Airport give a useful indication of specific conditions governing the ground running of aircraft engines. The amount of ground running permitted in defined areas has regard to the proximity of the aircraft to airport buildings and residential areas and the need to avoid hazards to personnel and vehicles. The conditions[78] specify that only essential ground running for maintenance or test purposes is permitted. The periods and locations available for aircraft engine ground running are specified and include a complete ban on ground running between 2300 and 0600 hours (night period). Full power running is allowed for propeller driven and turbojet/turbofan aircraft during the early morning shoulder period (0601–0700 hours) and the day-time period (0701–2259 hours), depending on the location of the airport. The ground running of engines at full power during the early morning shoulder period on weekdays is conditional and subject to a noise limit, an average daily exposure the equivalent of 78 dBL_{Aeq}. The morning shoulder restrictions apply on Mondays to Saturdays only. Engine ground running on Sundays is prohibited before 0800 hours. Ground running on aircraft stands is prohibited at night but permitted between 0601 and 2259 hours at idling speed only. Ground running on passenger stands is restricted to functional checks on one engine at a time, for a maximum of three minutes and only between 0601 (0801 Sundays) and 2259 hours, and subject to Apron Control prior approval. No ground running of turbojet/turbofan engines is allowed on Sundays and Good Fridays between 1030 and 1230 hours. Applications must be made to the Airport

---

[78] Airport Operational Instruction A01 01/07, 3rd May 2001.

Operations Duty Manager before any ground running takes place, other than check starts and ground idle, and the area to be used is determined after consultation with Air Traffic Control and takes account of expected aircraft movements, wind speed and direction and time of day. Safety is an important consideration in selecting the areas to be used for ground running of engines.

Noise control through airport charges

Under section 38(1) of the Civil Aviation Act 1982 "an aerodrome authority may, for the purpose of encouraging the use of quieter aircraft and of diminishing inconvenience from aircraft noise, fix its charges by reference, amongst other things, to any fact or matter relevant to:

(a) the amount of noise caused by the aircraft in respect of which the charges are made; or

(b) the extent or nature of any inconvenience resulting from such noise."

The Secretary of State also has power to direct an aerodrome authority to fix their charges in any manner he may determine.

At Heathrow, Gatwick and Stansted airports, the landing charge as calculated in accordance with the prevailing schedules of charges, is increased by 100% in respect of jet aircraft not certificated in accordance with Chapter 3 of I.C.A.O. Annex 16. In addition, quieter Chapter 3 aircraft receive a 10% discount. At the same airports, aircraft departures which infringe the noise thresholds as measured by the noise monitoring system operated by the relevant airport company may be subject to the following additional charges:[79]

    – within 3 dB(A) of the limit – £500;

    – more than 3 dB(A) above the limit – £1,000.

Similar schemes are in force at other B.A.A. plc owned airports.

---

[79] At Heathrow, all money raised by noise supplements is placed in a Noise Fines Fund which is channelled to local noise reduction related projects. Around £1 million has been raised since fines began in the mid-1990s.

The noise strategies at different airports can vary significantly. One study[80] looked at the policies, strategies and activities at 22 United Kingdom airports. Its findings can be summarised:

1. Airports with a low level of use or distant from urban areas tend to have less rigorous noise controls than those near urban areas.

2. Most airports have some form of noise policy and mid-sized airports, such as Norwich, Newcastle and Birmingham, have very detailed strategies.

3. The variation in schemes may make comparison difficult.[81] The Government consultation paper[82] suggests that the power under section 38(1) of the Civil Aviation Act 1982 might be amended to make it clearer that charges could relate, for example, to compliance with "noise preferential routes'" or other noise mitigation procedures.

Following the phasing out of Chapter 2 aircraft, many airports are re-examining their charging policies. European Community charging systems differ from one member state to another, and there are also differences within member states. In eight member states the charging system includes an environmental component. To assist and help harmonise airport charging policies across Europe, the E.U. has produced a proposal for a Directive dealing with this issue,[83] although the U.K. Government is apparently concerned that the proposed Directive might prohibit the flexibility referred to in paragraph 3 above.

Consultation facilities

The person managing an aerodrome must provide adequate consultation facilities for aerodrome users, nearby local authorities

---

[80] *Noise Controls at UK Airports*, SASIG Technical Note, January 2001.
[81] Although this situation may change depending on the outcome of the Government review into the control of civil aircraft noise.
[82] *Control of Noise from Civil Aircraft*, D.E.T.R., July 2000, para. 27.
[83] *Proposal for a Directive of the European Parliament and of the Council on the establishment of a community framework for noise classification of civil subsonic aircraft for the purposes of calculating noise charges*, COM (2001) 74 final, Brussels, 20th December 2001.

Aircraft noise

and other local representative organisations concerning its management or administration which affects their interests, if the aerodrome is designated for that purpose by the Secretary of State. Under the powers of section 35 of the Civil Aviation Act 1982, all national and regional aerodromes and some general aviation airfields, a total of 47, have been designated for consultation purposes. The Government's policy has been to designate those airports with an annual turnover exceeding £1 million and to designate smaller aerodromes in response to representations where designation was likely to alleviate local problems.

In its consultation paper,[84] the Government indicates that its policy is to continue to encourage the consultation process as a means of reconciling local difficulties. It also suggests that airport operators should have a range of sanctions to apply to pilots failing to comply with noise amelioration schemes.[85] It also suggests[86] that local planning authorities should be able to oblige an aerodrome to implement a compulsory noise amelioration scheme which is consistent with flight safety. This proposal would apply to airports designated under the proposed new powers.[87]

Air transport licences

Under section 64 of the Civil Aviation Act 1982, air transport licences are generally required for the air transport of passengers or cargo for reward by United Kingdom registered aircraft. The administration of the system is a function of the Civil Aviation Authority in accordance with section 65 and, subject to a right of appeal, the Authority can grant, revoke, suspend or vary the terms of a licence. There is also a general duty on the Authority in section 68(3) of the Act to have regard to the need to minimise, so far as is reasonably practicable, any adverse effects on the environment and any disturbance to the public, from noise and vibration attributable to the use of aircraft for civil aviation purposes.

---

[84] *Control of Noise from Civil Aircraft*, D.E.T.R., July 2000, para. 26.
[85] *Ibid*, para. 11.
[86] *Ibid*, para. 17.
[87] This power would not apply to non-designated airports.

AIRCRAFT NOISE CERTIFICATION

The Wilson Committee report[88] considered that the only satisfactory way in which the necessary reduction in noise could be achieved was by improvements in engines and aircraft. International developments have taken place since that time following a conference in London in 1966, from which emerged the idea of noise certification. International noise regulation is the responsibility of the International Civil Aviation Organisation (I.C.A.O.) and in December 1969 at a meeting of the I.C.A.O. a noise certification scheme was agreed. The United Kingdom has been one of the leading countries in the development of international noise certification rules. The rules prescribe noise limits for each type of aircraft relative to its maximum certificated weight. Broadly speaking, the noise level from new types of subsonic jet aircraft is required to be about half as much, weight for weight, as earlier types.

Supersonic aircraft are not at present controlled by noise regulations although during the design stage of Concorde the target for noise production was the level of comparable subsonic jets. However, the older subsonic jet aircraft are gradually being replaced by quieter aircraft and, if supersonic travel becomes economically viable, there will undoubtedly be a need to reduce the noise levels of these aircraft. I.C.A.O. Annex 16 Chapter 4 notes that any new supersonic aircraft should meet Chapter 3 noise levels.

The first aircraft noise standards to be agreed by I.C.A.O. were for subsonic jets. This was in 1970 and they were published as Annexe 16 to the Chicago Convention.

Since September 1970, an international Committee on Aircraft Noise (CAN) has met regularly to consider proposed aircraft noise standards presented by its various international working groups. The United Kingdom is represented on the I.C.A.O. Council, CAN and on all the international working groups who meet regularly to consider noise standards for various types of aircraft. It is also a member of the European Civil Aviation Conference of member states (E.C.A.C.). One of the working groups of this conference seeks to harmonise European regulations so that aircraft failing to

---

[88] Para. 310.

meet any noise standards are removed from national registers as soon as possible.

Because of the international nature of air transport, it is important to try and achieve reductions in aircraft noise on an international basis.

The European Community has a significant part to play in contributing to the regulation of aircraft noise. Its first directive on this matter[89] prevented the addition of any more non-noise certified aeroplanes to the civil registers of member states and required the removal of any such aeroplanes by 31st December 1986 (with some exemptions until 31st December 1988). An amendment to this directive[90] prevented non-noise certificated aircraft registered outside the community from landing in the community from 1st January 1989 (with some exemptions until 31st December 1989).

A further directive[91] limiting noise, banned, subject to certain exemptions, all aeroplanes fitted with engines having a by-pass ratio of less than two unless there was in force a noise certificate issued either to the standards of Chapter 3, or Chapter 2 (provided that, in this case, the certificate was issued within the previous 25 years). This ban applied to aircraft operating into the European Community after 1st April 1995. From 1st April 2002, all Chapter 2 aircraft are banned.

The I.C.A.O. has agreed a new and more stringent standard for new aircraft. A cumulative reduction of 10 dB on the Chapter 3 standards has been established. This will result in a Chapter 4 standard.[92] It is also likely that operators of existing Chapter 3 compliant aircraft may wish to have their aircraft comply with the Chapter 4 standards. Accordingly, the I.C.A.O. has established rules for the re-certification of aircraft from Chapter 3 to Chapter 4, although re-certification will be voluntary.

---

[89] Directive 80/51/EEC.

[90] Directive 83/206/EEC.

[91] Directive 92/14/EEC. Implemented in the United Kingdom by the Aeroplane Noise (Limitation on Operation of Aeroplanes) Regulations 1993, S.I. 1993 No. 1409, now repealed.

[92] The new Chapter 4 standards, if adopted, would become applicable to all new aircraft and their derived versions from 1st January 2006 – see *I.C.A.O. Journal*, Vol. 56, 2001, p. 16.

The European Union has progressively introduced Directives limiting aircraft noise. These various Directives[93] have been implemented through the Aeroplane Noise Regulations 1999.[94] Under the Regulations, the number of operations by Chapter 2 jets was reduced between 1995 and 2002. From 1st April 2002, civil sub-sonic jet aircraft with a maximum take-off mass of 34,000 kg or with a capacity of more than 19 passenger seats, and in either case fitted with engines having a by-pass ratio of less than 2, are required, if landing or taking off in the U.K., to be noise certificated to the stricter standards of Chapter 3. A further E.U. regulation[95] banned the addition to member state's registers, from May 2002, of aircraft meeting the Chapter 3 standards through the use of "hush kits". All such aircraft were to be banned from taking off and landing in the E.U. unless they began operating in the E.U. after 1st April 1995. Implementation of this regulation was the subject of dispute between the E.U. and the U.S.A. which considers that the requirement is discriminatory as it has a large number of aircraft fitted with "hush kits". Following discussions between the E.U. and the U.S.A., this regulation was repealed in March 2002 to be replaced by a new Directive establishing rules and procedures with regard to the introduction of noise related operating restrictions at E.C. airports.[96]

Air Navigation (Noise Certification) Order 1990[97]

The Order applies to:

(a) every propeller driven aeroplane having a maximum total weight authorised of 9,000 kg or less;

---

[93] 80/51/EEC; 83/206/EEC; 89/629/EEC; 92/14/EEC; 98/20/EC; and 1999/28/EC.

[94] S.I. 1999 No. 1452, as amended by the Aeroplane Noise (Amendment) Regulations 1999, S.I. 1999 No. 2253. They apply to the United Kingdom.

[95] 925/99/EC.

[96] Directive 2002/30/EC on the establishment of rules and procedures with regard to the introduction of noise related operating restrictions at community airports, O.J.E.C., 28th March 2002. See pp. 299–300 for more details of this "balanced approach".

[97] S.I. 1990 No. 1514, as amended by the Aeroplane Noise Regulations 1999, S.I. 1999 No. 1452. The Order does not apply to any aeroplane to which the Aeroplane Noise Regulations 1999 apply, i.e. civil propeller driven aircraft registered in the U.K. and falling within certain specified categories.

(b) supersonic civil aeroplanes first obtaining certificates of airworthiness on or after 26th November 1981 and conforming to prototypes, airworthiness certification of which was requested before 1st January 1975, or derivations of such prototypes;

(c) every microlight aeroplane;

(d) all other subsonic aeroplanes with certificated take-off distances of more than 610 metres;

(e) every helicopter, being a helicopter in respect of which applicable standards are specified in the Order.

The Order prohibits, subject to certain exceptions, the aircraft to which it applies from taking off or landing in the United Kingdom unless there is in force in respect of that aircraft a certificate of compliance[98] with the standards as to noise specified in the Order, and except on compliance with the conditions of the certificate. In addition, a subsonic aeroplane registered in the United Kingdom after 1st November 1990 and powered by turbojet or turbofan engines which either has a maximum total weight authorised of more than 34,000 kg, or is capable of seating more than 19 passengers, is prohibited from taking off or landing in the United Kingdom or in any other member state of the European Community without a valid noise certificate, and only if any conditions of the certificate are complied with.[99]

The Civil Aviation Authority has a duty to issue a noise certificate in respect of any aircraft covered by the Order if it is satisfied that it complies with the relevant noise standards in the Order.[100] Applicants for certificates have to produce such evidence and submit aircraft to such flying trials and tests as the Authority requires. The Authority has to issue noise certificates subject to conditions concerning the maximum total take-off and landing weights and can impose such other conditions as it thinks fit. Schedule 1 of the Order specifies the location of the noise measurement points on the take-off and landing approach paths.

---

[98] Art. 5.
[99] Art. 5(2).
[100] Art. 6 and Schedule 1, parts I to IX.

For smaller propeller driven aircraft the maximum permissible noise levels are expressed as the peak noise level in dB(A) at the specified measurement point. These vary between 68 and 80 dB(A). The noise levels in respect of microlight aircraft range from 76–84 LAX[101] at the specified measurement point. The helicopter standard varies between 88–110 EPNdB.

An aircraft is not allowed to take off or land in the United Kingdom unless it carries any noise certificate required under the law of its country of registration and United Kingdom registered aircraft must carry the requisite noise certificates when in flight, whether in the United Kingdom or elsewhere.[102] The aircraft commander must produce the noise certificate if required to do so by the Civil Aviation Authority or an authorised person.[103] The authority can provisionally suspend a noise certificate pending inquiries and afterwards may revoke, suspend or vary a certificate.[104] Breach of a condition of a noise certificate renders the certificate invalid during the continuance of the breach. It is an offence for any person to use any noise certificate which has been forged, altered, revoked or suspended, to which he is not entitled, to lend any certificate, or allow its use by any other person; or to make false representations for the purpose of obtaining the issue, renewal or variation of a certificate.[105]

The Order is not applicable to military aircraft or to the naval, military and air force authorities and members of any visiting force and any international headquarters.[106] It applies to aircraft owned or exclusively used by the Crown[107] and provision exists for the Civil Aviation Authority, after consultation with the Secretary of State, to exempt aircraft or persons from any of the provisions of the Order.[108]

---

[101] A single-event exposure level which takes account of the maximum A-weighted sound level and a duration allowance.
[102] Art. 7.
[103] Art. 8.
[104] Art. 9.
[105] Art. 10.
[106] Art. 15(2).
[107] Art. 15(1).
[108] Art. 16.

Supersonic aircraft

The Order is not applicable to supersonic aircraft like Concorde
which are capable of sustained level flight in excess of Mach 1.
Apart from Concorde, all supersonic aircraft in the United Kingdom
are military. The particular noise characteristic of supersonic
aircraft is the sonic boom. This occurs when an aircraft flies faster
than the local speed of sound. An aircraft travelling in supersonic
flight can produce a sonic boom audible over more than 50 km
either side of its ground track, according to its altitude and size.

Aeroplane Noise Regulations 1999[109]

Noise certification requirements for specified types of U.K. and
foreign registered aeroplanes are contained in the Aeroplane Noise
Regulations 1999. They make provision for implementing all of the
European Community obligations of the U.K. under the following
directives:

(a) 80/51/EEC on the limitation of noise emissions from subsonic
    aircraft as amended by Council Directive 83/206/EEC;

(b) 89/629/EEC on the limitation of noise emission from civil
    subsonic jet aeroplanes; and

(c) 92/14/EEC on the limitation of the operation of aeroplanes
    covered by Part II, Chapter 2, Volume I of Annex 16 to the
    Convention on International Civil Aviation, second edition
    (1988) as amended by Council Directive 98/20/EC of 30th
    March 1988.

Aeroplanes cannot operate in the territories of member states or
E.E.A. states unless there is in force a noise certificate granted by
the C.A.A. In relation to the certificate, the Regulations have
regard, amongst other things, to civil propeller-driven and jet
aircraft; maximum certificated take-off weights; the date of
applications for, and issue of, certificates of air worthiness; and the
aeroplane must comply with the relevant standards of Annex 16/
1988. The Regulations make provision as to the issue and validity

---

[109] S.I. 1999 No. 1452, as amended by S.I. 1999 No. 2253.

of noise certificates; requirements as to the carriage of certificates; the production of certificates on request; their revocation, suspension or variation; offences and penalties. In many respects the Regulations relating to enforcement are similar to the 1990 Order.[110]

The "balanced approach" to aeroplane noise management

E.U. noise legislation has proved controversial, with some countries and airlines arguing that the rules discriminate against older and noisier aircraft. The U.S. in particular argued that the rules are unfair[111] and complained to the International Civil Aviation Authority. Following discussions, the Commission secured agreement on a new Directive establishing rules and procedures with regard to the introduction of noise related operating restrictions at Community airports.[112]

The Directive repeals Regulation No. 925/1999 and must be implemented by the end of September 2003. It will apply to civil airports with more than 50,000 movements of civil subsonic jet aeroplanes per year. It allows member states to impose operating restrictions to control noise. However, in doing so, they must operate a "balanced approach", the concept of which was adopted by the 33rd I.C.A.O. Assembly in 2001. The balanced approach consists of identifying the noise problem at an airport and analysing the measures available to reduce noise by considering four principal elements, i.e. reduction of aeroplane noise at source, land use planning and management measures, noise abatement operational procedures and operating restrictions. The intention is to address the problem of noise in the most cost-effective way, but any measures adopted must not be more restrictive than needed to meet the environmental objective established for a specific airport. They must also be non-discriminatory regarding the nationality or identity of the aircraft carrier or manufacturer.

When member states decide to impose restrictions on the noise performance of aircraft, they must take account of the certification

---

[110] See pp. 295–296.
[111] See p. 295.
[112] Directive 2002/30/EC of 26th March 2002.

standards in Annex 16 of the Convention of International Civil Aviation. Following the removal of Chapter 2 aircraft from E.U. airports, the E.U. is now addressing the issue of aircraft which meet, by a specified margin, the certification limits of Chapter 3. These are termed "marginally compliant aircraft", i.e. that meet the Chapter 3 noise standard by a margin of 5 EPNdB (Effective Perceived Noise, in decibels). The Directive allows the introduction of restrictions aimed at the withdrawal of such aircraft, but only after an assessment of all the alternative available measures, including operating restrictions of a partial nature, has shown this to be necessary. Any withdrawal period must be not less than five years, although marginally compliant aircraft registered in developing countries may be exempted for ten years, subject to certain conditions. The Directive sets out how such restrictions may be applied. "City airports" (in the U.K., London City and Belfast City) get special treatment; more stringent rules are required for these airports in recognition of the "particular noise problems of airports which are located in the centre of large conurbations".

NOISE INSULATION GRANTS

Notwithstanding the improvements that can be secured by the development of quieter aircraft, noise certification and good planning, there are likely to remain many people who are seriously affected by aircraft noise from our major airports. For these people, sound insulation of their homes is the only practicable solution to the problem. This was recognised by the Wilson Committee.

Section 79 of the Civil Aviation Act 1982 gives the Secretary of State power by statutory instrument to make a scheme requiring the aerodrome manager to make grants towards the cost of insulating such classes of buildings or parts of buildings as he thinks fit. This power applies in relation to designated aerodromes only.[113] Any such scheme must specify the area or areas in which buildings must be situated for grants to be paid, the persons to whom grants are to be payable, the amount of the grants and the rate at which grants are to be paid. A scheme may make different provisions with respect to different areas or circumstances.

---

[113] Currently Heathrow and Gatwick by virtue of s. 80.

A scheme may authorise or require a local authority to act as agents for the aerodrome manager in respect of applications for and payment of grants. A scheme may require that where an application for grant is refused, a written statement of the reasons be given at the applicant's request.

Noise insulation schemes around five airports operated by B.A.A. plc are now completed, including Heathrow and Gatwick. An example of the type of current scheme in operation is that at Stansted Airport. This scheme is now completed. It is designed primarily for dwellings of standard brick construction in specified areas around the airport. The area covered by the noise insulation programme is based on a forecast of aircraft activity when Stansted is handling eight million passengers a year. The precise boundary is a combination of the predicted 66 dB(A) daytime L_{eq} and 57 dB(A) nightime L_{eq} noise contours and a sound exposure level (S.E.L.) footprint. Payment of up to 100% (subject to certain limits) of the cost of insulating up to two living rooms and all bedrooms is available and applies to dwellings completed before 1st June 1991. Similar schemes have been operated in relation to all major airports.

The scheme requires double glazing and the installation of ventilation systems to a specified standard and permitted optional works to improve roof insulation, seal chimneys and carry out incidental repairs.

AIRCRAFT NOISE INDEX

From 1963 the official unit of aircraft noise exposure in the United Kingdom was the Noise and Number Index (NNI). The Index was established following a social survey around Heathrow Airport. At that time it was found that there was a fairly close relationship between the level of noise and the number of aircraft heard, and the degree of annoyance caused. It became widely accepted as a basis for evaluating aircraft noise in the consideration of airport development and of land use planning around airports. However, its relevance as a method of assessing the extent of annoyance has been subject to numerous criticisms. Accordingly, a study[114] was

---

[114] Published in *United Kingdom Aircraft Noise Index Study,* D.O.R.A. Report 8402, 1985, Civil Aviation Authority.

carried out by the Civil Aviation Directorate of Operations Research and Analysis, on behalf of the Department of Transport, to investigate whether improvements might be possible. The study comprised a social survey and aircraft noise measurements in 23 areas around five major civil aviation airports – Heathrow, Gatwick, Luton, Manchester and Aberdeen. The main conclusion of the report was that there appeared to be a case for replacing the NNI system of measurement by one based on the 24-hour L_{eq} (Equivalent Continuous Sound Level) scale[115] for the following reasons:

1. Use of the 24-hour L_{eq} as an index shows a statistical improvement over NNI in terms of correlation with community annoyance reaction.

2. Since the NNI formula includes a cut-off at 80 PNdB it means that in future, with the progressive introduction of quieter aircraft, it will take proportionally fewer aircraft into account in its calculation. This could lead to an under-estimation of public reaction.

3. 24-hour L_{eq} takes account of all aircraft movements over the full 24 hours; it also takes account of the duration of the noise of each aircraft, which NNI does not.

4. The use of an L_{eq}-based index would lead to a greater consistency with other aspects of annoyance at aircraft noise where L_{eq} is already used, e.g. helicopters, general aviation and sleep disturbance.

5. The use of an L_{eq}-based index would be more generally consistent with practice worldwide where the majority of indices have the form of L_{eq} (in addition, L_{eq} is more amenable to "on-site" spot checks than is NNI).

The Department of Transport then went out to public consultation on the advisability of adopting L_{eq} (24-hour) as the United Kingdom

---

[115] L_{eq} is commonly used as a measure of noise exposure and is the level of that hypothetical steady sound which, over the measurement period, contains the same sound energy, weighted according to the response of the human ear, as the actual variable sound.

aircraft noise index. Over 88% of the respondents accepted the case for L_{eq} but many of them were unhappy about the proposal to calculate the daytime noise as a simple average over 24 hours.[116] The proposals for change were discussed with the Aircraft Noise Monitoring Advisory Committee and in September 1990 the Department of Transport announced that in future it would use L_{eq} (16-hour) dB(A) as the daytime index for aircraft noise.

The 16-hour measurement period is from 0700–2300 hours. Computer programs were devised to produce L_{eq} contours around the designated airports and, whilst not identical, there is generally good correlation between the NNI and comparable L_{eq} contours. Some comparative ratings are given below:

	NNI	*L_{eq} (16-hour)*
Low annoyance:	35	57
Moderate annoyance:	45	63
High annoyance:	55	69
Very high annoyance:	60	72

The primary uses of the index are in land use planning and assessing the eligibility of properties for works of sound insulation. Provided with information about, or an estimate of, the amount and pattern of traffic at an airport, the L_{eq} (16-hour) dB(A) contours can be produced as an indication of the extent of noise exposure in various areas. Each airport operating a Noise Insulation Grants Scheme produces maps showing the noise contours within which grants will be payable for domestic properties.

LAW OF NUISANCE

The proper management of aerodromes and enforcement of the statutory requirements described in this chapter is particularly important in mitigating the effects of aircraft noise, since the possibility of civil action in respect of such noise is limited. The Civil Aviation Act 1982 provides:

---

[116] A critique of technical issues raised is published as D.O.R.A. Report 9023, *The Use of L_{eq} as an Aircraft Noise Index*, 1990, Civil Aviation Authority.

"Section 76(1). No action shall lie in respect of trespass or in respect of nuisance, by reason only of the flight of an aircraft over any property at a height above the ground which, having regard to wind, weather and all the circumstances of the case is reasonable, or the ordinary incidents of such flight, so long as the provisions of any Air Navigation Order and of any orders under section 62[117] above have been duly complied with and there has been no breach of section 81[118] below."[119]

This section prevents any action being taken in respect of a private or other nuisance caused by aircraft flying over or near a potential plaintiff's airspace. The protection of the section is not limited to the right of passage over land; it extends to all flights provided they are at a reasonable height above the ground and comply with the other requirements of the section.[120] Protection is not given where aircraft fly below a reasonable height,[121] or to air displays or aerobatics. However, under the Land Compensation Act 1973 and the Land Compensation (Scotland) Act 1973, noise is one of the "physical factors" that can be taken into account in claiming compensation. Compensation is claimed in relation to the depreciation of land values due to public works – in this context an aerodrome.

An owner, or other person to whom an aircraft is let or hired for more than 14 days, may be liable under section 76(2) of the Act for material loss or damage to any person or property caused by a person in, or an article or person falling from an aircraft while taking off, landing or in flight. This includes loss or damage due to noise or vibration and loss or damage also includes loss of life and

---

[117] Which relates to control of aviation by the Secretary of State in time of war or emergency.

[118] Relating to dangerous flying.

[119] The Government consultation paper on the control of civil aircraft noise, paras. 28/29, proposes only a minor technical amendment to this part of the Order to reflect E.C. legislation.

[120] See *Lord Bernstein of Leigh v Skyviews and General Ltd.* [1977] 2 All E.R. 902.

[121] *Roedean School Ltd. v Cornwall Aviation Co. Ltd., The Times,* 3rd July 1926, where the school complained of trespass and nuisance due to frequent flights at low heights near to the school grounds.

personal injury.[122] The term "material" is not defined and its meaning has not been determined by the courts. It may be arguable that it refers to identifiable financial loss or physical damage.

In a European Court case,[123] it was argued that section 76(1) of the Civil Aviation Act 1982 was in violation of the European Convention on Human Rights in that the statute prevented claimants having a fair public hearing of what would otherwise be their nuisance claims, and that the noise permitted by the statute interfered with the claimants' homes and private lives contrary to the convention. The argument was rejected.

The protection provided by section 76 was considered in the *Report of the Noise Review Working Party 1990.* The Working Party decided that the protection against nuisance action was no longer appropriate, particularly in the case of private and leisure flying. It recognised that noise certification would result in the gradual phasing out of older and noisier air transport aircraft but concluded that, because of the number of exemptions, certification was less effective in the case of smaller aircraft. It recommended that section 76 should be amended to allow action in respect of nuisance to be taken against aircraft under a certain weight flying beyond the aerodrome zone. The Government rejected the recommendation in a subsequent consultation paper,[124] stating that light aircraft must comply with the Rules of the Air and accepted aviation practice, otherwise action for nuisance could be taken against them. It also said that a light aircraft flying overhead may be audible on the ground but will normally be no louder than traffic passing nearby. The Government's view remained unchanged by the representations on the consultation paper.

However, a judgment of the European Court of Human Rights in relation to Heathrow Airport may have a significant impact on Government thinking. In October 2000, the European Court held that current United Kingdom policies on night-time flying from

---

[122] Civil Aviation Act 1982, s. 105(1).
[123] *Powell and Rayner v United Kingdom* (1990) 12 E.H.R.R. 35, E. Ct. H.R.
[124] Consultation Paper: *Control of Aircraft Noise,* August 1991, Department of Transport.

Heathrow breached the basic human rights of nearby residents by failing adequately to protect them from night-time noise.[125] The eight individuals bringing the case, supported by several local authorities, alleged that the level of aircraft noise at night, and the increase that followed the 1993 noise quota scheme, breached Article 8 of the Convention. This provides that "Everyone has a right to respect for his private and family life, his home and his correspondence". The Convention allows public authorities to interfere with that right on certain public policy grounds, including the "economic well-being of the country" and "the protection of the rights and freedom of others". The court considered the developing noise restrictions at Heathrow, the basis of Government policies on aircraft noise, and the economic importance of night flights at Heathrow. Although the Government was not the operator of the airport or the aircraft, it had a positive duty to take reasonable and appropriate measures to secure the rights of the individuals affected. Of particular reference were two statements:

> "In the particularly sensitive field of environmental protection, mere reference to the economic well-being of the country is not sufficient to outweigh the rights of others."

> "States are required to minimize, as far as possible, the interference with these rights, by trying to find alternative solutions and by generally seeking to achieve their aims in the least onerous way as regards human rights."

The impact of this judgment, which is subject to the right of appeal,[126] on Government policies and practices remains to be seen. Under the Human Rights Act 1998, British courts are not strictly bound by European Court decisions but have to take account of them.

---

[125] *Hatton & Others v The United Kingdom* (application No. 36022/97), judgment of the European Court of Human Rights, Strasbourg, 2nd October 2001. See also a report and analysis of this case in *Human Rights and Aircraft Noise*, Richard Macrory, Prof. of Environmental Law, University College, London, ENDS Report 321, pp. 53/54, October 2001.

[126] To be heard in October 2002.

LAND USE PLANNING[127]

The Wilson Committee report[128] emphasised the need for adequate consultation and planning control having regard to the future noise impact of any potential airport and the Department of the Environment recommended criteria for development control to minimise the impact of aircraft noise.[129] In particular:

(a) minimum noise routes should be established so that they can be taken into account by local authorities in their long term planning;

(b) avoidance of the use of land adversely affected by aircraft noise for noise sensitive development. The use of the Noise and Number Index (now L_{eq} (16-hour) dB(A)) is recommended as the criteria for development control;[130]

(c) sound insulation – where for overriding reasons it is necessary to build houses within an area likely to be adversely affected by aircraft noise, a suitable standard of noise insulation should be provided.[131]

The *Report of the Noise Review Working Party 1990* recommended that, when the DoE Planning and Noise Circular 10/73 was revised, the DoE should consider giving further guidance on the legal position regarding the requirement for planning permission when the intensification of use of an airfield is proposed.[132] The Working Party further recommended that three action levels[133] be used as the basis for planning guidance in respect of noise sensitive development near airfields. This concept was accepted by the Government. Planning Policy Guidance Note 24 on planning and noise was subsequently published in 1994. It contains four Noise Exposure

---

[127] See generally Chapter 9.
[128] Para. 333.
[129] *Planning and Noise,* D.O.E. Circular 10/73, paras 14/23 and Appendix 1/3. Circular 10/73 is now replaced by P.P.G. 24 *Planning and Noise* which still follows the same basic principles.
[130] *Planning and Noise,* D.O.E. Circular 10/73, Appendix 2, and P.P.G. 24, paras. 6–8 and Annex 1.
[131] *Ibid,* Appendix 3 and Schedule 2.
[132] *Report of the Noise Review Working Party 1990,* Recommendation 25, page 18.
[133] *Ibid,* Recommendation 31, page 19.

Categories. Amongst other things, the guidance suggests that when dealing with strategic issues such as development of, or near, major aerodomes, it may be necessary to include some noise policies in Part 1 of the Unitary Development Plan and in structure plans. It also suggests that in trying to ensure that development does not cause an unacceptable degree of disturbance, local planning authorities should bear in mind that a subsequent intensification or change of use may result in greater intrusion and they may wish to consider the use of appropriate planning conditions. This could include limiting hours of operation and the number and type of aircraft. Noise sensitive development should not normally be permitted in areas which are, or are expected to become, subject to unacceptably high noise levels, such as near airports.

P.P.G. 24 includes a recommended range of noise levels for each of the Noise Exposure Categories applicable to air traffic. By using forecast Noise and Number Index Contours, it should be possible to determine approximately which areas fall within the different noise exposure categories. Local planning authorities are expected to seek the co-operation of aerodrome management to arrive at the most appropriate long term forecasts of air traffic and its effect on the noise contours. The advice on aircraft noise includes consideration of the impact of military aircraft and helicopters. Other than for designated aircraft, most noise is limited through planning controls on the number, type and operational times of aircraft.[134]

The White Paper *A New Deal for Transport: Better for Everyone*[135] announced the Government's intention to prepare a new U.K. airports policy looking some 30 years ahead. This remains an ongoing process. In its Planning Policy Guidance note *Regional Planning 2000*,[136] regional planning bodies have to include in their

---

[134] The outcome of the Heathrow Terminal 5 enquiry includes a planning condition limiting the number of flights at Heathrow to 480,000 per year to limit noise.

[135] CM 3950.

[136] P.P.G. 11, October 2000, applicable to England except Greater London. See also P.P.G. 13, *Transport*, Annex B, and the Town and Country Planning (General Permitted Development) Order 1995, Part 18, for details of what is permitted development at, within or near airports, and what development is not permitted.

regional transport strategies a "strategic steer" on the role and future development of airports in their regions, in the light of national policy. Local planning authorities are expected to consider the growth of regional airports; indeed the White Paper encourages regional airport growth where it is consistent with sustainable development. In looking at the role of small airports and airfields, general aviation growth (including commercial air transport) may be increasingly restricted at larger airports. Accordingly, in formulating their plans and policies, and in determining planning applications, local authorities will need to take account of the local impact of general aviation. Local authorities should consult D.E.T.R.'s Airports Policy Division on draft development plan policies and proposals relating to airports and airfields. The environmental impact of aviation proposals will always need careful consideration.[137]

HELICOPTER NOISE

The low frequency throbbing of helicopter rotor noise is associated with the helicopter lifting operation. The increased flight speed of the helicopter produces effects which give rise to the familiar buzzing noise which can usually be heard in advance of it flying over the observer. Because of their manoeuvrability, helicopters do not necessarily have to adhere to well defined flight paths. This can make it difficult to estimate the associated community noise. Helicopters can use temporary sites for landing and taking off, provided safety standards are observed. Those sites can include large gardens, car parks, paddocks, hotel grounds and open fields. Provided a helicopter is flying normally and adhering to the appropriate provisions of the Civil Aviation Act 1982 and Rules of the Air Regulations 1991,[138] it will be immune from nuisance proceedings under section 76 of the Civil Aviation Act 1982.

The Town and Country Planning (General Permitted Development) Order 1995 gives permitted development rights to use land outside the curtilage of a building for any purpose for up to 28 days in any

---

[137] See P.P.G. 24, *Planning and Noise*, September 1994. The annex to P.P.G. 24 suggests noise conditions.
[138] S.I. 1991 No. 2437.

calendar year, without the need to make a specific planning application. The days can be consecutive and the number of movements is not restricted. Subject to the Secretary of State's confirmation, a local planning authority may withdraw the rights by making a Direction under Article 4 of the General Permitted Development Order. The landing and taking off of a helicopter from the garden of a dwelling house, if this is incidental to the use of the house, is not "development" and planning permission is not required.

Landing and taking off on industrial or commercial land may be an ancillary use. There is no legal right to do this but planning controls will not be effective unless the ancillary use expands to become a use in its own right, e.g. the regular operation of flights from land for paying customers, assuming this falls outside the 28 day period, would require planning permission.

Relatively few studies have been undertaken on helicopter noise and annoyance.[139] However, the Noise Review Working Party 1990 felt that environmental considerations required some additional measure of control. It was particularly concerned that helicopters using sites and landing areas close to houses and other buildings could be a serious cause of noise nuisance from which there was no protection. It recommended that there should be provision for local authorities to regulate the use of helicopters at private landing sites through a licensing system.[140]

In its consultation paper *Control of Aircraft Noise,*[141] the Department of Transport commented that information was limited, although the number of helicopters on the U.K. register had increased in the ten years between 1981 and 1991 from 500 to just over 900. The responses to the consultation paper provided no evidence of persistent or widespread problems at temporary and private sites. The

---

[139] However, useful reference to the studies undertaken is in "Helicopters in London", Southwood, R.M., Hill, C. and Stanbury, C., *Environmental Health,* May 1991, pp. 117–121.

[140] *Report of the Noise Review Working Party 1990,* Recommendation 32, page 19.

[141] Department of Transport, August 1991, paragraphs 30–38.

Government's conclusion[142] was that a proposed new power to "designate" aerodromes for noise control purposes would cover company and private sites and could be used to deal with recurring but intermittent problems. It also said that proposed national guidance on what was feasible and reasonable to control aircraft noise would be helpful.

REDUCING NOISE NUISANCE FROM LIGHT AIRCRAFT

Whilst much of this chapter deals with noise from civil aircraft, light aeroplanes increasingly attract complaints from areas adjacent to small airfields. Research suggests that a number of complaints attributed to light aeroplane noise are in fact related to other, non-acoustical factors.[143] The research indicates that, although noise is initially the reason for most complaints, the main cause for concern may well be other factors, e.g. a negative view to leisure flying, poor community/airfield relations, fear of crashes, poor response to complaints, and low flying aircraft. It also suggests that dealing with these non-acoustical factors may have some impact on the level of noise complaints.

The Civil Aviation Authority indicates[144] that aspects of general aviation activity which have attracted complaints include circuit flying, aerobatics, glider and banner towing, parachuting and cross-country flying. The greatest cause of complaint is from circuit flying and aerobatics. The Authority suggests a number of ways of reducing noise from these various activities, including:

1. *Circuit flying:* keeping circuit height as high as possible; tailoring the circuit to local conditions to avoiding overflying noise sensitive areas; changing circuit direction; using angled

---

[142] *Review of aircraft noise legislation: announcement of conclusions*, Department of Transport, March 1993. The Government's position does not appear to have changed in the interim period.

[143] *A study of community disturbance caused by general and business aviation operations – final report,* University of Southampton Institute of Sound and Vibration Research, D.O.T., July 1998.

[144] In its report *Recommended measures to help reduce the noise related nuisance from light aeroplanes.*

take-off and approach paths to avoid overflying noise sensitive areas; using less sensitive sites for pilot training; varying power levels.

2. *Aerobatics:* aerobatics have long been the cause of complaint from those in the vicinity due to constant changes in power settings and manoeuvres over a relatively small area. Noise reduction measures may include the use of remote areas with little nearby population; flying at greater heights; varying the areas in which aerobatic manoeuvres are carried out.

The Authority emphasises the importance of good training, airfield management and communications through consultation committees.[145]

MICROLIGHT AIRCRAFT

The early versions of microlight aircraft used high speed small diameter propellers driven from poorly silenced engines. The high-pitched engine tone and propeller buzzing tone, together with the long fly-by times due to the low airspeed produced a particularly annoying noise. Pulley and toothed, belt driven, larger diameter propellers now produce reduced noise output. Nevertheless, the free-roaming nature of microlight aircraft can still cause considerable annoyance and they are subject to noise certification.

The British Microlight Aircraft Association publishes guidance on compliance with the Air Navigation Order and Rules of the Air. In particular it draws attention to the need for flying club members to report any enforced low flying (which may cause noise complaints) to its Chief Flying Instructor and to comply with any local airport noise restrictions.

---

[145] For the purposes of the Civil Aviation Act 1982, s. 35. P.P.G. 24 also suggests planning conditions, and most light aircraft aerodrome controls are applied in this way.

Chapter 9

PLANNING AND DEVELOPMENT

This chapter is not intended to cover in depth the complex matters of planning procedure, compulsory purchase and planning inquiries. It provides guidance on the broad aspects of planning control and how consideration of environmental noise issues fits into the planning and enforcement processes. Comprehensive guidance on the more detailed aspects of planning law may be found in other publications.[1]

The Industrial Revolution was the start of the manufacturing system which is largely responsible for the environmental noise problems that exist today. Demand for work in the new industrial areas of the country resulted in migration of people from rural areas to the developing towns and cities. Houses, many of which were occupied by the industrial employees, were built in the shadow of the new factories. Planning controls did not exist and no doubt the opportunity to earn a standard of living above the poverty line far outweighed the dirt, fumes and noise to which the new town dweller became exposed. New Public Health legislation was introduced to control and improve the poor housing conditions and to control the spread of infectious diseases. Gradually, new Housing, Public Health and Planning legislation began to bring about better control but town planning did not become a reality until 1909 when local authorities were given power to make town planning schemes in respect of land in the course of, or proposed for, development and to secure proper sanitary conditions, amenity and convenience in connection with the layout and use of land.[2] This was the first opportunity to control development as a whole rather than individual plots of land. It therefore enabled some provision to be made for protecting residential areas against undesirable industrial

---

[1] *An Outline of Planning Law, 10th edition,* Heap, Sir Desmond, 1991, Sweet and Maxwell. *The Encyclopaedia of Planning Law and Practice* – same author. *Planning Controls and their Enforcement, 7th edition*, Little, A.J., 2001, Shaw & Sons Ltd.

[2] The Housing, Town Planning, etc. Act 1909, s. 54.

development and provided planning authorities with the opportunity of setting aside areas for industrial development only.

It could not of course legislate for the removal of existing industry from residential areas and in many areas of the country such conditions still exist to the detriment of residential properties, although the planning process has developed to the stage where industry and people can co-exist without significant pollution problems due to the co-operation that takes place between the Planning Officer, Environmental Health Officer and Highway Engineer.

A succession of statutes followed the 1909 Act and these sought to improve the administrative process, consolidate the law, introduce powers of compulsory land acquisition and compensation, give local authorities power to undertake their own development and prohibit the carrying out of any development (subject to certain exceptions) without planning permission. The Town and Country Planning Act 1947 made an entirely new start by repealing all previous town planning legislation and enacting new planning law principles. As a result of continuing consideration of the need for improved planning legislation, further changes were recommended[3] which resulted in the enactment of the Town and Country Planning Act 1971. Since then, a series of legislative changes has taken place, resulting in four new planning Acts becoming law in 1990, the Town and Country Planning Act 1990 becoming the principal Act. Despite this consolidating legislation, the Government introduced further changes in the Planning and Compensation Act 1991 which came into operation through a series of commencement orders. This is the principal planning legislation controlling planning and development at the present time.[4]

During 2001 the Government published a Green Paper, *Planning: Delivering a Fundemental Change*, proposing a wholesale review of the planning system in England. It was subsequently followed by four "daughter" consultation documents on: Major Infrastructure

---

[3] White Paper *Town and Country Planning*, Cmnd. 3333.
[4] Comparable powers exist in Scotland under the Town and Country Planning (Scotland) Act 1972.

Projects; Compulsory Purchase and Compensation; the Use Classes Order; and Planning Obligations. Together they constitute the most radical review of the system since the 1947 Act. The proposals, if adopted, will affect all aspects of the system from regional planning, to a new system of development plans, changes in development control, the Use Classes Order, the General Permitted Development Order, Section 106 Agreements, compulsory purchase and compensation, and how major infrastructure projects are dealt with. A review of all national guidance issued via Planning Policy Guidance Notes (P.P.G.s) is also proposed. In July 2002, the Office of the Deputy Prime Minister, who became responsible for planning and environmental health matters following a reorganisation of Government departments, published a "policy response" to the Green Paper consultations and indicated its intention to proceed with a regional tier of stautory planning, a revised development plan process based on Local Development Frameworks, changes to the development control process, and proposals to speed up public inquiries.

Most Environmental Health Officers, Planning Officers and many householders will be aware that planning decisions have been made which have resulted in a worse noise environment in certain areas of their authorities than existed prior to development taking place. Failure to recognise the full impact of the operations of the developer can result in new development which emits noise at unacceptable levels. If planning controls have not been imposed to limit environmental noise, then the only satisfactory recourse may be action to abate a statutory noise nuisance[5] or by the institution of common law action by aggrieved persons. In the case of statutory law, however, the "best practicable means"[6] defence exists. Accordingly, if this defence is successfully used, people living in the vicinity of a noisy activity may remain subject to an unsatisfactory noise climate which could possibly have been prevented by proper planning. The Wilson Committee[7] recognised this difficulty and the need for more effective planning control was recommended by

---

[5]   See Chapter 2.
[6]   Environmental Protection Act 1990, s. 79(9).
[7]   *Noise,* Final Report, Cmnd. 2056, 1963, paras. 373–378.

the Scott Committee[8] and the Department of the Environment declared the Government's policy in 1973 concerning the control of noise by planning.[9] The Government accepted that "People increasingly resent being subject to noise, particularly in their homes ..." This Circular laid down, with particular reference to noise from roads, aircraft and industry, principles and specific criteria by which the Secretaries of State would be guided in taking planning decisions and on which they urged local planning authorities to base their own policies. In September 1994 the Government published *Planning Policy Guidance: Planning and Noise* – P.P.G. 24 which replaces and builds on the principles of the earlier circular and takes account of the recommendations in the report of the Noise Review Working Party 1990. It outlines some of the main considerations which local authorities should take into account in drawing up development plan policies and when determining planning applications for development which will either generate noise or be exposed to existing noise sources.

It is clear that the planning system has to have regard for environmental considerations. This is partly because of public and private recognition of environmental protection matters and also because of particular legal requirements, e.g. the Town and Country Planning (Environmental Impact Assessment) (England and Wales) Regulations 1999.[10]

The Government previously published its views on the issue of planning and pollution control in its White Paper *This Common Inheritance – Britain's Environmental Strategy.*[11] It said:[12]

"Planning control is primarily concerned with the type and location of new development and changes of use. Once broad land uses have been sanctioned by the planning process, it is the job of pollution control to limit adverse effects that operations may have on the environment. But in practice there is common

---

8   *Neighbourhood Noise,* Noise Advisory Council, 1971, paras. 94–105.
9   Circular 10/73, *Planning and Noise.* Advice now cancelled by *Planning Policy Guidance: Planning and Noise,* P.P.G. 24, September 1994, H.M.S.O.
10   S.I. 1999 No. 293.
11   Cmnd. 1200, September 1990.
12   Paragraph 6.39.

ground. In considering whether to grant planning permission for a particular development, a local authority must consider all the effects, including potential pollution; permission should not be granted if that might expose people to danger. And a change in an industrial process may well require planning permission as well as approval under environmental protection legislation."

The Government prepares national guidance to secure consistency of approach to planning decisions. The guidance has to be taken into account in preparing development plans and in making decisions on individual planning applications. The guidance is in the form of Planning Policy Guidance Notes (P.P.G.s). These progressively replace the guidance given in earlier planning circulars. They are intended to give "clearer, more accessible and systematic policy guidance".

In its first P.P.G.,[13] the Government discusses its approach to sustainable development, mixed use and design, and sets out general principles under which the planning system is to operate, including the following extracts:

"Sustainable development seeks to deliver the objective of achieving, now and in the future, economic development to secure higher living standards while protecting and enhancing the environment."[14]

"The planning system, and the preparation of development plans in particular, is the most effective way of striking the right balance between the demand for development and the protection of the environment."[15]

"One of the Government's key aims is to encourage economic development in a way which is compatible with its stated environmental objectives."[16]

---

[13] *Planning Policy Guidance: General Policy and Principles,* P.P.G. 1, March 1992, DoE, revised in February 1997.
[14] Paragraph 4.
[15] Paragraph 39.
[16] Paragraph 21.

> "Where development is proposed on land adjoining urban areas, its impact on its surroundings and nearby land uses should be considered carefully ... local authorities should have the aims of securing environmental improvement, reducing conflicts between neighbouring land uses ..."[17]

Noise is clearly a matter to be considered in addressing these principles. More particularly, P.P.G. 4[18] says that "The characteristics of industry and commerce are evolving continuously and many businesses can be carried on in rural and residential areas without causing unacceptable disturbance through increased noise ... Planning permission should normally be granted (for commercial and industrial activities) unless there are specific and significant objections, such as ... unacceptable noise ... Where they are disposed to permit industrial or commercial developments in residential and rural areas, planning authorities should bear in mind that subsequent intensification of the use may become unacceptably intrusive. Planning authorities should ... consider the use of planning conditions or planning obligations to safeguard local amenity, where they would be an appropriate means of preventing foreseeable harm."

In P.P.G. 23: *Planning and Pollution Control*,[19] the Government gives advice on the relationship between authorities' planning responsibilities and the separate statutory responsibilities of local authorities, including those under the Environmental Protection Act 1990. It emphasises that the planning system should not be operated so as to duplicate controls which are the statutory responsibility of other bodies, and encourages close co-operation between planning and pollution control authorities to prevent unnecessary duplication and conflict of interests. That P.P.G. deals more particularly with air, waste and water pollution, leaving P.P.G. 24 to address noise pollution.

Planning authorities should consider carefully whether particular proposals for new development may be incompatible with existing

---

17 Paragraph 31.
18 *Planning Policy Guidance: Industrial and Commercial Development and Small Firms*, P.P.G. 4, November 1992, DoE, paras. 14–19.
19 DoE, 1994. Applies to England only.

industrial and commercial activities. The juxtaposition of incompatible uses can cause problems for the occupiers of both the new and existing development. For example, where a residential development is proposed in the vicinity of existing industrial uses, the expectation of the residents may exceed the standards applied by the planning authority and may give rise to pressure to curtail the industrial use. This may be a particularly acute problem where other legislation, such as that relating to environmental pollution or public health, might subsequently result in costly new conditions or restrictions being imposed on the industry as a consequence of the new neighbouring development. Planning authorities should consider carefully the possible consequences of incompatible development encroaching on established businesses.

In other words, noise prevention is better than cure, and significantly cheaper!

DEVELOPMENT PLANS

"Development" means[20] (subject to defined exceptions) the carrying out of building, engineering, mining or other operations in, on, over or under land or the making of any material change in the use of any building or other land.

The Town and Country Planning Act 1947 introduced a system of development plans in order to set out longer term frameworks for land use planning and decision making. Part II of the Town and Country Planning Act 1968 amended the system by introducing a two-tier system of development plans: structure plans and local plans. A further variation was introduced by the Local Government Act 1985 – the unitary development plan. Full guidance on the preparation of development plans is contained in P.P.G. 12.[21] Development plans are the main guidance to planning decisions by local authorities and others. The plans, which should be consistent with national and regional planning policy, provide the principle

---

[20] Town and Country Planning Act 1990, s. 55(1).
[21] *Development Plans*, P.P.G. 12, December 1999, D.E.T.R. See also *Local Plans and Unitary Development Plans: A Guide to Procedures* (2000) and *Structure Plans: A Guide to Procedures* (2000), Circular 07/99, D.E.T.R.

means of reconciling conflicts between the need for development and the need to protect the environment. Section 54A of the Town and Country Planning Act 1990 requires planning decisions to be made in accordance with the development plan unless material considerations indicate otherwise. It is therefore important for plans to include development control policies which will apply to decisions on applications for development that would cause noise or would introduce noise sensitive development, such as housing and hospitals, into areas already exposed to noise from existing uses or development.[22]

A number of different plans[23] may constitute the development plan, depending on the subject and proposed development area:

(a) *structure plans* – set out the strategic policies in non-metropolitan areas and are produced by county planning authorities;

(b) *local plans* – contain detailed development policies in non-metropolitan areas and are generally prepared by local councils;

(c) *unitary development plans* – combine the functions of structure and local plans in London Boroughs, Metropolitan Districts and the Unitary Authorities in Wales.

The Mayor of London is required to prepare and publish a "spatial development strategy"[24] which has to include general policies in respect of the development and use of land in Greater London. Although this is not a development plan, the Unitary Development Plans of London Boroughs have to be in accordance with the spatial development strategy.

---

[22] For a useful case involving planning permission for the creation of a landing strip for light aircraft, see *R. v Mendip D.C. ex parte Fabre* [2000] J.P.L., August, p. 810. This case involved the granting of temporary planning permission and noise monitoring requirements by the Council's Environmental Health Officer.

[23] The Government in its Green Paper, *Planning: delivering a fundamental change*, December 2001, D.E.T.R., proposes simplifying the current hierarchical system of plans and replacing structure plans, local plans and unitary development plans with new Local Development Frameworks. See Introduction, p. xliii.

[24] Greater London Authority Act 1999, s. 334.

The local planning authority has a duty to keep under review the matters which may be expected to affect the development of its area or the planning of its development, and can at any time institute a fresh survey of its area.[25] The planning authority may have to use the services of its local Environmental Health Department or consultants if it requires information and advice on environmental noise levels in different areas. Areas where noise problems exist or are likely to exist can be determined by surveys so that proper consideration can be given to such matters in drawing up the plans. The Town and Country Planning (Development Plan) (England) Regulations 1999[26] underlined the role of development plans as a means of environmental protection through a requirement to have regard to environmental considerations.[27] Authorities must have regard to a wider range of environmental concerns than those traditionally used for land use planning and they must assess the environmental impact of their proposals as a whole. P.P.G. 12 advises[28] that:

> "The (environmental) appraisal process should be an important element of every stage of the development plan process ... finish the process with a clear set of environmental objectives ... it should be clear from the reasoned justification/explanatory memorandum of the plan what elements of the (environmental) appraisal have informed the policies and proposals in the plan."[29]

> "Plans should have key environmental and other indicators built into them which are capable of being monitored throughout the lifetime of the plan."[30]

> "The fact that a plan was subject to environmental appraisal does not take away the requirements for environmental

---

[25] Town and Country Planning Act 1990, s. 30(1).

[26] S.I. 1999 No. 3280. The Town and Country (Development Plan) Regulations 1991, as variously amended, still apply in relation to Wales.

[27] Reg. 20.

[28] *Development Plans*, December 1999.

[29] Paragraph 4.18. Guidance on environmental appraisal of development plans is given in *Environmental Appraisal of Development Plans: A Good Practice Guide*, 1993, DoE.

[30] Paragraph 4.21.

assessment of individual proposals where they are required by legislation."[31]

Noise is one of the most important environmental factors in considering planning issues and warrants detailed consideration. P.P.G. 24[32] includes advice that:

"Development plans should give developers and local communities a degree of certainty about the areas in which particular types of development will be acceptable and those in which special measures may be required in order to mitigate the impact of noise."[33]

"Plans should contain policies designed to ensure, as far as is practicable, that noise sensitive developments are located away from existing sources of significant noise ... potentially noisy developments are located in areas where noise will not be such an important consideration ..."[34]

"Where it is particularly difficult to separate noise sensitive development from noisy activities, plans should contain an indication of any general policies which the planning authority propose to apply in respect of conditions or planning obligations."[35]

The relevance of noise in the preparation of development plans is clearly indicated in P.P.G. 24[36] and must be included as one of the factors required to be considered by virtue of the requirements of the 1990 Act[37] which requires that the matters to be kept under review must include:

(a) the principal physical and economic characteristics of the area of the authority (including the principal purposes for which

---

[31] i.e. the Town and Country Planning (Environmental Impact Assessment) (England and Wales) Regulations 1999, S.I. 1999, No. 293.
[32] *Planning and Noise*, September 1994, DoE.
[33] Paragraph 3.
[34] Paragraph 5.
[35] Paragraph 7.
[36] Paragraphs 3–7.
[37] s. 11(2). This section is closely modelled on that (s. 30) for structure plans.

land is used) and, so far as they may be expected to affect that area, of any neighbouring areas;

(b) the size, composition and distribution of the population of that area (whether resident or otherwise);

(c) without prejudice to paragraph (a) above, the communications, transport system and traffic of that area and, so far as they may be expected to affect that area, of any neighbouring areas;

(d) any considerations not mentioned in paragraph (a), (b) or (c) which may be expected to affect any matters mentioned in them;

(e) such other matters as may be prescribed or as the Secretary of State may in a particular case direct;

(f) any changes already projected in any of the matters mentioned in any of paragraphs (a) to (e) and the effect which those changes are likely to have on the development of that area or the planning of such development.

If the planning authority needs to examine matters concerning the area of another authority, it must do so in consultation with that other authority.[38] This could presumably include the effects of noise from industry and roads in an adjacent authority, which might adversely affect potential future residential development near the boundary of the authority carrying out its survey and preparing its plans.

Structure plans

All areas of the country requiring a structure plan have one in place. The local planning authority, on completion of any review of its area under section 30 of the Town and Country Planning Act 1990, must submit its proposed structure plan alterations to the Secretary of State for his approval.[39] The Secretary of State can direct the authority to submit the alterations within a specified period and the

---

[38] s. 11(3).
[39] s. 32(1).

proposals may relate to the whole or part of the area to which the plan relates.[40] The structure plan indicates broad policy and general proposals in respect of the development and other use of land in its area (including measures for the improvement of the physical environment and the management of traffic) and any other matters prescribed or directed by the Secretary of State.[41] The Town and Country Planning (Development Plan) (England) Regulations 1999 deal with the detailed matters to be contained in the structure plans.[42]

The structure plan must take the form of a written statement and be illustrated by diagrams.[43] The structure plan diagram will usually show the proposed land usage, which will include industrial and other potential noise producing sources. The proposals must be justified by any fresh survey and have regard to strategic or regional planning guidance given by the Secretary of State, national policies and available resources for implementing the structure plan proposals.[44]

Examples of the type of policy statements that may be included to deal with environmental noise are:

> "3.6 In considering proposals for new development or redevelopment, the Council will seek to protect nearby uses from excessive noise, pollution and other environmental nuisance. Residential development will not normally be permitted in locations which experience high levels of environmental nuisance.
>
> 3.7 The Council will encourage the relocation of 'bad neighbour' uses from residential and other sensitive areas; where resources permit, the Council will seek to provide alternative sites to assist with this relocation."[45]

---

[40] s. 32(2).

[41] s. 31(2) and (3).

[42] See also *Development*, P.P.G. 12, December 1999, D.E.T.R. For Wales, see *Planning Guidance (Wales): Unitary Development Plans* (1996).

[43] Town and Country Planning Act 1990, s. 31(2) and (5).

[44] *Ibid*, s. 31(6). See also the Town and Country Planning (Development Plan) (England) Regulations 1999, S.I. 1999 No. 3280, and P.P.G. 12, *Development Plans*, 1999, D.E.T.R.

[45] Walsall Unitary Development Plan 1988–2001.

Local plans

The structure plan will not provide the land owner or developer with detailed information about how the district planning authority's proposals will affect the land in which it has an interest. The local plan must contain a written statement[46] setting out policies for the development and use of land, including the conservation of the amenity of the land, the improvement of the physical environment and the management of traffic. It must be in general conformity with the structure plan and should guide most day-to-day planning decisions. It is worth bearing in mind that if planning decisions on development proposals change the character of a neighbourhood by increasing noise levels, subsequent action in respect of nuisance may fail.[47]

In this respect the case of *Gillingham Borough Council v Medway (Chatham) Dock Co. Ltd. and Others* is most significant. The council was anxious to attract business and employment opportunities to the site of a former naval dockyard which was proposed for use as a commercial port. It was aware of the environmental effects which the port would produce and gave assurances that unrestricted access would be available to the port. Access to the port was only possible through a residential area and the passage of heavy goods vehicles to and from the port, which operated 24 hours a day, resulted in substantial interference with the residents' enjoyment of properties in streets through which the port traffic passed. The council brought a nuisance action seeking a declaration that the passage of heavy goods vehicles to and from the port between 7.00 p.m. and 7.00 a.m. constituted a public nuisance, and injunctions to restrain such traffic. There was no dispute about the fact that serious disturbance was caused by the movement of about 750 heavy goods vehicles every 24 hours. However, the dock company were operating the port in accordance with the planning permission. It was held that "where planning consent was given for a development or change of use, the question whether a particular user amounted to a public nuisance thereafter

---

46   Town and Country Planning Act 1990, s. 36(2).
47   See *Gillingham Borough Council v Medway (Chatham) Dock Co. Ltd. and Others* [1992] 3 All E.R. 923; [1992] 3 W.L.R. 449, Q.B.D.

fell to be decided by reference to the neighbourhood as it was with that development or change of use and not as it was previously ... since the council's claim in nuisance was to be judged by reference to the character of the neighbourhood as affected by the planning permission ... to use the former dockyard as a commercial port, which the council had been aware at the time of granting planning permission would be used 24 hours a day, the disturbance to residents ... was not actionable." This case emphasises the need for adequate consultation between Planning and Environmental Health Officers to avoid development causing major noise problems.

Unitary development plans

A unitary development plan applies to London Boroughs and metropolitan areas, and unitary authorities in Wales.[48] It has two parts: Part I is analogous to the structure plan in non-metropolitan areas and consists of a written statement of the planning authority's general policies for the development and use of land in its area. Part II is analogous to the local plan in non-metropolitan areas and contains a written statement of the proposals for development and use of land, a map showing these proposals and a reasoned justification for the proposals.

Noise policies and guidance in development plans

Planning authorities need to ensure that development plans contain clear land use policies for different types of industrial and commercial development. Consideration must be given to the changes introduced in the Town and Country Planning (Use Classes) Order 1987,[49]

---

[48] Under the Local Government (Wales) Act 1994, each new Welsh council, as local planning authority, is required to prepare a unitary development plan for its area. Until then, existing plans remain in force. In relation to London, the Mayor is required by the Greater London Authority Act 1999, Pt. VIII, to prepare and adopt a spatial development strategy for London. This is not a development plan for the purposes of this Act but it creates a strategic framework for the unitary development plans of the Boroughs. London Boroughs cannot adopt a unitary plan or amendments to an existing plan unless they are in general conformity with the spatial development strategy.

[49] S.I. 1987 No. 764, as variously amended.

particularly the business use class (B1). The Order allows the use of a building for any purpose specified in one of the sixteen classes, to be changed to any other purpose falling within the same class, without the need for planning permission because such change does not constitute development. However, this provision must be considered in light of the decision in *Corporation of City of London v Secretary of State for the Environment and Another.*[50] In this case it was established that conditions attached to a planning permission can restrict further changes in the use of land even though those changes would not constitute development by virtue of the 1987 Order. P.P.G. 4 advises that the business use class introduces a clear distinction between business uses and general industry, based on environmental factors. It presents an opportunity for development plans to provide positively for enterprise and investment, whilst affording environmental protection. It recognises that plans should provide specifically for polluting industries, whilst ensuring that such industries are separated from sensitive land uses.

The Department of the Environment's P.P.G. on planning and noise goes further. In relation to noise, the following statement in P.P.G. 24[51] is important: "The aim of this guidance is to provide advice on how the planning system can be used to minimise the adverse impact of noise without placing unreasonable restrictions on development or adding unduly to the costs and administrative burdens of business. It builds upon the principles established in Circular 10/73 *Planning and Noise* and takes account of the recommendations of the Noise Review Working Party which reported in October 1990.[52] It outlines some of the main considerations which local planning authorities should take into account in drawing up development plan policies and when

---

[50] *Corporation of City of London v Secretary of State for the Environment and Another* [1971] 23 P. & C.R. 169. Additionally, a change of use from one class to another will not *necessarily* constitute development unless the use is a *material change*. See *Rann v Secretary of State for the Environment* (1980) 40 P. & C.R. 113.

[51] Paragraph 1. For Wales, see Technical Guidance Note (Wales) 11, *Noise*, 1997.

[52] It recommended an urgent review of Circular 10/73 (which is now superseded) and the introduction of Noise Action Levels.

determining planning applications for development which will either generate noise or be exposed to existing noise sources."

The guidance suggests various types of development and use which are susceptible to exposure by noise from transport and other sources. In particular, to assist in the appraisal of development proposals it introduces the concept of "noise exposure categories" for residential development. There are four categories ranging from Category A, where noise is unlikely to be a significant factor, to Category D, where it is such an important factor that planning permission for an incompatible use should normally be refused in the absence of strong planning reasons to the contrary.

P.P.G. 24 contains a recommended range of noise levels for each "Noise Exposure Category", although in some cases it may be appropriate for local planning authorities to decide what levels of noise they wish to attribute to each of the categories and to define the type of development to be considered most sensitive to noise, in the light of local circumstances and priorities. The policies must be contained in district local plans or Part II of the unitary development plans. The Secretary of State considers that housing, hospitals and schools should normally be regarded as "noise sensitive development", although planning authorities may wish to include other developments or uses.

The determination of the proposals to be contained in unitary development plans or local plans will be dependent on the knowledge gained as a result of surveys.

Some planning authorities adopt policies for the relocation of industries causing pollution which cannot be satisfactorily resolved by statute or are in other ways environmentally unsatisfactory. In such cases, including those where noise is significant, it may be that the "best practicable means" defence available under the Environmental Protection Act 1990 is applicable and relocation may be the only satisfactory way to resolve the problem. These policies will often be detailed in local plans and unitary development plans. Similarly, new industries may be restricted from coming into a particular area.

APPLICATIONS, PLANNING PERMISSION, CONSENT CONDITIONS

Definition of development

The Town and Country Planning Act 1990 defines "development" as:[53]

> "the carrying out of building, engineering, mining or other operations[54] in, on, over or under land, or the making of any material change in the use[55] of any buildings or other land."

The Act also provides that certain matters will or will not constitute development.[56] Development does not include the change of use of buildings or other land where the change is from one use to another within the same use class specified in the Town and Country Planning (Use Classes) Order 1987.[57] The Town and Country Planning (General Permitted Development) Order 1995[58] grants planning permission for 85 types of development contained in 32 different categories.[59] This may not always apply universally – Article 4 of the Order makes provision for the local planning authority, or the Secretary of State, to make a direction requiring specific planning permission to be obtained for any of those works that would normally be in the permitted category. In addition, an original application can be conditioned to restrict the activities to a certain use. Noise is a significant factor in determining into which

---

[53] ss. 55(1) and 336.

[54] *Cheshire C.C. v Woodward* [1962] 2 Q.B. 126 held that there is no one test to find out what physical characteristics constitute development of land, it depends on all the circumstances and on the degree of permanency of the building, engineering, mining or other operations. The definition in s. 55(1) is similar to that in s. 60(1), Control of Pollution Act 1974 and presumably certain activities could be controlled under either legislation so as to control noise. Generally speaking, the Control of Pollution Act will most satisfactorily control this type of work whilst in progress due to the more immediate remedial action available. Planning action is more appropriate to the use of the building after completion.

[55] Noise could be the sole factor in deciding a material change of use.

[56] See s. 55(2).

[57] s. 55(2)(f).

[58] S.I. 1995 No. 418. The Order applies to England and Wales.

[59] Town and Country Planning Act 1990, s. 59 and Art. 4 and Sched. 2 of the Order.

use class a particular building falls. For example, Class B1 defines a business use for the purposes of an office (except for financial and professional services), research and development of products or processes, or for any industrial process "being a use which can be carried out in any residential area without detriment to the amenity of that area by reason of noise, vibration ...".

The reference to "any residential area" is general and not specific to the actual area surrounding the site. It is, therefore, irrelevant that the actual site may be in a noisy area, or in a primarily industrial area, or that the geography of the site may result in the nearest neighbours being protected from emissions.[60] It is the impact of the industrial activity that is particularly important. Accordingly, the design of a particular building, and especially any measures incorporated into the building design to minimise noise emissions, are highly relevant factors. So, for example, a builder's yard used for joinery and metal fabrication is more likely to be detrimental to the amenity of the area and therefore outside this class[61] than a properly insulated building put to the same use. Account can be taken of the measures, such as noise insulation, which can, and customarily are, installed to control the polluting effect.[62]

In Class B2 of the Order, a general industrial use is for the carrying on of an industrial process other than one falling within Class B1 or one of the five Special Industrial Groups. In the case of a Class B2 building, noise could be detrimental to the amenities of the area.

The determination of what constitutes a Class B1 use may present the planning authority with some difficulty unless they have particular knowledge of the effects that certain machinery and processes can have in connection with noise emissions. Situations can often occur where badly designed factories and poorly laid out equipment cause environmental noise problems. Equally, good design and layout can result in minimal impact on the environment. The question therefore seems to rest on the word *can*. It can be

---

[60] See *W.T. Lamb Properties Ltd. v Secretary of State for the Environment* [1983] J.P.L. 303 where the building was adjacent to Gatwick Airport.

[61] See *Essex County Council v Secretary of State for the Environment* [1974] J.P.L. 286.

[62] *Blight & White Ltd. v Secretary of State for the Environment* [1993] 1 P.L.R.

helpful therefore, to avoid any conflicting views about a particular
class use, for the planning authority to consult the public health
authority to determine whether certain buildings are *capable of
operation* without causing detrimental noise problems. Close liaison
is essential to ensure correct judgment on planning applications and
it is useful for planners and Environmental Health Departments to
have regular meetings to consider planning applications which may
be a source of noise, e.g. industry, transport installations, airports
and places of entertainment. This liaison will help to determine the
correct use class to be applied, enable investigations to take place
into the detailed proposals so as to provide information on which to
base realistic noise controls in the planning consents, and also to see
if the development proposals are likely to entail works of construction
which ought to be controlled so as to minimise noise.[63]

Change of use
It is permissible to change from one use to another within the same
class use without the need for planning permission. However,
development will occur if there is a material change of use of the
building, land or structure, and planning permission will be required.
The interpretation of the term "material change of use" by the
courts has led to four criteria that have to be considered:

1. A distinction has to be drawn between the "primary" use of land
    and the ancillary uses which accompany it and are thus protected
    through their link with the primary use.

2. A change need not be a change to a different kind of use
    altogether (such as from residential to industrial) before it may
    be regarded as material, and changes in the "character" of a use
    may be sufficient.

3. A material change may occur where an existing use is
    "intensified", so that although the same description may still be
    applied to it, it has undergone a change in character.

4. The concept of the "planning unit" has evolved as a means of
    determining the most appropriate physical area against which
    to assess the material change.

---

[63] See generally Chapter 5, pp. 168–172 *ante*.

Planning and development

A number of decisions in the courts, although not necessarily concerned with particular noise problems, involve changes of use which could give rise to noise nuisance. They therefore have some relevance.

Birmingham Corporation v Minister of Housing and Local Government and Habib Ullah[64] – it was held that if a house, formerly occupied by a single family, is let out in flats to a number of families, there may be a material change as a matter of degree and fact, notwithstanding that the use of the house remains residential throughout.

Brooks and Burton v Secretary of State for the Environment[65] – there may be a material change of use where an existing use has become intensified.

London Borough of Newham v Secretary of State for the Environment[66] – in this case, planning permission which had been refused for conversion of houses into flats was granted on appeal. The council appealed to the High Court on the grounds that the inquiry inspector had failed to take into account a material consideration, namely the sound insulation requirements of the proposed development. The inspector had considered that sound insulation was generally a matter for environmental health legislation and not a planning matter. The appeal was upheld and it was clear that the noise problems created by the sub-division of a simple dwelling house were material considerations as they were attributable to the character of the use of the land.

Trio Thames v Secretary of State for the Environment and Reading Borough Council[67] – the Divisional Court held that where a building with planning permission for a "restaurant with dine and dance facilities" had come to be used as a night club and restaurant, the

---

[64] *Birmingham Corporation v Minister of Housing and Local Government and Habib Ullah* [1963] 3 All E.R. 668.

[65] *Brooks and Burton v Secretary of State for the Environment* [1977] 1 W.L.R. 1294.

[66] *London Borough of Newham v Secretary of State for the Environment* [1986] J.P.L. 607.

[67] *Trio Thames v Secretary of State for the Environment and Reading Borough Council* [1984] J.P.L. 183.

Secretary of State was right to regard the planning permission as one of a primary use for a restaurant and therefore not authorising a dual or mixed use for restaurant and night club.

Wallington v Secretary of State for Wales[68] – this case involved intensification of an ancillary use, where the keeping of 44 dogs had gone beyond the primary use of the private dwelling house involved. The court upheld an enforcement notice reducing the number of dogs being kept to six.

The Town and Country Planning (Use Classes) Order 1987 followed a review of the 1972 Order by the Property Advisory Group at the request of the Secretary of State. Although the 1987 Order generally provides that change within a use is not material, and therefore does not require planning permission, not all uses of land fall within the specified classes. Certain uses, most of which have the potential to cause environmental noise problems, are excluded from the provisions of the Order. These are amusement arcades or centres, funfairs, theatres, launderettes and dry cleaners (subject to some exceptions), sale of motor fuel and motor vehicles, car hire or taxi businesses, scrapyards and vehicle breakers. There are no reported cases of intensification of use relating to industrial noise.

The answer to the avoidance of problems in determining whether a material change of use has occurred may well be to impose conditions when planning permission is granted, preventing the use of the land from being changed from the use stated in the planning application. This can be done even though such other use is within the same use class as the use covered by the planning permission, and is not technically development at all.[69] However, the Secretary of State has, as a matter of policy, established a presumption against such conditions and will regard them as unreasonable unless there is clear evidence that the uses excluded would have serious effects on the environment or on amenity and are not susceptible to other control.[70] If a change of use is subsequently desired, it will be

[68] *Wallington v Secretary of State for Wales* [1990] J.P.L. 112.
[69] *Corporation of City of London v Secretary of State for the Environment and Another* [1971] 23 P. & C.R. 169. See also DoE Circular 1/85, paragraphs 66–71; DoE Circular 13/87, paragraph 12.
[70] Town and Country Planning Act 1990, s. 192.

necessary to submit a further planning application which can then be conditioned according to the proposed new use.

In cases where it is not clear whether a particular activity or change of use constitutes development, there is provision for the determination of doubtful cases by an application to the local planning authority. The application is for a Certificate as to the Lawfulness of the Proposed Development.[71]

Planning applications procedure

If the development proposed is not "permitted development" by virtue of the Town and Country Planning (General Permitted Development) Order 1995,[72] it will be necessary to obtain a formal grant of planning permission under the Town and Country Planning Act 1990.[73] Any applicant could usefully consult the various Planning Policy Guidance Notes. The method of applying for planning permission is dealt with partly in the Town and Country Planning (Applications) Regulations 1988[74] and partly in the Town and Country Planning (General Development Procedure) Order 1995.[75]

An application to a local planning authority must be made in the manner prescribed by regulations.[76] The application has to be made on a form issued by the local planning authority. There is no prescribed form. The application must contain the particulars required. It must be accompanied by a plan of the land and other plans, drawings and information necessary to describe the development. An application can be for outline or detailed planning permission. An application for outline permission may be made by a developer before he buys his land or incurs the cost of preparing detailed plans. He will then get to know if his proposals are likely to be acceptable in principle before incurring undue expense. Fees

---

71 Town and Country Planning Act 1990, s. 191.
72 S.I. 1995 No. 418.
73 s. 58(1)(b).
74 S.I. 1988 No. 1812.
75 S.I. 1995 No. 419.
76 Town and Country Planning Act 1990, s. 62 and S.I. 1988 No. 1812.

are payable with planning applications.[77] A local planning authority cannot charge a fee for time spent on consultations relating to proposed development.[78] A developer may wish to discuss noise issues with the authority's Environmental Health Department (a useful exercise to undertake in advance of a planning application).

An applicant for planning permission does not need to have a legal interest in the land to which the application relates. The application may be, and often is, made by a prospective developer. Therefore, development orders[79] provide for notice to be given of applications for planning permission. Of particular interest will be development involving "bad neighbour" development with the potential for causing environmental noise problems. In general, planning applications have to be publicised by the local planning authority. This must take the form of a local advertisement and a site display on or near the land in question for at least 21 days,[80] but is often supplemented by further local publicity using neighbour notification letters. In the case of planning applications requiring a formal environmental assessment under the Town and Country Planning (Environmental Impact Assessment) (England and Wales) Regulations 1999,[81] a site display for at least 21 days is required, together with a local advertisement. In the case of "major development", there is a similar advertisement requirement as well as a requirement to give notice of the proposals to any adjoining owner or occupier or to display a site notice. Any representations made to the local planning authority must be taken into account by the authority.[82] The types of defined major development most likely to produce noise problems include:

---

[77] Town and Country Planning Act 1990, s. 303 and the Town and Country Planning (Fees for Applications and Deemed Applications) Regulations 1989, S.I. 1989 No. 193.

[78] *McCarthy and Stone (Developments) Ltd. v Richmond upon Thames London Borough Council* [1991] 4 All E.R. 897.

[79] Currently the Town and Country Planning (General Permitted Development) Order 1995, S.I. 1995 No. 418.

[80] Town and Country Planning (General Development Procedure) Order 1995, S.I. 1995 No. 419, Art. 8.

[81] S.I. 1999 No. 293. See also the Channel Tunnel Rail Link (Assessment of Environmental Effects) Regulations 1999, S.I. 1999 No. 107.

[82] Town and Country Planning Act 1990, s. 71(2) and (2A).

(a) the winning and working of minerals or the use of land for mineral-working deposits;

(b) waste development (defined as any operational development designed to be used wholly or mainly for the purpose of, or a material change of use to, treating, storing, processing or disposing of refuse or waste materials).

Access to information on planning applications is also available to the general public by virtue of the Local Government (Access to Information) Act 1985. Access is available to decision-making committees, to agendas and reports and other related documents. The Environmental Information Regulations 1992[83] also impose a requirement on public authorities to provide information relating to the environment to anyone who requests it. This may include information relating to noise.

Determining planning applications

The majority of planning applications where noise is an issue will be those involving the introduction of noise-sensitive development into areas exposed to existing noise sources, e.g. major roads, aerodromes, railway lines and industrial sites. The Town and Country Planning Act 1990 requires that planning decisions have regard to the development plan, so far as it is material to the application, and to any other material considerations.[84] Where the development plan is material to the development proposal, the application, or subsequent appeal, must be determined in accordance with the plan, unless material considerations indicate otherwise.[85] A material consideration must be a proper planning consideration, i.e. regulating the development and use of the land in the public interest. Accordingly, matters such as the impact of noise on a neighbourhood will be material considerations.

When determining applications for development which will be exposed to an existing noise source, local planning authorities

---

[83] S.I. 1992 No. 3240, as amended by S.I. 1998 No. 1447.
[84] s. 70(2).
[85] s. 54A. See also P.P.G. 24 *Planning and Noise*, paragraph 2.

should take account of both the noise exposure at the time of the application and of any increase that may reasonably be expected in the future, i.e. noise levels forecast to be produced when the existing noise source is used to its full capacity. Any prediction that noise is likely to be reduced at some future date should be supported by a properly produced assessment. The local planning authority should not hesitate to require an applicant to provide information about the noise impact of a development or the assessed effect of an existing noise source on a proposed development.[86]

Many applications will require very detailed consideration and this may be essential in the case of large scale industrial development where factors such as noise, air pollution, nature conservation, traffic generation, large scale drainage schemes and associated matters have to be taken into account.[87] The liaison between relevant officers and authorities is even more important if such applications are to be processed in the requisite time period. Consideration of the noise implications will generally involve the Environmental Health Department whose action can be summarised:

1. Contact the developer to determine his detailed proposals regarding:

    (i) types of plant and equipment to be used and their noise output;

    (ii) the layout of noise producing equipment within the building;

    (iii) the type of building construction to be used so that the sound attenuation properties can be assessed;

    (iv) proposed arrangements for delivery of materials to and from the development after completion;

    (v) hours of work envisaged.

2. The layout of the site will be considered in detail to ensure that, as far as possible, recommendations can be made to ensure that

---

[86] The Town and Country Planning (Applications) Regulations 1988, Art. 4(a) and (b).

[87] But see pp. 339–344 for information on environmental assessment.

noisy activities are remote from site boundaries close to other noise sensitive development.

3. Noise level readings will usually be taken at or near the perimeter of the proposed development site together with readings near to existing sensitive development. These will establish the existing noise climate and will be used to assess the likely effect of the development on completion.

If the application contains sufficient detail, or the developer can provide adequate information, it will usually be possible to calculate the noise emission from the development and compare this information with existing levels. It can then be determined whether the predicted noise is likely to affect other people adversely. Accordingly, control over noise levels may be included as part of the planning consent. Care must be exercised on the manner in which these noise levels are specified to ensure that they can be readily understood and are "certain".[88] Alternatively, conditions may be imposed in terms of the use of the land, the structure of the building containing the noise or other forms of noise shielding.

In some cases, where outline permission is sought and adequate detail concerning noisy processes and machinery is not available, it may be necessary to condition the permission by specifying noise levels at the boundary of the development such as will avoid nuisance to other sensitive development in the area, or alternatively to make the consent conditional on the submission of a scheme to minimise noise to the satisfaction of the local planning authority who will no doubt be advised by its Environmental Health Department. Once outline permission has been granted, the planning authority is restricted to considering matters of detail.[89]

However, there are difficulties in using outline permission procedure in cases where environmental impact assessment is required because of the need to undertake a full assessment of the likely environmental

---

[88] *The use of conditions in planning permissions,* DoE Circular 11/95 (Welsh Office Circular 35/95), gives valuable advice.

[89] Defined as "reserved matters". Town and Country Planning (General Permitted Development) Order 1995, Arts. 1(2), (3) and (4); Town and Country Planning (Applications) Regulations 1988, Regs. 2 and 3(2).

effects. A basic outline application cannot comply with the requirements of the Town and Country Planning (Environmental Impact Assessment) (England and Wales) Regulations 1999.[90] Nevertheless, a way of addressing this issue by conditioning an outline planning permission was dealt with in the case of *R. v Rochdale Metropolitan Borough Council ex parte Milne*.[91]

It is important that the developer provides as soon as possible the detail on noise production so that his application can be processed quickly. The planning authority may well require the applicant to provide predictions of the corrected noise levels at the boundaries of the application site.[92]

Environmental assessment

Environmental assessment is the systematic evaluation of the environmental impact of a proposed project. In relation to decision making on major development proposals it is now well established. E.C. Directive 85/337, as amended by Directive 97/11, requires an environmental assessment to be carried out before planning consent is given for certain types of projects. The Directive's main aim is to ensure that the authority giving the primary consent for a particular project makes its decision in the knowledge of any potentially significant effects on the environment. The Directive sets out a procedure to be followed before the specified projects can be given "development consent". The Environmental Impact Assessment (E.I.A.) procedure draws together, in a systematic way, an assessment of a project's likely significant environmental

[90] S.I. 1999 No. 293.
[91] Unreported but cited in *Encyclopedia of Planning Law and Practice*, Sweet & Maxwell, Vol. 4, p. 39509. See also *Berkeley v Secretary of State for the Environment and Others* [2000] 3 All E.R. 1018, Q.B.D. In this appeal involving the 1988 Regulations, documents were submitted in support of a planning application which were purported to represent an environmental impact assessment, although they did not accord with the provisions of the Regulations. Although the planning authority supported the application and granted planning permission, which was upheld by the Secretary of State following a public enquiry, the House of Lords quashed the planning permission as the application had not been dealt with in accordance with the requirements of the Regulations.
[92] Town and Country Planning (Applications) Regulations 1988, Art. 4(a).

effects. It has been implemented by the Town and Country Planning (Environmental Impact Assessment) (England and Wales) Regulations 1999.[93] Crucial to this process is consultation between developers, the local planning authority and Environmental Health Departments with expertise in noise control. This consultation should then influence the design, layout, construction and type of plant and equipment used, so as to minimise the environmental noise impact.

Environmental assessment is compulsory if the particular development proposed is considered likely to have significant effects on the environment. The regulations list two sets of projects. Those in Schedule 1 *must* be subject to an environmental assessment, and include the carrying out of building or other operations or the change of use of buildings or other land (where a material change) to provide a crude oil refinery, certain types of large power station, radioactive storage or disposal facility, steel works, major chemical installation, major road, railway or aerodrome, a trading port and certain types of waste disposal and treatment facility. A lengthy list of projects in Schedule 2 requires an environmental assessment if the development would be likely to have significant effects on the environment by virtue of factors such as its nature, size or location. Where an environmental assessment is required, the likely effects of noise will be one of the considerations to be dealt with in the resultant environmental statement prepared by the developer and submitted with the planning application.[94]

For all Schedule 2 development, the local planning authority must make its own formal determination of whether or not E.I.A. is required. This is referred to in the Regulations and circular as a "screening opinion". This can be done before a planning application

---

[93] S.I. 1999 No. 293. These Regulations consolidate all previous Regulations on this subject. Similar provision is being made for Scotland and Northern Ireland.

[94] Reg. 3 requires the environmental information to be taken into account before granting planning permission. Development falling below the thresholds or meeting none of the criteria in the second column of the table in Sch. 2 does not require E.I.A. However, if small developments might give rise to significant environmental effects, the Secretary of State can use his powers of direction under Reg. 4(8) to direct that an E.I.A. is required.

is submitted[95] or afterwards.[96] In making the determination, the planning authority must take account of the relevant "selection criteria".[97] Developers may appeal to the Secretary of State for a "screening direction" where a local planning authority adopts a screening opinion that E.I.A. is required.[98] The authority must make all screening opinions and directions available for public inspection.[99] The selection criteria for Schedule 2 developments include:

Characteristics of development
1. The characteristics of development must be considered having regard, in particular to:

    (a) the size of the development;

    (b) the cumulation with other development;

    (c) pollution and nuisance.

Location of development
2. The environmental sensitivity of geographical areas likely to be affected by development must be considered, having regard, in particular, to:

    (a) the existing land use;

    (b) the absorption capacity of the natural environment …

Characteristics of the potential impact
3. The potential significant effects of development … having regard in particular to:

    (a) the extent of the impact;

    (b) the magnitude and complexity of the impact;

    (c) the probability of the impact;

---

[95] Reg. 5.
[96] Reg. 7.
[97] Sch. 3.
[98] Regs. 6 and 8.
[99] Reg. 20.

(d) the duration, frequency and reversibility of the impact.

An environmental statement must include specified information[100] which is defined as:

"1. Description of the development including in particular–

PART I
    (a) a description of the physical characteristics of the whole development and the land-use requirements during the construction and operational phases;

    (b) a description of the main characteristics of the production processes, for instance, nature and quantity of the materials used;

    (c) an estimate, by type and quantity, of ... emissions (... noise, vibration ...) resulting from the operation of the proposed development.

2.   An outline of the main alternatives studied by the applicant or appellant and an indication of the main reasons for his choice, taking into account the environmental effects.

3.   A description of the aspects of the environment likely to be significantly affected by the development ...

4.   A description of the likely significant effects of the development on the environment, which should cover the direct effects and any indirect, secondary, cumulative, short, medium and long-term, permanent and temporary, positive-negative effects of the development, resulting from:

    (a) the existence of the development;

    (b) the emission of pollutants, the creation of nuisance ... and the description by the applicant of the forecasting methods used to assess the effects on the environment.

---

[100] 1999 Regulations, Reg. 2(1) and Sch. 4, pt. 1. See also the advice in Circular 2/99, *Environmental Impact Assessment.*

5. A description of the measures envisaged to prevent, reduce and where possible offset any significant adverse effects on the environment.

6. A non-technical summary of the information ...

7. An indication of any difficulties (technical deficiencies or lack of know-how) ... in compiling the required information.

PART II
1. A description of the development ... site, design and size ...

2. A description of the measures envisaged in order to avoid, reduce and, if possible, remedy significant adverse effects.

3. The data required to identify and assess the main effects ... on the environment.

4. An outline of the main alternatives studied ... and an indication of the main reasons for the applicant's choice ...

5. A non-technical summary of the information."

Environmental Health Departments[101] can provide a valuable input into the environmental assessment process in a number of ways:

(a) advising on suitable noise monitoring locations;

(b) advising on existing local noise pollution problems;

(c) conducting noise surveys for departmental reference or inclusion in the environmental statement;

(d) carrying out predictive noise exercises to assess the developer's proposals and check the developer's own evaluation;

(e) advising on methods of mitigating noise;

(f) providing technical judgments to the planning committee on the environmental acceptability of a project;

---

[101] And the Environment Agency in respect of installations subject to Integrated Pollution Prevention and Control. See generally Chapter 7.

(g) suggesting appropriate planning conditions to ensure that noise problems do not occur if permission is granted.

It may be necessary to conduct a survey to determine noise emission limits. Agreement ought to be reached on noise measurement criteria for pre- and post-application evaluation.

A proper environmental assessment is a lengthy and complex process. It requires careful planning, covering as it does a wide range of environmental factors, of which noise is one. It must withstand rigorous examination by planning officers and their Environmental Health colleagues. The kind of development to which this type of assessment applies, especially the Schedule 1 activities, may well result in considerable objections from those people living in the neighbourhood of the development proposals. If so, there will be pressure on the local planning authority to refuse permission. Developers should anticipate such objections and seek to address them in the thoroughness of the assessment. A well structured and considerate public consultation exercise may enable the developer to gauge public reaction to the proposals and identify particular concerns which can then be specifically considered in the environmental statement. In assessing the potential impact of noise, those criteria likely to be used by the local planning authority should be taken into account.[102]

In its P.P.G. 24,[103] the Department of the Environment gives advice on some particular types of development, some of which will require environmental assessment in accordance with the regulations.

A number of general, commonsense principles can be extracted from P.P.G. 24 which are applicable to most situations:

(i) wherever practicable, noise-sensitive developments should be separated from major sources of noise;

(ii) new development involving noisy activities should, if possible, be sited away from noise-sensitive land uses;

---

[102] Referred to in specific chapters of this book. See also Environmental Assessment Circular 2/99, DoE.

[103] *Planning Policy Guidance: Planning and Noise*, P.P.G. 24, September 1994, H.M.S.O.

(iii) where such separation is not possible, local planning authorities should consider the use of planning conditions or planning obligations;

(iv) consideration should be given to the possible intrusion that may be caused by an intensification or change of use;

(iv) the character of industrial noise, e.g. sudden impulses, irregular noise and particular tonal qualities, should be considered in addition to the noise level;

(vi) proposals for noise-sensitive development should not normally be permitted in areas which are – or are expected to become – subject to unacceptably high noise levels, especially where high noise levels will continue throughout the night;

(vii) in residential development, people should expect a reasonable degree of peace in gardens and amenity areas.

Roads
In considering potential new development near major new or improved roads, future predicted noise levels, e.g. over 15 years, should be considered with the assistance of the local highway authority. Some new or improved roads may have been subject to predictions for the purposes of the Noise Insulation Regulations 1975[104] as amended by the Noise Insulation (Amendment) Regulations 1988.[105] For others, reference should be made to the *Calculation of Road Traffic Noise* manual.[106]

In preparing local plans, Part II of their U.D.P.s and dealing with their development control duties, local planning authorities should aim to ensure that noise sensitive developments are not sited close to roads with high levels of traffic noise. Any particular constraints on achieving this separation may have to be achieved by planning conditions or planning obligations,[107] e.g. using design features to

---

[104] S.I. 1975 No. 1763.
[105] S.I. 1988 No. 2000.
[106] Department of Transport, 1988.
[107] Town and Country Planning Act 1990, ss. 106, 106A and 106B. Often referred to as "planning gain" by achieving things that could not be covered by planning conditions.

act as noise barriers or limiting development to sound insulated dwellings or single aspect dwellings with gardens sited furthest away from the noise source.

Aircraft

The problem of aircraft noise[108] is a continuing area of concern for the public and local authorities, and careful consideration of development, particularly near to major international airports, is necessary as part of the long term planning process. The *Report of the Commission on the Third London Airport* (Roskill Report) concluded that "... aircraft will not have learned to live with people by the end of this century. We cannot base our site choice on the hope of a major reduction of aircraft noise at source at least for a long time ahead". Whilst noise from individual aircraft has been reduced,[109] aircraft noise overall remains a major issue, as reflected in the Government White Paper, *A New Deal for Transport: Better for Everyone*[110] and the advice contained in Planning Policy Guidance Note 13, *Transport.*[111]

Where land is, or is likely to become, subject to significant levels of aircraft noise, local planning authorities should determine approximately which areas are likely to fall within the different noise exposure categories. For major aerodromes, noise contours[112] are published to show noise exposure levels expressed in terms of L_{eq} dB(A). These contours are the best average description of exposure to noise produced by aircraft taking off and landing, having regard to the type of aircraft and the time of day. The contours are subject to regular variation as aircraft movements change and developing technology produces quieter aircraft. Aerodrome management generally produce noise contours which reflect long term predictions of air traffic. 60 dB(A) is regarded as a desirable upper limit for major new noise sensitive development. Local planning authorities will also need to have regard for arrival and departure routes which will usually comprise a wide corridor

---

[108] See Chapter 8, pp. 263–267 *ante.*
[109] See generally Chapter 8.
[110] Cmnd. 3950, July 1998, D.E.T.R.
[111] P.P.G. 13, *Transport*, 27th March 2001, para. 5–360.16.
[112] See Chapter 7.

of tracks to take account of operational and safety considerations. Noise contours and take-off and landing routes for the three London airports are available from the Department of Transport. At other major airports, the information will be available from the airport management.

If the construction of an aerodrome includes a runway length of 2,100 metres or more, an environmental assessment will be mandatory. Otherwise an assessment will be required if there are likely to be significant environmental effects. In general, the following matters should be considered:

(a) the effect of the proposal on environmental noise and the number of people likely to be affected;

(b) the effect of changes to the noise abatement flight paths;

(c) changes in hours of operation and the intensity of use;

(d) effects of noise from ground operations, e.g. engine testing, taxiing and auxiliary power units, and the impact of possible noise control measures;

(e) arrangements for monitoring compliance with proposals;

(f) public consultation arrangements.

The use of noise contours is not applicable to other than the major airports or those handling military aircraft where the Ministry of Defence has produced contours but night flying (particularly charter aircraft), training and club flights may all produce noise problems for people in the vicinity. In these latter cases, planning action cannot be used to control aircraft in flight as the object of planning control is related to the development of land. However, limitation of the number and type of aircraft using the airport or airfield, the hours of landing and taking off and ground running of engines may help avoid unnecessary disturbance.

Railways
Railway noise is associated with a variety of sources including operational railway lines (wheel/rail noise and locomotive noise),

marshalling operations and station activities including announcements. Both noise and vibration from railway tracks can be a particular problem and proposals for nearby residential development may require an assessment of the impact of the noise and vibration. Where levels are high, care will be needed to ensure that the construction and layout minimises the effects on noise-sensitive areas. The construction of railways requires an Environmental Impact Assessment.[113]

Construction and waste disposal sites
These activities are not permanent although waste disposal sites may operate for many years. Much of the noise will be generated by vehicular traffic and the varying hours of operation, particularly on construction sites, may well add to the annoyance. Noise may be controllable by planning conditions but restrictions using Part III of the Control of Pollution Act 1974 may also be appropriate. In this respect P.P.G. 24 refers to BS5228, dealing with noise control on construction and open sites, which provides valuable guidance on practical noise control measures.[114] Waste disposal sites are required to have a waste management licence issued under Part II of the Environmental Protection Act 1990. An essential prerequisite is a valid planning permission. The licence may also condition activities in a manner likely to control noise emissions, e.g. by limiting hours of operation and the frequency of deliveries to the site. Noise control from mineral extraction is dealt with in the DoE's Minerals Planning Guidance Note No. 11, *The Control of Noise at Surface Mineral Workings.*

Sporting and recreational activities
For these activities, which include open air pop concerts, the local planning authority will have to take account of how frequently the noise will be generated and how disturbing it will be, and balance the enjoyment of the participants against nuisance to other people. For open air events, selection of a suitable site may be difficult. It

---

[113] Under Sch. 1 of the Town and Country Planning (Environmental Impact Assessment) (England and Wales) Regulations 1999 where they are "long-distance". Otherwise in accordance with Sch. 2 where the area of works exceeds 1 hectare.
[114] See generally Chapter 5.

may be possible to use an already noisy site, e.g. next to a main road, or a location well away from noise sensitive development may be more appropriate. Many operating bodies publish codes of practice giving useful guidance on noise control measures appropriate to particular sporting activities. If a noisy activity in the open air is covered by the permitted development rights in Article 3 and Schedule 2 of the Town and Country (General Permitted Development) Order 1995, planning control will not be available unless a direction is made removing those rights in accordance with Article 4 of the Order. The activity will be subject to control under the relevant statutory nuisance provisions and may also require licensing under the law relating to the licensing of public or private entertainment.[115]

Industrial and commercial premises
The impact that bad planning can make on the noise climate in an area should not be underestimated. The introduction of industry into a residential area, if not properly considered and controlled, can result in environmental pollution having adverse effects that may not subsequently be controlled sufficiently by other statutory powers. The introduction of noisy businesses requires very careful consideration. The effect that a particular type of activity may have in any area is best left to Environmental Health Departments who generally have staff with the training and experience to give advice, or to consultants. It is as important to ensure that new industry or commerce does not cause annoyance in existing residential areas, as it is to protect new residential or other noise sensitive development from the effects of existing industrial or other noise producing activities.[116]

Many planning authorities will have designated areas specifically for industrial use in their structure, local and unitary development

---

[115] See generally Chapter 3.
[116] Notwithstanding this, the Government is increasingly promoting "mixed use" areas, i.e. housing, shops, offices, entertainment, etc., all in close proximity and often in the same area or building. If such development is to take place, it will present significant challenges to ensure that such mixed activities can operate in harmony. Indeed, it may also require far different expectations from the occupiers of residential properties close to noisier activities. The author is not optimistic!

plans. Also, residential development may well be planned close to such areas. It should not be automatically presumed that the allocation of land in this way makes it suitable for any type of development. Applications for planning permission to develop land are refused at times because the development proposed does not conform with the development plan.

This would usually be only one of a number of reasons for refusal and it is important to ensure that adjacent land uses do not conflict. In considering development where this kind of conflict may arise, the following matters should be considered and, where appropriate, consent conditions should be formulated taking these factors into account:[117]

1. The use of some form of noise barrier between the noise source and the nearest sensitive development. These can include:

    (i) areas of open space suitably landscaped;

    (ii) the use of suitable acoustic barriers or sound insulation, e.g. the use of a solid factory wall designed to give appropriate sound attenuation. Although sound insulation measures can reduce noise to acceptable levels inside buildings, people may also reasonably expect peaceful enjoyment of amenity areas such as gardens;

    (iii) the construction of earth barriers (again properly designed and landscaped) to provide both a noise and visual barrier. It must be recognised that the use of earth barriers and tree screens will not be effective unless properly designed. The use of tree screens is not generally effective in reducing noise unless the trees are very dense and of the evergreen kind;[118]

    (iv) on industrial estates, buildings which generally have a lower noise output, e.g. warehouses and light industrial

---

[117] See also DoE Circular 11/95, *The Use of Conditions in Planning Permissions*.
[118] "A review of the influence of meteorological conditions on sound propagation", Ingard, U., *Journal of the Acoustical Society of America Vol. 75*, May 1953.

buildings, may be sited between the most noisy factories and the nearest sensitive development. Provided the buildings intended to act as barriers are of sufficient size and located so that they do not reflect sound towards areas it is intended to protect, they can be a useful means of control.

2. Noise and vibration arising from traffic using industrial development will be a mixture of light vehicles (employees' cars, small vans) and heavy traffic (articulated vehicles transporting materials). Careful siting of entrances and loading areas is essential to avoid disturbance to adjacent properties. Internal traffic circulatory systems should also be designed to consider both safety and the effects of noise outside the development.

3. Good design of buildings is essential. Development designed to minimise the impact of noise on people in the surrounding area need not cost any more to construct than that in which noise is not properly considered. The arrangement of noisy equipment and activities away from noise sensitive boundaries of the development will offer significant noise reduction and the incorporation of adequate sound attenuation features will minimise noise emissions. It is important therefore to know what the noise emissions from the various types of plant and machinery are likely to be.

4. Noise emissions should be calculated and the likely effect on nearby noise sensitive development predicted. P.P.G. 24 suggests the use of the BS4142:1997 – *Method for Rating Industrial Noise affecting mixed residential and industrial areas* to assess the effect of noise emission from industrial and commercial developments. In relation to the assessment of transportation noise, the P.P.G. advocates the use of well-established criteria derived from research into the effects of such noise on people. Care is necessary, as adherence to these recommendations will not necessarily mean that complaints will not subsequently arise, and these recommendations should only be used as a *guide*. In fact, the introduction of new noise

sources into an area is likely to result in a creeping growth of the ambient noise level and a consequent deterioration in the quality of the environment, even though each of the new noise sources, considered separately against BS4142:1997, would not be liable to give rise to complaints. The P.P.G. gives examples of conditions that planning authorities may wish to consider in setting conditions to any planning consent.

Other important factors to take into account in setting conditions are given below. If these are not given proper consideration, planning permission may not give the desired control and situations may arise where noise requires action under other statutory law, e.g. Environmental Protection Act 1990.

(i)   Where noisy processes are included in the development, the noise control features that have been incorporated in the design should be *constructed before these processes are put into use.* If this is not done an intolerable situation can arise for people exposed to the noise. It is understandable that where high capital costs are incurred, industry will wish to complete those parts of its proposals that will provide a return on expenditure as soon as possible. Consent conditions must therefore ensure that screen walls, earth barriers and other noise control features are among the first works to be carried out. Care should be exercised in considering specifications for noise screens or barriers, as although these may be suitable for the initial use to which premises are put, permissible changes of activity may occur which do not require planning approval. Such changes could result in increased noise which is not as effectively controlled by the screening originally installed. The use of planning obligations[119] as well as planning conditions may well have a role in the control of noise.

(ii) In conjunction with the above, it may be useful to control noise at the boundary of the site so as to prevent complaints of nuisance. The ways in which this can be done are numerous

---

[119] Town and Country Planning Act 1990, s. 106. See also Circular 1/97, *Planning Obligations* (applicable to England) and Welsh Office Circular 13/97.

and include control over peak noise levels, establishment of a level related to pre-existing ambient levels and control of noise levels at certain times of day. The Environmental Health Department should always be consulted on the appropriate method of control related to the local circumstances. Care must be taken to avoid conflict with any proposals of the local authority to control noise from the development under the Noise Abatement Zone provisions of the Control of Pollution Act 1974.[120]

(iii) Certain activities are inherently noisy and may be difficult to control satisfactorily by setting noise levels, e.g. transport movements, certain types of press and stamping work, and use of internal loudspeaker systems. In such cases, if it is not possible to exercise control by careful siting of equipment, noise level control or building design, consideration may be given either to refusing the application for that particular activity or controlling the hours of operation so that especially noisy events do not occur when the adverse effect is likely to be greater, e.g. restriction to daytime operations and weekdays only.

(iv) Certain changes within the same class use may occur and, although not requiring planning permission, they may be inherently more noisy than another industry in the same class. For example, the old Class B4 (Special Industrial Group B)[121] includes: "(b) converting, refining, heating, annealing, hardening, melting, carburising, forging or casting metals or alloys, other than pressure die casting, and (e) pickling or treating of metal in use." Clearly the processes in (b) are inherently noisier than those in (e) but the changes of process can take place without the need for planning permission.[122]

---

[120] s. 67 provides for control of new development occurring in an operative Noise Abatement Zone.

[121] Town and Country Planning (Use Classes) Order 1987, S.I. 1987 No. 764, as variously amended.

[122] The Order as amended now includes only two Class B uses; the concept of "special industrial use" disappears, to be replaced by Class B2 General Industrial Use.

However, the 1995 Order[123] revoked the special industrial classes. The permitted development under the Order now makes no specific reference to what might otherwise be termed a special industrial use and the standard conditions specified in the Order as applying to the various classes of permitted development have little to say about environmental pollution (including noise) controls. It would, therefore, appear necessary in cases where a development is permitted by the Order but likely to result in significant environmental noise problems, to rely on the powers of the Secretary of State or the local planning authority to give a direction[124] that the development proposed shall not be carried out unless permission is granted on application or, if appropriate, to require an environmental impact assessment.[125] It may therefore be desirable to restrict the permission to allow only the activities to be carried on for which the application is made. Any change would then require a fresh application and the new proposals could be properly assessed.

In deciding to grant planning permission subject to conditions, the planning authority cannot do just as they please. Section 70 of the 1990 Act allows conditions to be imposed "as they think fit" from a planning viewpoint and those conditions must not only have regard to the development plan but also to any other material considerations.[126] Noise is clearly a material consideration.

If the planning authority considers that the predicted noise is likely to cause a statutory nuisance and that planning conditions or obligations will not resolve the situation, planning permission should normally be refused. There will be cases where there is less

---

[123] S.I. 1995 No. 418.

[124] Art. 4(1).

[125] Town and Country Planning (Environmental Impact Assessment) (England and Wales) Regulations 1999, S.I. 1999 No. 293, as amended by S.I. 1999 No. 416 and S.I. 2000 No. 2867.

[126] There are tests to be applied to any condition proposed to be attached to a consent. They are: is it necessary; is it relevant to planning; is it relevant to the development to be permitted; is it enforceable; is it precise; is it reasonable?

certainty about the situation. In such cases, if planning permission is granted, remedial action may only be available under the statutory nuisance provisions of Part III of the Environmental Protection Act 1990.[127] However, a planning consent which changes the character of a neighbourhood may make nuisance proceedings more difficult to uphold.[128]

NOISE EXPOSURE CATEGORIES FOR DWELLINGS

In assessing proposals for new noise sensitive development, the Noise Review Working Party 1990 thought it would be preferable to set a range of noise levels which would provide guidelines for authorities responsible for assessing such proposals. The Working Party proposed the idea, put forward by the Building Research Establishment, of using "Action Levels". These have been translated in P.P.G. 24 *Planning and Noise* into four Noise Exposure Categories (N.E.C.s) ranging from Noise Exposure Category A – for proposals in this category noise need not be considered as a determining factor – to Noise Exposure Category D: for proposals in this category planning permission should normally be refused. Rather than use the traditional indices to describe noise from different sources, all noise levels are expressed in the P.P.G. in terms of $L_{Aeq,T}$ over the periods 07.00–23.00 or 23.00–07.00.

Noise Exposure Categories are only intended to be used when considering new residential development near to an existing noise source. They are not intended for when a new noise source is proposed in a residential area as the P.P.G. advises that, in general, developers are under no statutory obligation to offer noise protection measures to existing dwellings which will be affected by a proposed new noise source.

A recommended range of noise levels for each of the N.E.C.s is given for dwellings exposed to noise from road, rail, air and "mixed sources". These are tabled overleaf:

---

[127] In relation to England and Wales.
[128] See *Gillingham Borough Council v Medway (Chatham) Dock Co. Ltd. and Others* [1992] 3 All E.R. 923; [1992] 3 W.L.R. 449, Q.B.D.

RECOMMENDED NOISE EXPOSURE CATEGORIES FOR
NEW DWELLINGS NEAR EXISTING NOISE SOURCES

Noise levels[0] corresponding to the Noise Exposure Categories for new dwellings $L_{Aeq,T}$ dB				
	Noise Exposure Category			
Noise source	**A**	**B**	**C**	**D**
road traffic 07.00 – 23.00 23.00 – 07.00[1]	<55 <45	55 – 63 45 – 57	63 – 72 57 – 66	>72 >66
rail traffic 07.00 – 23.00 23.00 – 07.00[1]	<55 <45	55 – 66 45 – 59	66 – 74 59 – 66	>74 >66
air traffic[2] 07.00 – 23.00 23.00 – 07.00[1]	<57 <48	57 – 66 48 – 57	66 – 72 57 – 66	>72 >66
mixed sources[3] 07.00 – 23.00 23.00 – 07.00[1]	<55 <45	55 – 63 45 – 57	63 – 72 57 – 66	>72 >66

Notes

[0] **Noise levels:** the noise level(s) ($L_{Aeq,T}$) used when deciding the N.E.C. of a site should be representative of typical conditions.

[1] **Night-time noise levels (23.00 – 07.00):** sites where individual noise events regularly exceed 82 dB L_{Amax} (S time weighting) several times in any hour should be treated as being in N.E.C. C, regardless of the $L_{Aeq,8h}$ (except where the $L_{Aeq,8h}$ already puts the site in N.E.C. D).

[2] **Aircraft noise:** daytime values accord with the contour values adopted by the Department of Transport which relate to levels measured 1.2 m above open ground. For the same amount of noise energy, contour values can be up to 2 dB(A) higher than those of other sources because of ground reflection effects.

[3] **Mixed sources:** this refers to any combination of road, rail, air and industrial noise sources. The "mixed source" values are based on the

lowest numerical values of the single source limits in the table. The "mixed source" N.E.C.s should only be used where no individual noise source is dominant.

To check if any individual noise source is dominant (for the purposes of this assessment), the noise level from the individual sources should be determined and then combined by decibel addition (remembering first to subtract 2 dB(A) from any aircraft noise contour values). If the level of any one source then lies within 2 dB(A) of the calculated combined value, that source should be taken as the dominant one and the site assessed against the appropriate N.E.C. for that source, rather than using the "mixed source" N.E.C.s.

If the contribution of the individual noise sources to the overall noise level cannot be determined by measurement and/or calculation, then the overall measured level should be used and the site assessed against the N.E.C.s for "mixed sources".

Having assessed a proposal for residential development near a noise source and determined into which of the Noise Exposure Categories the proposed site falls, local planning authorities are expected to have regard to the advice in the appropriate N.E.C. as shown below:

N.E.C.	
A	Noise need not be considered as a determining factor in granting planning permission, although the noise level at the high end of the category should not be regarded as a desirable level.
B	Noise should be taken into account when determining planning applications and, where appropriate, conditions imposed to ensure an adequate level of protection against noise.
C	Planning permission should not normally be granted. Where it is considered that permission should be given, for example because there are no alternative quieter sites available, conditions should be imposed to ensure a commensurate level of protection against noise.
D	Planning permission should normally be refused.

Speculative development

This type of development can present particular problems as the developer may have no idea of the type of future activity that will take place in the buildings and on the land. Accordingly, the type of structure and layout may be unsatisfactory for certain industries. Considerable care is therefore necessary in setting conditions on any planning permission to protect the interests of people in adjoining buildings. The speculative developer may not be particularly concerned about the conditions as they are attached to the land and not to him. However, revised enforcement powers in the 1991 Act enable the local planning authority to serve "breach of condition" notices.[129] These are served on the person responsible for the breach and therefore the developer may be subject to further action.

Publicity

Article 8 of the Town and Country Planning (General Development Procedure) Order 1995 specifies the publicity requirements for planning applications. In its Circular 15/92, *Publicity for Planning Applications*,[130] the Department of the Environment draws attention to those matters relating to the publicity requirements for certain types of development. The General Permitted Development Order defines "major" developments, requiring either site notices or neighbour notification and, in either case, a newspaper advertisement. The circular states that it is the responsibility of the local planning authority to decide, on a case by case basis, which developments falling outside the "major" category are likely to create wider concern. It suggests that such developments may warrant newspaper advertising in addition to either site notices or neighbour notification. The likely types of such development include:

(a) those affecting nearby property by causing noise ... vibration;

(b) those attracting crowds, traffic and noise into a generally quiet area;

---

[129] Town and Country Planning Act 1990, s. 187A.

[130] Strangely, not replaced to reflect changes in the law relating to such matters.

(c) those causing activity and noise during unsocial hours.

Where a planning application is accompanied by an environmental statement under the Town and Country Planning (Environmental Impact Assessment) (England and Wales) Regulations 1999, the local planning authority has to publicise the application and the statement. If the environmental statement is submitted after the planning application, the developer has to publicise the statement.

PLANNING CONDITIONS

Well considered conditions on a planning permission are invaluable in controlling noise. Equally, uncertain and imprecise conditions can make noise control through planning conditions very difficult. Department of the Environment Circular 11/95, *The use of conditions in planning permissions* and P.P.G. 24 *Planning and Noise* contain invaluable advice on the use of conditions and include useful models of acceptable conditions.

Section 70 of the Town and Country Planning Act 1990 allows the local planning authority, in granting planning permission, to impose "such conditions as they think fit". This power is not as wide as it seems and has to be interpreted having regard to legal decisions on what is reasonable. In practice, it is essential that developers liaise with local planning officers and their environmental health colleagues. This will enable an applicant to take account of their requirements in formulating the development proposals in advance of submitting a planning application. This will increase the likelihood of the proposals being approved and should limit the need for extensive noise control conditions. The value of such prior consultation should not be underestimated.

Conditions should usually be consistent with national planning policies, as contained in Government circulars, Planning Policy Guidance Notes and other published material. The Secretary of State has established the criteria to be applied in setting down planning conditions. They should only be imposed where they are:

(a) necessary;

(b) relevant to planning;

(c) relevant to the development to be permitted;

(d) enforceable;

(e) precise;

(f) reasonable in all other respects.

A condition should not be imposed unless there is a need for it and conditions should be used to deal with specific noise problems, e.g. the noise attenuation standards for a building or limiting aircraft take-off and landing during certain hours. Some matters may be capable of control under other legislation but, although it has been suggested that planning conditions should not normally be used to secure objectives achievable under other legislation,[131] prevention is obviously better than cure and noise control will be cheaper if considered and implemented at the development stage. In the case of *London Borough of Newham v Secretary of State for the Environment and East London Housing Association Ltd.*[132] it was argued that the matter of sound insulation in a proposed conversion of houses into flats was generally a matter for environmental health legislation and not a planning matter. It was also argued that the likelihood of noise being emitted within a building so that noise from one flat might disturb the occupants of another, was not a material consideration. In discussing the appeal, the court implicitly held that noise control conditions could legally be imposed, as paragraph 19 of Circular 1/85[133] advocated the use of such conditions in particular circumstances. This is logical as the granting of planning permission is the sensible stage at which to impose sound insulation requirements. This decision is also consistent with the Department of the Environment's views in the P.P.G. on planning and noise in which it says that the planning system should ensure that, wherever practicable, noise-sensitive developments are separated from major sources of noise. Where it is not possible to achieve such separation, local planning authorities should consider

---

[131] *Planning Policy Guidance: General Policy and Principles,* P.P.G. 1, February 1997 (England only).
[132] *London Borough of Newham v Secretary of State for the Environment and East London Housing Association Ltd.* [1986] J.P.L. 605.
[133] Now Circular 11/95.

control through the use of conditions or planning obligations. Circular 11/95 advises[134] that "... local planning authorities should consider whether it is practicable to control or reduce noise levels, or to mitigate the impact of noise, through the use of conditions or planning obligations." This is quite clearly a case for preventing a statutory noise nuisance by the imposition of noise control conditions.

Noise control conditions must be enforceable. It is no good setting noise levels that cannot be measured, for example because they are significantly below existing background levels, or without stating the measurement location and measurement criteria. Unless there is certainty and precision in the requirements, they will be unenforceable. A condition may be unreasonable if it is unduly restrictive, although it would usually be reasonable to restrict the hours of an industrial use if the activity outside those hours would create noise problems. However, it would be unreasonable to control hours to such an extent as to make it impossible for the occupier to run his business properly.[135]

Because of the general presumption against restrictions on permitted development or on changes of use that are not development, care should be taken in imposing restrictions on further development on a site. It would not usually be right to control noise using a condition restricting uses if an alternative, specific condition, e.g. restricting noise levels emitted from the site, would achieve the same end.[136]

Section 70(1) of the Town and Country Planning Act 1990, as conditioned by section 72(1)(b), provides a power to impose conditions requiring that a use be discontinued after a specified period. Where an application for permanent planning permission is made for a use which may be a "bad neighbour" to existing noise sensitive uses but there is insufficient evidence to enable the authority to be sure of its character or effect, it may be appropriate to grant a temporary permission. This should be an infrequently used control in relation to potentially noisy activities, as there is a

---

[134] Paragraph 77.
[135] See *Gillingham Borough Council v Medway (Chatham) Dock Co. Ltd. and Others* [1992] 3 All E.R. 923; [1992] 3 W.L.R. 449, Q.B.D.
[136] See Circular 11/95, Appx. A, for examples of acceptable noise conditions.

power to require whatever additional information may be needed to determine an application.[137]

ENFORCEMENT OF PLANNING CONTROL

Section 172 of the Town and Country Planning Act 1990 allows a local planning authority to issue an enforcement notice in any instance where it appears that there has been a breach of planning control.[138] This includes development which fails to comply with conditions attached to a planning consent and will therefore include failure to comply with noise control requirements. Action has generally to be taken between four and ten years from the date of the breach, depending on the nature of the breach, although in some cases action must be taken before the expiration of four years.

The authority may issue an enforcement notice if it appears that it is expedient to do so having regard to the provisions of the development plan and to any other material considerations.[139] An enforcement notice must specify the matters alleged to be a breach of planning control, together with the steps needed to remedy the breach, including "... remedying any injury to amenity caused by the development".[140] The notice may, for example, require[141] the alteration of any buildings and stop any activity being carried on except as specified. This would seem to include the possibility of requiring sound insulation works, or stopping noisy activities outside specified hours.

In such cases, if a noise nuisance exists, the local planning authority may wish to consider whether action under the statutory nuisance provisions of the Environmental Protection Act 1990 or Noise Abatement Zone provisions of the Control of Pollution Act 1974, if appropriate, would bring about a speedier resolution to the problem. It should be recognised that, even if enforcement action is taken by the planning authority in connection with breaches of planning control, it may still be necessary for the Environmental

---

[137] Town and Country Planning (Applications) Regulations 1988, Art. 4(a).
[138] Defined in s. 171A.
[139] s. 172(1)(b).
[140] s. 173(4). "Amenity" will presumably include noise.
[141] s. 173(5).

Health Department to proceed under the statutory nuisance powers. Enforcement action may be prolonged and could take a considerable time before any particular matter is determined by the Secretary of State on appeal. It will usually be possible for action taken under the Environmental Protection Act 1990 to be completed much earlier. If the planning authority's grounds for enforcement action are mainly failure to comply with noise conditions, then the grounds for such action could be weakened by alternative action to control noise nuisance under the Environmental Protection Act 1990. This must be accepted as a risk, as although it is a *discretionary* power to take enforcement action, a local authority has a *mandatory* duty to serve notice in respect of noise nuisance.

This dilemma is addressed in P.P.G. 18, *Enforcing Planning Control.* In its advice on the general approach to enforcement,[142] it says that local planning authorities should be guided by:

(a) whether enforcement action may be necessary in the public interest;

(b) there may be "maladministration" if the authority fails to take effective enforcement which is plainly necessary;

(c) whether the breach of control would unacceptably affect public amenity or the existing use of land meriting protection in the public interest;

(d) it would usually be inappropriate to take formal action against a technical or trivial breach which causes no harm to local amenity.

The guidance note also suggests that it may be appropriate to consider whether the environmental health authority is better able to take action. This may well be the best course of action in the case of a statutory noise nuisance.

In cases where these alternative courses of action exist, it should be made quite clear that in serving notice under the Environmental

---

[142] December 1991, para. 5. For Wales, see Technical Advice Note (Wales) 9, *Enforcing Planning Control* (1997). See also DoE Circular 10/97, *Enforcing Planning Control.*

Protection Act 1990 to abate a noise nuisance, the local authority is not condoning contraventions of planning control and that the person responsible, before carrying out works, should consider whether or not he would be better advised to discontinue the use giving rise to the noise nuisance, rather than waste money on carrying out works which may well prove to be abortive if effective enforcement action is taken against him. This particular kind of situation strengthens the need for co-operation between planning enforcement officers and Environmental Health Departments to ensure that there should be no misunderstanding concerning the requirements of the Environmental Protection Act 1990.

Stop notices

Under section 183 of the Town and Country Planning Act 1990, the local planning authority has power to serve a "stop notice". The stop notice may prohibit any specified activity which is, or is included in, a matter alleged in an enforcement notice to constitute a breach of planning control.[143] There are certain exceptions in respect of buildings used as dwelling houses, and continuation of any activity which commenced more than four years earlier, unless the activity is, or is incidental to, building, engineering, mining or other operations or the deposit of refuse or waste.

Stop notices will generally be considered when unauthorised development has taken place and the local planning authority considers that the breach of control took place in full knowledge that planning permission was required; the person responsible for the breach refuses to submit a planning application; and, most

---

[143] s. 183(1). There is no limit to the number of stop notices that can be served or be effective at any one time, and there is no duty of consultation prior to service. See *R. v Hounslow London Borough Council ex parte Dooley* [2000] J.P.L., Q.B.D., pp. 750–752. For an interesting compensation case involving noise from moto-cross scramble meetings, see *Bolton v North Dorset D.C.* (1997) 74 P. & C.R. 73 (Lands Tribunal: J.C. Hill, F.R.I.C.S.). This did not involve stop notices but related to the withdrawal of permitted development rights for the holding of moto-cross meetings and making express planning permission necessary for such development. Planning permission was then refused and compensation sought for the refusal of planning permission formerly granted by the development order. The applicant's claim was upheld.

importantly, the breach is causing serious harm to public amenity in the neighbourhood of the site. The procedure allows an authority to impose a ban, almost immediately, on activities being carried on in breach of planning control.

A stop notice can only be served when the local planning authority has served an enforcement notice and before the expiry of the time period for compliance, and the activity prohibited by the notice must be included as a matter alleged by the enforcement notice to constitute a breach of planning control. It can relate to the whole of a building operation or use, or alternatively to a particular activity which forms part of that operation or use. Clearly this could involve activities producing noise. No appeal against the stop notice exists as such, it stands or falls with the enforcement notice to which it relates. Generally, if a stop notice is withdrawn or quashed on appeal, the local planning authority will be liable to pay compensation for loss or damage directly attributable to the prohibition in the stop notice.[144] The circular[145] accompanying the Act gives valuable advice on the use of stop notices and some of the principle points are summarised below.

Circular 10/97
Subject to some limited exceptions, a stop notice may prohibit any, or all, of the activities comprising the breach of planning control alleged in the related enforcement notice. The prohibition can be directed at a use of land that is ancillary, or incidental, to the main use of the land, or a particular activity taking place only on part of the land specified in the enforcement notice, or an intermittent or seasonal activity.

The compensation provisions of the 1990 Act make it clear that no compensation is payable in respect of the prohibition in a stop notice of any activity which, *at any time when the notice is in force,* constitutes or contributes to a breach of planning control.[146]

Once the local planning authority has decided to serve a stop notice,

---

[144] s. 186.
[145] 10/97, England only. For Wales, see Technical Advice Note (Wales) 9, *Enforcement of Planning Control* (1997).
[146] s. 186(5)(a).

it must act speedily and effectively. The Planning and Legal Departments must be clear about their individual responsibilities for preparing the notice, serving it and assessing its practical effect. Service of a stop notice is an infrequent occurrence and it will usually be best to maintain the essential knowledge in a small group of officers. When the decision to serve the notice has been taken, implementation becomes top priority. The effect of serving the notice will usually be to stop the breach of control, or the specified activity, almost immediately. A quick and thorough assessment of the possible costs and benefits of a stop notice should therefore be carried out. The costs to the recipient may vary from relatively cheap modifications to a production process, to the cessation of a business and its impact on jobs, contracts and future viability. The effect of prohibiting a particular activity should, therefore, be carefully examined, e.g. prohibition of a noisy but essential production process could result in the complete cessation of manufacturing activity.

Section 183(1) and (2) of the 1990 Act allows a stop notice to be directed at any activity specified in the enforcement notice, or any part of an activity, or any associated activity. Accordingly, the local planning authority should ensure that a stop notice prohibits only what is essential to safeguard amenity or public safety, or prevent serious or irreversible harm to the environment. Excessive noise could well be an amenity issue which could give rise to a stop notice, although action under the statutory nuisance procedures of the Environmental Protection Act 1990 will generally be the preferred alternative. In deciding whether to serve a stop notice, the local planning authority should consider how many people are likely to benefit from the action and the impact on their amenities if it is not served. A stop notice must specify the date when it is to come into effect and this must be between 3 and 28 days from the date on which it is first served.

Action in default

Where an enforcement notice is not complied with, the local authority, according to the circumstances of the case, may enter on the land and do what the notice requires under section 178 of the

1990 Act, institute a prosecution for penalties under section 179, or seek an injunction restraining contravention of the notice. A person wilfully obstructing someone exercising the default powers is liable on summary conviction to a fine not exceeding level 3 on the standard scale.

Penalties

Additional to the power of the local planning authority to take default action, where the enforcement notice requires steps to be taken, the owner of the land at the time of service of the notice, if the steps are not taken, will be liable to a fine up to £20,000 on summary conviction, or an unlimited fine on conviction on indictment.[147] Similar penalties apply to failure to comply with a stop notice.

PLANNING APPEALS

Section 78 of the Town and Country Planning Act 1990 provides a right of appeal to the Secretary of State within such period as is specified in the development order[148] or such longer period as may be agreed by the applicant and the authority, against a decision of the planning authority. The appeal can be lodged generally against a refusal to grant planning permission for development or the conditions associated with a grant of permission. Section 174 contains similar provisions for appeals against enforcement notices.

A number of appeal cases serve to illustrate the attitude of the Secretary of State to particular noise issues.

Potential noise nuisance is a planning consideration[149]
This case involved an appeal against an enforcement notice relating to the development of a boules pitch and extension of a car park at a public house. The activities resulted in the service of an abatement notice under the Control of Pollution Act 1974, in respect of noise in the garden area of the public house. The result of that action is not

---

[147] s. 179.
[148] See ss. 59 and 336(1). Subject also to Arts. 6 and 7 of the Town and Country Planning (General Permitted Development) Order 1995.
[149] [1985] J.P.L. 567.

recorded. In determining the appeal it was said in the decision notice "... the potential noise nuisance arising from the development the subject of the inquiry is ... properly a planning consideration". The decision reflected the inquiry inspector's view that additional noise and disturbance to local residents caused by spectators, and the likely additional noise associated with a proposed car park, were unreasonable in the residential surroundings.

Noise from a motorway near to residential development[150]
In two cases, the inquiry inspector referred to the severe exposure to motorway noise, agreeing to restrict development so that no dwelling was subject to an external noise level in excess of 68 dB(A) on the L_{10} index. He recommended limiting such development to part of the site, redesign of the site and/or erection of suitable noise barriers.

Planning permission refused for conversion of houses into flats[151]
The council refused planning permission for the conversion of several two-storey houses into flats. On appeal, the inspector allowed each conversion. The council appealed to the High Court to have the decision quashed on the grounds that the inspector failed to take into account a material consideration, i.e. the sound insulation requirements of the proposed development. The inspector had decided that sound insulation was generally an environmental health matter, not one for planning legislation. All parties to the case accepted that the proposed change of use could cause additional noise disturbance. It was held that *the issue of sound insulation was a material consideration* and the inspector had failed to take account of the advice in Circular 1/85,[152] *The Use of Conditions in Planning Permissions.*

NOISE FROM PUBLIC INFRASTRUCTURE

The value to the country of public infrastructure, such as airports and new roads, is clear. To those people living close to these works,

---

[150] [1975] J.P.L. 110 and 111.
[151] *London Borough of Newham v Secretary of State for the Environment and Another* [1986] J.P.L. 607.
[152] Now Circular 11/95.

however, there is likely to be a distinct disbenefit and depreciation of the value of their property resulting from their use. That depreciation has been termed "injurious affection".[153]

Depreciation

The Land Compensation Act 1973 provides[154] a right of compensation where the value of a person's interest in land is depreciated by certain physical factors caused by the use of public works. The factors involved include noise and vibration[155] and the public works are: any highway, any aerodrome and any other public works on the land provided or used in the exercise of statutory powers.[156] The source of those physical factors must be on or in the public works, except in the case of aircraft where arrivals and departures are taken into account whether the aircraft are within the airport boundaries or not.[157] Depreciation must have occurred on or after 17th October 1969.[158]

No compensation is payable in respect of public works whilst their construction is in progress, irrespective of the length of the construction period.[159] Compensation is not payable in respect of any depreciation that may occur as a result of intensifying a particular use, e.g. increasing traffic flow on an existing road or an increasing number of flights from an airport.[160] Compensation may, however, be payable in respect of certain major works of alteration,

---

[153] ss. 63 and 68, Land Clauses Consolidation Act 1845 and s. 2, Compulsory Purchase Act 1965.

[154] s. 1.

[155] s. 1(2).

[156] s. 1(3).

[157] s. 1(5). See also generally Chapter 8, pp. 300–301 *ante*.

[158] s. 1(8).

[159] See however The Noise Insulation Regulations 1975, Reg. 5, which provides a highway authority with discretionary powers concerning the sound insulation of eligible buildings likely to be seriously affected by noise from highway construction works.

[160] See however Chapter 7 generally and pp. 301–303 regarding the use of the equivalent continuous noise level (L_{eq}) as an aircraft noise index which takes account of factors including the number of aircraft movements in assessing the degree of eligible sound insulation works to dwellings affected by aircraft noise.

extension or reconstruction to existing highways and other public works and, in relation to airports, major alteration or addition to existing runways, taxiways or aprons.[161]

The responsible authority is, in the case of a highway, the highway authority and, in respect of other public works, the person managing the works.[162] Compensation is not payable for noise and vibration caused by the use of public works other than a highway unless the responsible authority has statutory immunity from actions for nuisance in relation to that use or, in the case of an aerodrome and aircraft noise, the aerodrome is one to which the Civil Aviation Act 1982, s. 77(2) applies giving immunity from action for nuisance.[163]

A claimant for compensation must, on the relevant date,[164] be the resident owner/occupier (or freeholder or tenant for a term of years certain, of which not less than three years remain unexpired at the date of the claim) of a dwelling house or other hereditament not exceeding a prescribed rateable value, or of an agricultural unit.[165] A notice of claim must be served on the responsible authority and must not usually be made before the expiration of twelve months after the public works were first open or used[166] (or altered or changed in accordance with s. 9(1)). The claim must contain details of the land in respect of which the claim is made, the relevant interests in the land, the public works and the amount of compensation claimed.[167]

Compensation is not payable unless it exceeds £50[168] and will be assessed by reference to prices current on the first day of the claim

---

[161] s. 9.

[162] s. 1(4).

[163] s. 1(6).

[164] Defined in s. 1(9), i.e. the date on which a highway is first open to public traffic and, in respect of other public works, the date they were first used after completion.

[165] See also s. 10 for provisions relating to mortgages, trusts for sale; s. 11 – interests acquired by inheritance; s. 12 – tenants entitled to enfranchisement or extension under Leasehold Reform Act 1967; and s. 13 – ecclesiastical property.

[166] s. 3(2) and (3).

[167] s. 3(1).

[168] s. 7.

period,[169] *minus* any reduction in the depreciation which has occurred or will occur as a result of works carried out under Part II of the Act (the Noise Insulation Regulations 1975 were made under section 20 for the purpose of reducing the effects of increased road traffic noise), or as a result of sound insulation works under section 15 of the Airports Authority Act 1965, section 29A of the Civil Aviation Act 1971, section 79 of the Civil Aviation Act 1982, corresponding local enactments, or sound proofing grants in respect of buildings near an aerodrome. Any improvements such as landscaping and tree planting carried out in accordance with section 27 will also be taken into account. Certain assumptions are made in assessing compensation in connection with the development potential of the land subject to the claim.[170] It is assumed that planning permission would be granted, subject to Schedule 10 to the Town and Country Planning Act 1990, for any development of a class specified in paragraph 1 of Schedule 3 to that Act and also development of a class specified in paragraph 2 of Schedule 3. It must not be assumed, however, that planning permission would be granted where certain classes of development have already been the subject of refusal or conditions bringing into operation the compensation provisions of the Town and Country Planning Act 1990.[171] Where planning permission has been granted for development, it has to be assumed that it has not in fact been granted in respect of any development that has not been carried out.

Disputes relating to compensation claims must be referred to the Lands Tribunal.[172] Compensation paid is eligible for interest[173] and, where compensation is payable, reasonable valuation or legal expenses must also be paid by the responsible authority.[174]

Purchase and other controls

Section 246 of the Highways Act 1980 gives highway authorities certain powers for the acquisition of land by agreement so as to

---

[169] s. 4(1).
[170] s. 5.
[171] s. 5(3)(c).
[172] s. 16. In Scotland, to the Lands Tribunal for Scotland.
[173] s. 18.
[174] s. 3(5).

mitigate the adverse effects of a highway or proposed highway. This would seem to give the facility to provide "buffer zones" that may separate the highway from surrounding areas adversely affected by noise. In addition, a similar power exists to acquire land seriously affected by works of highway construction or improvement, or by the use of the highway.

Section 282 enables the highway authority to carry out works on land in its ownership or on the highway, which will mitigate the adverse effects of the works or use of the highway. The works may include planting of trees, shrubs or plants and the laying out of any area of grassland. These powers are discretionary.

Powers are also contained in sections 26 and 27 of the Land Compensation Act 1973 allowing other authorities responsible for public works to exercise similar powers.

Without prejudice to section 106 of the Town and Country Planning Act 1990[175] relating to agreements between local planning authorities and landowners regulating the development and use of land, section 253 of the 1980 Act empowers the highway authority to enter into agreements with persons interested in land adjoining or in the vicinity of a highway. Such agreements may restrict or regulate the use of the land permanently or during a specified period so as to mitigate the effects of the highway on its surroundings. The agreement may relate to the planting and maintenance of trees, shrubs or plants on the land and restricting the lopping or removal of them. Any such agreement is binding on persons subsequently purchasing the land and the agreement is registrable as a local land charge.

Expenses for temporary removals

Section 28 of the Land Compensation Act 1973[176] empowers the authority responsible for the public works to pay the reasonable

---

[175] In Scotland, s. 50, Town and Country Planning (Scotland) Act 1972.

[176] This section should also be read in conjunction with the provisions of the Noise Insulation Regulations 1975 which allow for the provision of specified sound insulation works prior to construction work in connection with a public highway to which the Regulations apply.

expenses of any occupier of a dwelling adjacent to the site of providing suitable alternative accommodation where the construction or alteration of those works affects the enjoyment of the dwelling. This may be payable for the whole or any part of the period during which the works are being carried out. No payment can be made unless the agreement of the authority has been obtained prior to the expenditure being incurred. This provision does not apply to the occupiers of commercial premises.

BUILDING DESIGN AS A MEANS OF CONTROL

The problem of noise within buildings, particularly the transmission of sound between dwellings is especially important as it can be difficult to introduce acceptable control measures once buildings have been constructed and are occupied. The Wilson Committee in its report *Noise*[177] recognised that at that time more people were concerned about external noise sources, e.g. traffic, when they were in their homes, than they were about internal noise, e.g. from neighbours. However, the 1991 national noise attitude survey demonstrated that, of all the categories of environmental noise, noise from neighbours attracts the greatest proportion of objections relative to all the people who can hear it.[178] Complaints are frequently made to local authorities and the police about noise from neighbours' parties, television sets and other forms of entertainment in the home. The methods of statutory control are dealt with in Chapters 2 and 3 but it is relevant to discuss the principles of sound transmission in buildings in order to appreciate the problems associated with controlling noise between dwellings. The relevance of the Building Regulations 2000[179] is also considered.

Sound transmission in buildings: basic principles

Sound transmission may occur in two ways:

1. A sound source may produce airborne sound waves which produce vibrations in a wall or floor. That vibration energy will

---

[177] Para. 115.
[178] *Effects of environmental noise on people at home,* Grimwood, C.J., B.R.E. Information Paper IP 22/93, December 1993.
[179] S.I. 2000 No. 2531.

become airborne sound again on the other side of the wall or floor. The vibrations can be, and often are, transmitted along a separating wall to be re-radiated into rooms not immediately adjacent to that containing the sound source. This may explain what happens when a neighbour's radio or television set operating in their ground floor room can be heard in the bedroom of the adjacent house. It is called flanking transmission and can occur either horizontally or vertically.

2. Direct impact noise can produce similar problems although in this case it is the actual impact that produces the vibration in the adjoining structure rather than the sound waves impinging on it.

The manner in which the sound transmission takes place is illustrated below.

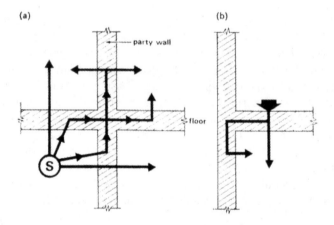

Fig. 12. Vertical sections illustrating paths of sound transmission.
(a) Airborne.   (b) Impact.
(*reproduced by permission of the Building Research Establishment*)

The building of residential flats, other similar multi-storey buildings and conversion of buildings into multi-occupancy for residential use has, because of the type of construction, often resulted in the structure providing a ready transmission path. Many cases have accordingly occurred where, for example, the noise from a basement boiler installation can be heard in flats several storeys above ground level. Similarly pop music played in clubs or discotheques in a large integral development complex may be heard in residential property forming part of that complex, even though the source and receiver are a considerable distance apart. In these cases the sound is often structure borne.

The Building Regulations 1965 first introduced sound insulation as one of the construction requirements for new buildings. Sound insulation for separating walls and floors had to be "adequate". There was also a list of constructions that were "deemed to satisfy" the requirement. In 1985 the Regulations were reviewed and reduced to simple functional requirements, e.g. requiring that sound insulation should be "reasonable". Non-mandatory technical guidance is contained in a number of Approved Documents. Builders are not obliged to adopt any particular solution contained in an Approved Document if they prefer to meet the relevant requirement of the Regulations in another way. Unfortunately, compliance with the Regulations offers no guarantee that a noise source in one room or building will not cause annoyance to the occupiers of another area.

The scale of the problem in residential accommodation is indicated in the 1996 English House Condition Survey which revealed that 4.7 million householders were bothered by noise, either from traffic, industry or neighbours, and 670,000 householders were bothered by noise from neighbours which they attributed either to poor design of the building or a combination of poor design and behaviour of the neighbours.[180] The current standards of sound insulation in dwellings can be traced back to surveys conducted in the 1950s and studies by the Building Research Establishment[181] indicate that the successive Building Regulations, and guidance in Approved Document E dealing with resistance to the passage of

---

[180] *The Building Act 1984. The Building Regulations 2000. Proposals for Amending Part E – Resistance to the Passage of Sound*, consultation paper produced by Department of Environment, Transport and the Regions, January 2001. The consultation paper, also referred to in the Introduction to this book, proposes alterations to the Building Regulations as well as more comprehensive changes to Part E.

[181] Referred to in the document in fn. 180 above.

sound, do not always produce satisfactory standards of sound insulation. One study revealed that about 25% of people living in dwellings meeting the current standards rated the insulation as poor or very poor. Another study looking at sound insulation between dwellings approved under the Building Regulations 2000 found a poor level of compliance with the standards. Apart from a wide range of performance for some constructions, the Building Research Association estimated that up to 40% of new separating floors and 25% of separating walls might fail to meet the required standards.

Accordingly, good sound insulation is extremely important as is the design and layout of buildings and the use to which they are put.[182] Buildings likely to contain sources of high noise levels should be expertly designed and constructed to ensure that they provide good sound attenuation and buildings exposed to external noise should be similarly considered. If a club or discotheque is intended in a building complex, for example, a study by experts should be carried out to ensure either that sound will not be transmitted to adjacent properties to the detriment of the occupants or, if that possibility exists, properly designed acoustic treatment is applied to the rooms containing the sound sources.

Building Regulations 2000

The Building Regulations[183] control the construction of buildings. They specify the criteria for materials to be used and include structural and fire safety arrangements, ventilation and drainage requirements, and heating and fuel conservation requirements. They apply throughout England and Wales. The review which resulted in the 2000 Regulations also updated the Approved Document E, *Resistance to the Passage of Sound.* The Regulations are enforced by local authorities and require:[184]

---

[182] This is particularly so as national planning policy increasingly favours mixed use developments, particularly in town and city centres, and the Government is committed to increasing the density of all residential development.

[183] S.I. 2000 No. 2531.

[184] Part E of Schedule 1.

Airborne sound (walls)

E1. A wall which–
(a) separates a dwelling from another building or from another dwelling, or
(b) separates a habitable room or kitchen within a dwelling from another part of the same building which is not used exclusively as part of the dwelling,
shall have reasonable resistance to the transmission of airborne sound.

Airborne sound (floors and stairs)

E2. A floor or a stair which separates a dwelling from another dwelling, or from another part of the same building which is not used exclusively as part of the dwelling, shall have reasonable resistance to the transmission of airborne sound.

Impact sound (floors and stairs)

E3. A floor or a stair above a dwelling which separates it from another dwelling, or from another part of the same building which is not used exclusively as part of the dwelling, shall have reasonable resistance to the transmission of impact sound.

The sound insulation requirements apply to new buildings and to "material changes of use",[185] i.e. where there is a change in the purposes for which, or the circumstances in which, a building is used, so that after that change the building:

(a) is used as a dwelling where previously it was not;

(b) contains a flat where previously it did not;

(c) contains a greater or lesser number of dwellings than it did previously.

Two new sections were added to the 1992 version of Approved Document E.[186] The first describes an approval procedure for new

---

[185] Building Regulations 2000, Reg. 5.
[186] There has been no substantial revision of Approved Documents since 1992. In the Government's proposals for change, although the proposed E1 still asks for *reasonable* sound insulation, the proposed guidance on the Regulations includes explicit sound insulation performance targets for dwellings.

building, the second gives guidance to cover the material change of use of a dwelling, such as conversion of a house into flats. The requirements for England and Wales, Scotland and Northern Ireland have been harmonised in their respective technical documents. The Scottish and Irish documents still contain reference to "deemed to satisfy" requirements but this term no longer applies in England and Wales. In considering the provisions relating to material changes of use, such as conversion of a house into flats, an important factor is the level of sound insulation to aim for as being "reasonable". It should preferably be the same as for new buildings. However, with new building, flanking transmission can be taken into account but, with conversion work, as much of the existing structure as possible needs to be used on economy grounds. This limits extensive work, such as the use of wall linings to control flanking transmission. This in turn limits the degree of sound insulation compared with new building.

These statutory requirements are the result of many years' experience and detailed investigations by the Building Research Establishment including field measurements of sound transmission in buildings. Unfortunately it has been shown that in a significant number of cases measured by the Establishment, the performance standard required by the Building Regulations has not been obtained.

The standard for sound insulation was originally based on the performance of a 9 in. brick wall which was a common type of construction for party walls in the early 1960s. Present day construction methods involve the use of sturdy but lightweight materials which do not have the equivalent mass of a 9 in. brick wall and therefore the sound insulation value may be of a lower standard. Although the Part E provisions may be met in practice, the Local Authority Building Inspector is under no obligation to accept the sound insulation guidance in Part E and may be satisfied with alternative methods. There is also power to relax the requirements.[187] In fact, the Regulations say that in connection with material changes of use, any work must comply with Part E[188] or, if it does

---

[187] Reg. 11.
[188] Reg. 6.

not, the completed work must be no more unsatisfactory than before the work was carried out.[189]

Therefore, building work may be accepted which fails to meet the "reasonable" provisions. In practice it is often impossible to determine what level of noise may be generated in any room and therefore even compliance with the "reasonable" provisions will not necessarily avoid the transmission of unacceptable levels of noise from one room to another, particularly where the source of noise may be from electronically amplified sound or appliances fixed to the separating wall.

Building methods

There are a number of common deficiencies in the methods of constructing walls which reduce the efficiency of the structure to attenuate sound and every attempt should be made to eliminate them. They include:

(a) bricks laid "frog" downwards – this may reduce the amount of mortar required to construct a wall but the cavity then left between the mortar and the brick effectively reduces the mass of the wall. Bricks laid "frog" upwards will result in the "frog" being filled with mortar ensuring fewer voids and better insulation;

(b) when large building bricks or blocks are used, the joints tend not to be properly filled, the mass is again reduced and air paths are left through the wall;

(c) the tendency to use a combination of different building materials in any one building makes it less certain that consistent results in sound reduction will be achieved;

(d) the use of lightweight concrete blocks may provide the load bearing standards required but these have less mass and therefore may provide lower sound attenuation than, say, brickwork;

---

[189] Reg. 4.

(e) general shoddy workmanship – gaps in structure, improperly sealed cavities, etc. reduce the sound reduction capabilities of a building.

Control by planning and design

The first line of defence to external noise is the design and layout of the development site. Several factors influence the sound level experienced by the occupants of a dwelling. Architects can exercise control by:

(a) suitable location of the buildings on a site;

(b) screening of the site;

(c) internal layout of the building;

(d) the type of building and its orientation.

Fig. 13 illustrates some design features which may help to minimise the effects of traffic noise initially. As far as possible, external noise should be controlled by site and building planning, so that building design can be primarily concentrated on reducing sound transmission between individual rooms or adjacent buildings.

Even adequate standards of building construction will not necessarily control internally transmitted noise to a satisfactory extent and therefore special care has to be taken in the planning and design stage of buildings, especially those used for residential purposes. This chapter deals generally with planning controls and it is clear that any limitations of the Building Regulations must be taken into account by:

(a) the avoidance of incompatible but adjacent uses;

(b) the proper design and layout of buildings to be used to house a particular noise source so as to minimise the effect on adjacent properties;

(c) the proper internal design of dwellings taking into account any limits of control in the Regulations.

The form and layout of buildings may provide
some defence against noise by screening

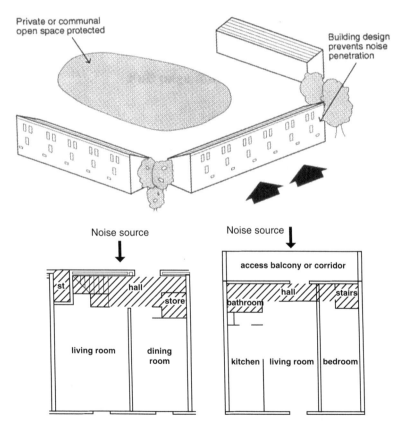

Fig. 13. Some design features to minimise noise.

There are a number of factors that can be taken into account to avoid those internally generated noise problems which appear to cause most concern:

(a) the avoidance of flanking transmission (which is extremely difficult to control once a building is constructed and occupied) requires compliance with the Building Regulations, proper standards of workmanship and correct materials;

(b) avoid designs which result in w.c.s, refuse chutes and other noisy appliances next to living rooms and bedrooms;

(c) avoid designs which allow the fixing of power sockets, switches and central heating pumps on party walls as these can be a source of annoyance in adjacent rooms;

(d) layout of rooms in buildings is no less important than external appearance and the following matters should be considered;

    (i) lounges (see diagram below) tend to contain the greatest number of sound sources – amplified music, radios, television sets, and problems of direct and flanking sound transmission may occur. This is difficult to avoid in most designs but in semi-detached houses or flats it is possible to place halls and stairways side by side;

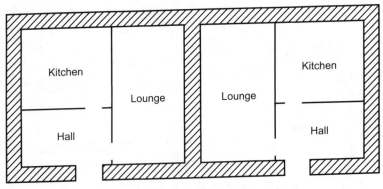

Fig. 14. Arrangement of rooms likely to increase the possibility of sound transmission between the most frequently used rooms.

(c) adoption of action plans by the member states, based upon noise mapping results, with a view to preventing and reducing environmental noise where necessary, and particularly where exposure levels can induce harmful effects on human health, and to preserving environmental noise quality where it is good.

2. ... providing a basis for developing community measures to reduce noise emitted by specific sources, in particular means of transport and outdoor equipment."

The Directive will apply[198] to environmental noise to which humans are exposed in built-up areas, public parks or other quiet areas in urban areas with populations exceeding 100,000, quiet areas in open country, and near schools, hospitals and other noise-sensitive buildings and areas. It will not apply to noise caused by the exposed person himself, noise from domestic activities, noise created by neighbours, noise at work places or noise inside means of transport or due to military activities in military areas.[199]

Member states will have to designate the competent authorities and bodies responsible for implementing the Directive.[200] Strategic noise maps[201] will have to be made and approved for all urban areas with more than 250,000 inhabitants, for all major roads which have more than six million vehicle passages a year, major railways which have more than 60,000 train passages a year, and major airports within their territories.[202] Neighbouring member states must co-operate on strategic noise mapping near borders. Strategic noise maps must be reviewed and revised, if necessary, at least every five years. Specified noise indicators[203] will have to be used in the noise mapping process, although until common assessment

---

[198] Art. 2.
[199] Other categories of noise emissions are already covered by Community legislation, detailed in the common position document p. 3(4).
[200] Art. 4.
[201] Defined as "... designed for the global assessment of noise exposure in a given area due to different noise sources or for the overall predictions for such an area": Art. 3(a). They must satisfy the minimum requirements of Annex IV.
[202] Art. 7. The maps must show the position in the preceding calendar year.
[203] Arts. 5 and 6. L_{den} and L_{night} as defined.

methods have been established by the commission, member states will be able to use existing national noise indicators and may use supplementary indicators for special cases.

Following strategic noise mapping, member states will have to draw up action plans designed to manage noise issues and effects, including noise reduction if necessary. This requirement[204] applies to those areas to which strategic noise mapping applies. Action plans have to be reviewed at least every five years after their approval.[205] The public has to be consulted about proposals for action plans,[206] their preparation and review, and advised of the decisions taken. Strategic noise maps and action plans have to be made publicly available.[207] The Commission has to receive information from member states as specified[208] and the Commission is obliged to report to the European Parliament and the Council on the need for further community actions on environmental noise and any strategies to address specific issues.[209] The Directive defines the noise indicators[210] to be used, assessment methods for the noise indicators,[211] harmful effects,[212] and the minimum requirements for strategic noise mapping[213] and action plans.[214]

Although the European Commission's 1996 Green Paper suggested the use of noise mapping, there was no practical experience in the U.K. in the use of modern noise mapping techniques. Subsequently, Birmingham City Council conducted a comprehensive noise mapping exercise in conjunction with the Department of Environment and the Building Research Establishment. The overall project objective "was to produce 'state of the art' noise maps of the City of Birmingham in sufficient detail to allow them, after further

---

[204] Art. 8.
[205] As specified in Art. 7.
[206] Art. 8, para. 7.
[207] Art. 9.
[208] Art. 10 and Annex VI .
[209] Art. 11.
[210] Annex I.
[211] Annex II.
[212] Annex III.
[213] Annex IV.
[214] Annex V.

development, to serve as a strategic planning and noise reduction tool and as an aid for day to day decision making on many environmental noise matters". The project resulted in sound emission contour maps being produced for the whole of Birmingham, covering selected major roads, all train lines, aircraft in flight at Birmingham International Airport and 21 industrial sites. The exercise utilised experience and expertise from Germany and involved both noise measurements and computer based calculation and modelling techniques. Whilst the resultant comprehensive report[215] concludes that the noise mapping exercise was a success, it also contains recommendations for further research which the authors consider essential to develop the process sufficiently to address the future requirements of the Directive.

---

[215] Birmingham City Council, *A report on the production of noise maps of the City of Birmingham*, Environmental Services Department, D.E.T.R., February 2000.

Chapter 10

OCCUPATIONAL NOISE EXPOSURE

The effects of exposure to noise are considered generally in Chapter 1. The most recent report[1] estimates that, in 1995, around two million people in Great Britain were suffering from an illness they believed was caused by their current or past work. Of that total, deafness, tinnitus or other ear conditions accounted for about 170,000 cases.[2] A joint report[3] by the T.U.C. and the Royal National Institute for Deaf People has concluded that more than one million people are subjected to noise above the level[4] which puts their hearing at risk.

However, although exposure to environmental noise can produce psychological effects, it does not usually result in physical damage to the ear. Records exist to indicate that the deleterious effect of noise on human hearing was recognised centuries ago. The effect of noise on workers in certain occupations was recorded by Ramazzini in his book *De Morbis Artificum* published in 1713. In the chapter on diseases of coppersmiths, he writes "In every city e.g. at Venice these workers are all congregated in one quarter and engaged all day in hammering copper ... from this quarter there arises such a terrible din that only workers have shops and homes there; all others flee from the disagreeable locality". He goes on to state that "to begin with the ears are injured by that perpetual din, and in fact the whole head, inevitably, so that workers of this class become hard of hearing and, if they grow old at this work completely deaf."

No particular efforts to quantify the degree of hearing loss associated with particular occupations appear to have been carried out until the end of the last century. Research carried out by Dr. T. Barr, a

---

[1] *Health and Safety Statistics 2000/01*, Health & Safety Commission, H.M.S.O., 2001.
[2] *Ibid*, p. 86, para. 2.16.
[3] "Indecent Exposure", reported in *Croner's Health and Safety Case Law Briefing*, Issue 21, 12th April 1999.
[4] 85 dB(A).

surgeon at Glasgow Ear Hospital, was reported in a paper presented to the Royal Philosophical Society of Glasgow in March 1886. This dealt with the effect of noise on those workers employed in the boiler making industry.[5]

Dr. Barr was unable to measure the noise levels associated with particularly noisy tasks but from the knowledge available today it is clear that the exposure levels would be totally unacceptable today without proper hearing protection. Very little action, however, was taken until 1962 when a joint investigation by the Medical Research Council and the National Physical Laboratory was commenced. Its terms of reference were:

"(a) To compare the state of hearing of persons with various known histories of noise exposure.

(b) To secure pre-exposure audiograms and to monitor the state of hearing of people throughout the early years of working in noise locations by means of serial audiograms.

(c) To determine, if possible, whether any significant relationship exists between temporary and persistent threshold shift.

(d) To relate the physical properties of industrial noises, with particular reference to those experienced by the groups studied in (a) and (b) above, and to determine by statistical procedures the physical features of the noises which constitute an effective set of criteria for measuring exposure as judged by correlation with its effect on hearing.

(e) To obtain data on hazards to hearing and to make recommendations on measures to avoid them."

The Wilson Committee in its chapter "Occupational Exposure to High Levels of Noise" commented on the effects of noise on the ear and the different ways in which damage to hearing can occur, viz:[6]

---

[5] *Enquiry into the effects of loud sounds upon the hearing of boilermakers and others who work amid noisy surroundings.*

[6] *Noise,* Cmnd. 2056, July 1963, para. 508

(a) temporary reductions in sensitivity of hearing for varying periods of time after exposure to noise (temporary hearing loss);

(b) permanent reductions in sensitivity of hearing due to damage to the ear caused by exposure to certain types of noise over a prolonged period (permanent hearing loss);

(c) sudden gross damage caused by noise of very high intensity and short duration.

The gap in the available knowledge on noise-induced hearing loss was recognised and it was stated[7] that investigations must be undertaken into the problem. Shortly afterwards in 1963, the Department of Employment published a guide on occupational noise exposure.[8] In 1970, the report of Burns and Robinson,[9] undertaken by the National Physical Laboratory and Medical Research Council, was published. The results of these and other[9] research findings have subsequently been incorporated in guidance on occupational noise exposure.

RELATIONSHIP BETWEEN NOISE EXPOSURE AND HEARING LOSS[10]

There are many variables that may affect the possibility of hearing loss due to noise exposure. Briefly, these can be summarised as follows:

Sound pressure level and frequency – generally, the greater the sound pressure level, the greater the degree of temporary and permanent threshold shift. However, the same sound level displayed on a sound level meter can be produced by different noises. The frequency of the noise may also be significant. The significance of

---

[7] *Noise,* Cmnd. 2056, July 1963, para. 509.

[8] *Noise and the Worker,* Health and Safety at Work Booklet No. 25, 1971.

[9] *Hearing and Noise in Industry,* Burns, W. and Robinson, D.W., 1970, H.M.S.O. For a useful summary of research work on the effects of occupational noise, see *The Effects of Occupational Noise on Hearing: Recent Developments,* Review SHE, 4th April 1991, The Loss Prevention Council.

[10] See also Chapter 1, pp. 9 and 10.

the sound pressure level is taken into account in the regulations controlling occupational noise exposure.[11]

Duration of exposure – if noise is likely to produce hearing loss, the extent of the loss will increase with time and accordingly the total exposure time must be taken into consideration.

Personal susceptibility – the degree of hearing loss varies considerably between individuals subject to a given noise exposure.

OCCUPATIONAL DEAFNESS – COMMON LAW

An employee who suffers injury to his hearing due to noise at work may be entitled to take action under the common law of negligence. Under common law the courts also seek to provide compensation in cases of excessive exposure resulting in chronic hearing defects.

Duty of care

It is well established that an employer has certain responsibilities to his employees. The duty of care which has developed as a result of common law action over many years is now also taken into account in statutory controls. An employer has the following basic duties:

(a) he must take reasonable care not to expose his employees to unnecessary risks;

(b) he must provide his employees with a safe place in which to work.

These principles have been used in certain cases concerning hearing damage connected with occupational noise exposure. The following judgment should be especially borne in mind as it seems to state quite clearly what is required of an employer in relation to his duty of care:

"The overall test is still the conduct of the reasonable and prudent employer, taking positive thought for the safety of his workers in the light of what he knows or ought to know; where

---

[11]   The Noise at Work Regulations 1989, S.I. 1989 No. 1790.

there is a recognised and general practice which has been followed for a substantial period in similar circumstances without mishap, he is entitled to follow it, unless in the light of common sense or newer knowledge it is clearly bad; but where there is a developing knowledge, he must keep reasonably abreast of it and not be slow to apply it; and where he has in fact greater than average knowledge of the risks he may be thereby obliged to take more than the average or standard precautions. He must weigh up the risk in terms of the likelihood of injury occurring and the potential consequences if it does; and he must balance against this the probable effectiveness of the precautions that can be taken to meet it and the expense and inconvenience they involve. If he is found to have fallen below the standard to be properly expected of a reasonable and prudent employer in these respects, he is negligent."[12]

The following cases may serve to show that the courts take into account these factors in arriving at their judgment as to whether negligence exists:

Slater v Ministry of Defence[13]
The plaintiff in this case claimed that his substantial deafness was due wholly or partly to the noise to which he was exposed whilst employed at a Ministry of Defence Ammunition Proof and Trial Unit. He was employed as an examiner in proofing ammunition. He was given a routine medical examination on his transfer to the firing ranges which indicated some slight deafness. He was not advised of this and was not aware of any hearing loss until after an incident on the range when a gun on the range fired several shots, without warning, close to him. He claimed that he immediately experienced pain in his ears and loss of hearing. However, he made no complaint and did not report the matter until a few days later. He did not report the matter to his doctor for another fortnight and continued working. It was found that he was suffering from inflammation of the middle ear (*otitis media*).

---

[12]   *Stokes v Guest, Keen and Nettlefolds (Bolts and Nuts) Ltd.* [1968] 1 W.L.R. 1776; 112 S.J. 821; 5 K.I.R. 401.
[13]   Unreported, 25th November 1970, Stafford Assizes.

The judge in this case was not satisfied that the incident complained of had in fact occurred but expressed the view in any case that the hearing loss was most likely to be associated with chronic inflammation of the middle ear and not the impulsive noise.

This case bears out the importance of medical examination and monitoring of employees' hearing in assessing the effects of exposure in a noisy working environment.

Berry v Stone Manganese Marine Ltd.[14]
In this case, the plaintiff had been employed on processes involving the shaping of manganese bronze propellers by pneumatic hammers. Extremely high noise levels existed which allegedly:

(a) frightened the plaintiff out of his life; and

(b) bordered on the threshold of pain according to another witness.

Noise levels in the order of 115/120 decibels existed. The plaintiff became aware of his hearing loss in 1960 but took no action until 1964 when his doctor was approached. No action was taken as a result of this but he consulted his doctor again in 1967 and he was seen by a consultant surgeon and was subjected to an audiometric test. Further hearing loss occurred and he commenced proceedings for negligence and a breach of statutory duties by his employers. The court found the defendant to have been negligent. Some important failings of the defendant had occurred:

(a) the earplugs available were only provided in a limited range of sizes;

(b) no facilities existed to aid the choice of suitable earplugs;

(c) no supervision of choice was provided.

The following points, which are associated with the judgment in this case, need to be considered by employers:

1. In cases where a danger to hearing is obvious, protection must be provided and employees made aware it is available.

---

[14] *Berry v Stone Manganese Marine Ltd.* (1971) 12 K.I.R. 13, 22–3.

2. In some instances the risk to hearing may not be so obvious but serious hearing impairment may still occur. The reasonable employer should take steps to establish the possible risks of exposure to a noisy working environment.

3. The correct type of hearing protection must be provided under supervision and not left solely to the individual. The protection must be adequate, e.g. ear muffs rather than ear plugs may be required.

4. It is pointless to argue that the employee would not wear hearing protection even if it had been supplied. The employer has a duty to *educate* the employee to ensure that the ear protection is used, and to supervise the wearing of it.

Bolton v Hawker Siddeley Aviation Ltd.[15]
The plaintiff in this case worked in the defendants' engine shed. He claimed that he was exposed to high noise levels from the testing of aircraft engines outside the shed where he worked during several weeks in 1966 and on one day was directly exposed to a high level of noise that knocked him over and caused pain for two days. It was shown that he had a pre-existing degenerative condition in his left ear and his hearing in that ear had deteriorated since the incident. Although the hearing loss was not great in his left ear, it was attributed to the defendants' negligence. The following important facts emerged:

(a) the defendants had been warned of the disturbing noise;

(b) the defendants' own doctor had advised that earplugs would not provide adequate protection;

(c) earmuffs were necessary but had not been provided;

(d) noise intensity tests had been advised but not undertaken;

(e) current literature at the time[16] advised monitoring audiometry and where necessary the relocation of employees particularly susceptible to noise to a less noisy environment.

---

[15] Unreported, 9th March 1973, Chester Crown Court.
[16] Earlier edition of Department of Employment's Health and Safety at Work Booklet No. 25, *Noise and the Worker.*

The value of audiometric tests is referred to in more detail in this chapter but in the *Berry* case the judgment was that the employers' duty of care did not include the need for audiometric tests to establish whether the employee's hearing was being affected. However, it has been established that:

(a) if an employer knows that an employee has a particular disability or is particularly susceptible, he has an *increasing duty of care*;[17]

(b) where an employer is aware of circumstances and events necessitating medical examination of employees, then he should advise the employee to be subjected to proper medical examination.[18]

Degree of employer's liability

A number of particularly important questions were considered in the case of *Thompson and Others v Smiths Ship-repairers (North Shields) Ltd.*[19] This was a consolidated action involving six plaintiffs, each of whom had worked on various noisy jobs, either solely for the defendant company or in addition to other noisy occupations for other employers. All suffered varying degrees of hearing loss and were individually awarded damages which took account of the following:

(a) the date from which legal liability was considered to begin;

(b) what was considered to be the breach of duty;

(c) the apportioning of liability between employers;

(d) the apportionment of liability in cases where the onset of deafness occurred before the employer could be expected to take preventative measures to protect employees.

---

[17] *Paris v Stepney Borough Council* [1951] A.C. 367. *Bux v Slough Metals Ltd.* [1973] 1 W.L.R. 1358 deals with the employer's duty to educate and persuade concerning the use of safety devices and techniques.

[18] *Wright v Dunlop Rubber* (1971) 11 K.I.R. 311.

[19] *Thompson and Others v Smiths Ship-repairers (North Shields) Ltd.* [1984] All E.R. 881.

In this case, it was determined that employers are liable in negligence if they fail to take reasonable steps[20] to protect employees from known sources of danger.

Each plaintiff complained of hearing loss and difficulty hearing ordinary sounds such as the telephone, doorbell, television set, music and normal conversation. They also argued that an employer who contributed to any degree to the injury could be made liable for the whole injury. These latter arguments were rejected and the judge ruled that there was no need to apply the whole liability on the employer when his legal liability was clearly less than 100%.

The judgment found that since 1963 all employers are taken to know of the danger of injury to employees' hearing as a result of exposure to excessive noise.[21] Since this date, employers are liable to compensate employees for:

(a) physical injury to hearing;

(b) the resultant loss of amenity;

(c) the consequent social handicap;

which occur as a result of the employer's breach of duty.

Where the injury occurs progressively through successive employment, an apportionment of liability must be made between each employer. An apportionment is also to be made to allow for injury occurring before 1963, for which no liability arises, and injury occurring after that date. In this apportionment it was recognised that in most cases the progression of hearing loss was most rapid during the first six to thirteen years of exposure (this was the best knowledge available at that time and was based on work of the National Physical Laboratory).

---

20 See also *McCafferty v Metropolitan Police Receiver* [1977] 2 All E.R. 756 where it was also held that the defence that the employer had delegated the duty of caring for his own hearing to the employee could not stand.

21 In 1963 the Ministry of Labour published *Noise and the Worker* advising of the dangers of noise, and earplugs and sound absorbent cotton wool were available. Therefore, there existed the knowledge and means to protect the employees.

Time of knowledge of risk

In the case of *Kill v Sussex Coastline Buses Ltd.*,[22] the plaintiff claimed damages for noise induced hearing loss allegedly caused by his having driven a Leyland double decker bus with a large diesel engine in proximity to the drivers compartment, over a period of up to six hours during the relevant periods. The plaintiff contended that the relevant date that his employer should have had requisite knowledge of the dangers of noise induced deafness was 1963 when *Noise and the Worker* was published by the Ministry of Labour. The defendant contended that the document related only to factories and, in any event, there was nothing within it that should have put them on notice of potential deafness problems for drivers of that type of vehicle. In giving judgment, it was held that there was no evidence of complaints having been made to the defendant company at the time of the 1962 document which would have prompted the company to realise that its bus drivers were being exposed to noise levels which might damage their hearing, and the requisite knowledge on the defendant's part could not predate the relevant codes published in 1972.

Levels of compensation

In the case of *Fry and Others v Ford Motor Company Ltd.*,[23] the employer admitted exposing four employees to noise levels averaging over 90 dB(A) for between 15 and 30 years. It was decided that, in assessing compensation, the effect of hearing loss on each individual should be taken into account. The following points were relevant:

(a) although there was no pain or suffering in the same way as physical injuries, there was disruption of family and social life and intolerance of others who became irritated by a person who was hard of hearing;

(b) deterioration of hearing was age related and thus the age at which the injury occurred was important in calculating the

---

[22] (2000) *Current Law Year Book 2000*, p. 1115.
[23] *Fry and Others v Ford Motor Co. Ltd.* (1990) H.S.I.B. 174, Q.B.D.

years of hearing loss up to the date of the trial and the likely years following the trial;

(c) the frustration and irritation caused by the condition varied considerably between individuals and must be taken into account;

(d) therefore, in deciding compensation, account must be taken of the plaintiff's age, length of time hearing loss had been suffered, whether he suffered from tinnitus, the effect on social, work and family life, and any aids required in the future.

Duty to keep ahead of contemporary knowledge

In the case of *Baxter v Harland and Wolff*,[24] the plaintiff had been employed for a total of 25 years by the defendant company prior to retirement in 1962. After retirement he suffered deafness caused by high noise level exposure during his period of employment. He sought damages in 1984.

It was held that the employers had failed in their duty of care as they failed to take action to reduce noise levels during the plaintiff's period of employment. The employers knew that people were suffering hearing loss because of the noisy work environment and were required to take reasonable care to keep ahead of contemporary knowledge in relation to accident prevention and safety. The Ministry of Labour published noise guidelines in its booklet *Noise and the Worker* in 1963 but there had been sufficient legal, medical and scientific knowledge available before 1963. As the employers had failed to consider this knowledge, they were liable for noise levels before then.

Negligence

In the case of *Cropper v Ford Motor Co. Ltd.*,[25] the judge had regard to a number of the judgments referred to above and, in relation to liability, raised three questions:

---

[24] *Baxter v Harland and Wolff* [1990] I.R.L.R. 516, C.A. Northern Ireland.
[25] *Cropper v Ford Motor Co. Ltd.* (1992) Liverpool Crown Court, 17th November, Unreported.

1. To what levels of noise and over what duration was the plaintiff exposed?

2. Had he sustained hearing loss from such exposure?

3. Was his exposure such as to establish negligence or breach of statutory duty by the defendants?

The judge found that the hearing loss had been suffered by exposure to noise at work, in this case an L_{eq} level of 87/88 dB(A). He was satisfied that, by the standards of the late 1960s, the defendants exposed the plaintiff to noise they ought to have anticipated might damage his hearing and they could have taken measures to reduce the noise that were both reasonably practicable and cost effective, and commensurate with the risks involved. In particular, they could have provided suitable ear protection and warned of the hearing risk if it was not used. Further, in view of the lack of any education programme or advice, the plaintiff had not been contributorily negligent.

Limitation on proceedings

Section 2 of the Limitation Act 1980 stipulates that actions founded on tort shall not be brought after the expiration of six years from the date on which the action accrued. All civil rights of action must be commenced within time limits set down in the Limitation Act. In the case of action for damages for negligence, nuisance or breach of duty, whether the duty exists by virtue of a contract or of provision made by or under a statute or independently of any contract or any such provision, where the damages claimed consist of or include damages in respect of personal injuries to the plaintiff or any other person, the limitation period is three years from the date on which the cause of action accrued, or the date of knowledge, if later, of the person injured.[26] If the injured person dies before the end of the three years, the beneficiaries of the estate can pursue the action by virtue of the Law Reform (Miscellaneous Provisions) Act 1934 within three years from the date of death, or the date of the personal representative's knowledge, whichever is the later.

---

[26] Limitation Act 1980, s. 11(4).

Personal injuries include any disease and any impairment of a person's physical or mental condition. This will include injury due to noise exposure. References to a person's date of knowledge are references to the date on which he first had knowledge[27] of the following:

(a) the injury was significant; and

(b) the injury was attributable in whole or in part to the act or omission which is alleged to constitute negligence, nuisance or breach of duty; and

(c) the identity of the defendant; and

(d) if it is alleged that the act or omission was that of someone other than the defendant, the identity of that person and the additional facts supporting the action.

Accordingly, in a case where instantaneous damage occurred such as in the case of *Bolton v Hawker Siddeley Aviation Ltd.* there would be little doubt when the limitation period started. In the case of gradual injury occurring over a much longer period associated with regular exposure to high noise levels, it may be more difficult to establish when the cause of action accrued. The Limitation Act 1980 deals with this by defining an injury as being *significant* if the person whose date of knowledge is in question would reasonably have considered it sufficiently serious to justify taking proceedings for damages against a defendant who did not dispute liability and who was able to satisfy a judgment.[28] A *person's knowledge* includes that which he might reasonably have been expected to acquire from facts observable or ascertainable by him with or without the help of medical or other expert advice.[29]

In the case of disability there may be no limitation period.[30] In a decision involving a serious brain injury, although a writ was served the year after the injury occurred, no proceedings were taken and the plaintiff applied for the writ to be struck out. The decision

---

[27] s. 14(1).
[28] s. 14(2).
[29] Limitation Act 1980, s. 14(3).
[30] *Turner v W.H. Malcolm Ltd.* (1992) *The Times*, 24th August 1992, C.A.

was that section 28 of the Act provided that there was, in effect, no limitation period for a plaintiff who was under a permanent disability if the action was not proceeded with expeditiously. Although the case did not relate to an injury suffered at work, it may be of considerable significance in such cases where an employee has suffered permanent disability, e.g. permanent hearing loss.

The limitation acted against the plaintiff in the case of *Berry v Stone Manganese Marine Ltd.* as it was established that he had been aware that he was growing increasingly deaf due to noise at his place of work, yet he did nothing about it for several years. The court held that the long period of increasing deafness was a matter that should have led a reasonable man to seek advice before he did. He was not entitled to the relief in the 1963 Act and his claim concerning matters before 1967 was statute barred.

However, a different view was taken in the case of *Sykes v Chief Constable of West Yorkshire Police.*[31] The plaintiff had worked as a firearms instructor from 1978 to 1983. During this time he had been exposed to the noise from one million pistol shots and 300,000 shotgun rounds. Between 1979 and 1980 he suffered ringing in his ears, a source of constant discomfort to him. He did not complain for fear of affecting his promotion prospects and only sought legal advice in 1994. He started legal proceedings in 1996 and applied for a preliminary ruling on the question of limitation. The County Court decided, on the basis of medical evidence, that the permanent ringing in the man's ears was a significant work-related injury. In relation to the delay in complaining to his employer, the judge ruled that it was reasonable for a career policeman not to put his job at risk and allowed the action to continue.

Damages

Damages in respect of personal injury in civil claims usually consist of a lump sum awarded by the courts after assessment of the effect of the hearing loss on the successful plaintiff. The judgments made

---

[31] *Sykes v Chief Constable of West Yorkshire Police*, 21 January 1997, *Current Law Year Book 1997*, p. 226/7. For an interesting case involving the application of the Limitation Act 1980 to a company that had been voluntarily wound up, see *Isaac v Duport Steels Ltd., Current Law Year Book 1997*, p. 227.

to date indicate that damages may be awarded in successful actions in respect of:

(a) *Loss of amenity* – in the case of *Berry v Stone Manganese Marine Ltd.*[32] damages of £1,250 were awarded. The plaintiff had difficulty in taking part in certain conversations and he was handicapped in respect of his enjoyment of radio and television. In *Thompson and Others v Smiths Ship-repairers (North Shields) Ltd.*[33] damages of between £250 and £1,645 were awarded. This reflected the varying loss of amenity which in turn was related to the different levels of hearing loss suffered by each plaintiff.

(b) *Loss of career prospects and future earnings* – in the case of *Darby v Short Brothers and Harland Ltd. and the Ministry of Aviation Supply,*[34] the plaintiff not only suffered hearing loss which the High Court in Northern Ireland took into account but his career prospects had been reduced as a result and with it the possibility of increasing his income. In this case, damages of £27,000 were awarded which would have been higher but for an element of contributory negligence on the part of the plaintiff.[35]

It is not possible to draw conclusions on the level of damages likely to be awarded in any particular case although it does appear that in the cases so far taken, compensation related to loss of earnings is greater than that associated with the amenity loss.

STATUTORY RIGHT TO BENEFIT AS A RESULT OF HEARING LOSS

In 1969 the Secretary of State for Social Services asked the Industrial Injuries Advisory Council to consider and advise:

---

[32]   *Berry v Stone Manganese Marine Ltd.* (1971) 12 K.I.R. 13, 34–5.
[33]   *Thompson and Others v Smiths Ship-repairers (North Shields) Ltd.* [1984] 1 All E.R. 881.
[34]   *Daily Telegraph* (1972) 6th/7th June.
[35]   See also the case of *Dyer v Metropolitan Police*, reported in the *Health and Safety Practitioner*, December 1998, in which the police were ordered to pay damages of £175,792 in respect of irreparable hearing damage suffered by a police officer after using a police issue earpiece during regular surveillance operations. Exposure levels of up to 90 dB(A) were reported.

(a) whether there are degrees of hearing loss attributable to exposure to noise in the course of employment which satisfy the conditions for prescription as an industrial disease[36] and, if so;

(b) what arrangements would need to be made to deal with claims for benefit; and

(c) what, if any, special conditions should be placed on eligibility for benefit.

This request resulted from the conclusions of the Industrial Diseases Sub-Committee of the Industrial Injuries Advisory Council who appraised the final report on the research into noise in industry and its effect on hearing.[37] The Sub-Committee recommended that in view of the scientific and medical evidence and statistics, a formal reference of the question of prescription should be sought from the Secretary of State.

In a subsequent report[38] the Industrial Injuries Advisory Council concluded, "Deafness is a condition which only rarely leads to incapacity or affects earning power, but we are satisfied that it can become severely disabling socially and in our view it is a proper subject for compensation under a scheme based on loss of faculty rather than loss of earnings." The Council felt that occupational deafness should be prescribed as an industrial disease, provided that:

(a) the deafness due to occupational noise was substantial;

(b) appropriate technical and medical services were available for diagnosis and assessment;

(c) there was closely drawn occupational care.

Hearing loss due to noise exposure at work is the largest single category of prescribed industrial disease that has been compensated by the Department of Social Security. Since 1983, 1,200–1,500 cases each year have been recorded.

---

[36] As laid down by the National Insurance (Industrial Injuries) Act 1965.
[37] *Industrial noise and its effects on hearing,* Cmnd. 4145, 1969.
[38] *Occupational Deafness,* Cmnd. 5461, October 1973, para 89, p. 38.

Occupational deafness has been a prescribed disease since 1974 and is currently subject to the Social Security (Industrial Injuries) (Prescribed Diseases) Regulations 1985.[39] The Regulations set out a list of prescribed diseases and injuries and the occupations for which they are prescribed, in relation to all people employed on or after 5th July 1948. The Regulations define the degree of permanent hearing loss due to occupational exposure which must be experienced to be considered "occupational deafness" and therefore eligible for industrial injuries disablement benefit. There is a requirement that the affected person must have actually worked:

(i) in one or more of certain specified jobs for at least ten years; and

(ii) in one or more of those jobs at some time during the five years prior to the benefit claim.

The jobs are:

(a) using, or working very near, powered (but not hand powered) grinding tools on metal (other than sheet metal or plate metal);

(b) using, or working very near, pneumatic percussive tools on metal;

(c) using, or working very near, pneumatic percussive tools for drilling rock in quarries or underground or in mining coal (or in sinking shafts or for tunnelling in civil engineering works);

(ca) using, or working very near, pneumatic percussion tools on stone in quarry works;

(d) working very near a plant (but not a power press plant) involved in the forging (including drop stamping) of metal by means of closed or open dies or drop hammers;

(e) working in textile manufacturing all of the time or most of the time in rooms or sheds where there are machines which are

---

[39] S.I. 1985 No. 967, as variously amended. The Regulations were made under the Social Security Act 1975 and implement the provisions of the Social Security Contributions and Benefits Act 1992, Part V, by prescribing diseases and injuries in respect of which benefits are payable under the Act.

weaving man-made or natural (including mineral) fibres or in the high speed false twisting of fibres;

(f) working all of the time or most of the time very near machines which are cutting, shaping or cleaning metal nails;

(g) using, or working all of the time or most of the time very near, plasma spray guns which are depositing metal;

(h) using, or working all of the time or most of the time very near, any of the following machines which are working wood or material made partly of wood: multi-cutter moulding machines, planing machines, automatic or semi-automatic lathes, multiple cross-cut machines, automatic shaping machines, double-end tenoning machines, vertical spindle moulding machines (including high-speed routing machines), edge banding machines, band sawing machines with a blade width of not less than 75 millimetres, and circular sawing machines in the operation of which the blade is moved towards the material being cut;

(i) using chain-saws in forestry;

(j) air arc gouging or working wholly or mainly near such work;

(k) using, or working all or most of the time very near to band saws, circular saws or cutting discs for cutting metal in the metal founding or forging industries;

(l) using, or working all or most of the time very near to circular saws for cutting products in the manufacture of steel;

(m) using, or working all or most of the time very near to burners or torches for cutting or dressing steel based products;

(n) working all or most of the time very near skid transfer banks;

(o) working all or most of the time very near knock out or shake out grids in foundries;

(p) mechanical bobbin cleaning or working all or most of the time near such activity;

(q) using, or working all or most of the time near vibrating metal boxes in the concrete products industry;

(r) using, or working all or most of the time near high pressure jets of water or a mixture of water and abrasive material in the water jetting industry (including work under water);

(s) work in ships' engine rooms;

(t) using, or working all of the time or mainly very near circular saws for cutting concrete masonry blocks during manufacture;

(u) burning stone in quarries by jet channelling processes, or working all of the time or mainly near such processes;

(v) work on specified testing of gas turbines;

(w) using, or working all of the time or mainly very near certain types of automatic machines for the production of glass containers and hollow ware; spinning machines using compressed air to produce glass or mineral wool; glass toughening furnaces.

Specified vibration induced injury to the hands is also included when associated with particular industries and occupations.

When claims are made then, subject to the employment conditions of the regulations being satisfied, the Department of Social Security will arrange for medical examination. If diagnosis shows that the degree of permanent hearing loss satisfies the requirements of the regulations, an independent medical board will assess the degree of disability and determine the benefit to be paid.[40] Occupational deafness is defined for the purpose of the regulations as "sensorineural hearing loss amounting to a least 50 dB in each ear, being the average of hearing losses at 1, 2 and 3 kHz frequencies and being due in the case of at least one ear to occupational noise."

---

[40] For advice on claims see *Ill or disabled because of a disease or deafness caused by work?*, Leaflet SD6, October 2001, Department for Work and Pensions. It is estimated that 14,250 people were receiving disablement benefit for occupational deafness in April 2000. See *Health and Safety Statistics 2000/01*, Health and Safety Commission, H.M.S.O., 2001.

STATUTORY DUTY

Workplace (Health, Safety and Welfare) Regulations 1992[41]

Regulation 5(1) requires that "The workplace and the equipment, devices and systems to which this regulation applies shall be maintained ... in an efficient state, in efficient working order and in good repair." "Efficient" in this context means efficient from the point of view of health, safety and welfare.

It is possible a high noise level in a factory could make it an unsafe place to work under these provisions. This possibility was considered by Justice Ashworth in the case of *Berry v Stone Manganese Marine Ltd.* where the plaintiff suffered damage to his hearing over a number of years as a result of exposure to high noise levels from pneumatic hammers.[42] The plaintiff's claim was originally based on common law negligence alone but, by an amendment allowed at the trial, he alleged that the defendants were in breach of the duty to make and keep safe so far as reasonably practicable the plaintiff's place of work, contrary to section 29(1) of the Factories Act 1961 and its predecessors in law.[43] The counsel for the defence conceded that he could not successfully contend that section 29 of the Act applied only to the place or premises at which a person works but also to injurious processes carried on in that place but he reserved the right to contest the matter in a higher court. The court discussed the various steps that could have been taken to reduce the noise exposure, including acoustic linings to the walls of the work place, the provision of acoustic barriers, a quiet rest area, reduction of the number of employees in the particular work area (and accordingly a reduction in the level of noisy activities) and the use of "damping" techniques of the noisy processes. No judgment was given in

---

[41]   S.I. 1992 No. 3004.

[42]   Under current legislation, statutory action would no doubt be taken under the Provision and Use of Work Equipment Regulations 1998, S.I. 1998 No. 2306.

[43]   s. 26(1), Factories Act 1937, as amended. Section 29 of the Factories Act 1961 was repealed by the 1992 Regulations and it is reasonable to presume that judgments relating to the 1961 Act in respect of noise will form the basis of any similar actions taken under the Regulations. Exposure to high levels of noise could also be contrary to the general duties of employers under s. 2(2)(d) and (e) of the Health and Safety at Work etc. Act 1974.

respect of the statutory position as it as concluded that, having regard to the success of the common law claim, it was not necessary to establish a breach of statutory duty.

In a similar case in Scotland, however, a judgment was made on the application of section 29 of the Factories Act 1961 in respect of noise.[44] In the Scottish Outer House, Lord Maxwell considered a claim submitted by a man working on a drop-hammer in respect of partial deafness allegedly due to constant exposure to the noise of the drop-hammer. This action was based on common law negligence and breach of section 29(1) of the Factories Act 1961. The court was asked to decide whether the action could proceed on both counts. Proof was allowed before answer on the case on both negligence at common law and breach of statutory duty. In his judgment, Lord Maxwell did not see why the safety referred to in section 29(1) should not be just as much concerned with safety from heat, light and noise as from things with more tangible form. In this case, it had also been argued that, as danger only arose from prolonged exposure to noise, then at any one point in time a dangerously noisy place was not, at that instant, dangerous. Whilst appreciating the difficulty, Lord Maxwell was of the opinion that if a workplace at which men do in fact work for prolonged periods is not safe by reason of noise, for these men the work place is not "made and kept safe for any person working there".

Notwithstanding judgments on statutory law, plaintiffs may still take action in common law.

The Health and Safety at Work etc. Act 1974

Part I of the Act provides for a comprehensive and integrated system of law to deal with the health, safety and welfare of persons at work, and the health and safety of the public as they may be affected by work activities.[45]

The provisions of Part I of the Act relating to the making of health and safety regulations and the preparation and approval of

---

[44] *Carragher v Singer Manufacturing Co. Ltd.,* 1974, S.L.T. Notes, page 28.
[45] s. 1(1).

codes of practice enabled existing legislation[46] to be progressively replaced by a system of regulations and approved codes of practice, operating in combination with other provisions of Part I of the Act.[47]

General duty
The Act places a general duty on employers so far as is reasonably practicable:

(a) to ensure the health, safety and welfare at work of all their employees;

(b) to consult their employees on joint action on health and safety matters;

(c) to present a written statement of their safety policy arrangements.[48]

There is also a general duty on employees and the self-employed to ensure, so far as is reasonably practicable, that their activities are not conducted in such a way as to expose themselves or others[49] to risks to their health and safety.[50]

The Act established the Health and Safety Commission and the Health and Safety Executive to be responsible for administration of

---

[46] 3rd column, Schedule 1 and including *inter alia* the Mines and Quarries Act 1954, the Agriculture (Safety, Health and Welfare Provisions) Act 1956, the Factories Act 1961 and the Offices, Shops and Railway Premises Act 1963.

[47] s. 1(2).

[48] s. 2(3). A written policy is required if there are five or more employees.

[49] e.g. employees of sub-contractors, see *R. v. Swan Hunter Shipbuilders Ltd.* [1982] 1 All E.R. 264. Also employees who, in accordance with an agreement, used ... machinery which was defective and had been left on their employers' premises by ... contractors, were held to be affected by the way in which the ... contractors conducted their undertaking. *R. v Mara* [1987] 1 All E.R. 478; [1987] 1 W.L.R. 87.

[50] s. 3. s. 6 also deals with the duty of manufacturers, designers, importers and suppliers of any article for use at work to ensure it is designed and constructed so as to be safe and without risks to health when properly used. There is also a requirement to provide adequate information about any condition necessary to ensure its safe use – this could also include hearing protection.

Part I of the Act. Agricultural matters remain the responsibility of the Ministry of Agriculture. The function, powers and constitution of the Executive are contained in sections 10–14 and Schedule 2 of the Act.

Policy statements
The Health and Safety Commission considers the written policy statement to be extremely important. The Commission states "For each employer it is the blueprint on which his entire health and safety at work policy, organisation and activity are based. It should therefore be drafted clearly so that the entire labour force, management and employed, understands it and knows what its responsibilities are."[51]

Section 2(3) of the Health and Safety at Work etc. Act 1974 states:

> "Except in such cases as may be prescribed, it shall be the duty of every employer to prepare and as often as may be appropriate revise a written statement of his general policy with respect to the health and safety at work of his employees and the organisation and arrangements for the time being in force for carrying out that policy, and to bring that statement and any revision of it to the notice of all his employees."

Consultation is important in producing the general policy and detailing working arrangements and procedures for implementation of the policy. Employers will find it advisable to consult their employees through their safety representatives and safety committees. Policy statements will vary according to the particular circumstances of each employer and employers can also contact the Health and Safety Executive for advice on the production of written policy statements.

Contents of statement
Model statements have not been produced as they would not apply

---

[51] *Guidance notes on employers' policy statements for Health and Safety at Work,* Health and Safety Commission leaflet HSC 6, page 2. This leaflet offers very valuable guidance and poses and answers questions on the matters that should be considered in preparing a policy statement.

to every situation. They must contain the essential parts referred to in the Act:

(a) general policy; and

(b) the organisation and arrangements for carrying it out.

The following is one example of general policy on noise incorporated in a more detailed policy statement.

Good Standards for Health and Welfare

"Where there is a noise problem, the company will do whatever is reasonably practicable to reduce the exposure of employees to noise, by modifying machinery or buildings. Personal protection will be provided where appropriate."[52]

In some cases, particularly larger organisations, it may be better to produce the statement in two forms:

1. A concise statement of the general policy, organisation and arrangements in a single document, usually a booklet, which can be distributed to all employees and which would make reference to:

2. A more detailed document or collection of documents (e.g. including manuals of rules and procedures) which could be held in a central position in each location for all to see on request or posted where it could be seen by all employees.

In large groups of companies, not only is it important to produce a group safety policy, but the individual companies should be aware of their own particular responsibilities and produce their own policy.

The responsibility of particular employees at different levels within the organisation should be defined and the functions of any specialists in relation to health and safety should be made clear. This should include the person(s) delegated responsibility concerning noise control.

---

[52] Reproduced by permission of Courtaulds Ltd. from The International Paint Co. Ltd. publication *Your Safety – Policy and Guide.*

Identifying hearing hazards

The statement should ensure that those people exposed to a hearing risk are aware of the hazards and the reasons for controlling working practices to take account of the hazards. It should also state the role of the individual in maintaining a safe working environment.

ASSESSING THE EXISTENCE OF AN OCCUPATIONAL NOISE PROBLEM

The Robens Committee in its report[53] expressed its concern that prevention was the better approach to the problem of hearing loss at work rather than compensation. It studied the available evidence on the effects of occupational noise exposure in coming to this opinion and did in fact recommend powers to require employers to monitor and record noise levels from specified processes. However, it was not until 1981 that the Health and Safety Executive proposed new legislation specifically to control noise but this was shelved until the European Noise Directive was produced in 1986. This provided a four year deadline to introduce domestic legislation.

The Health and Safety at Work etc. Act 1974 empowers the Secretary of State to make health and safety regulations for any of the general purposes of Part I of the Act[54] and, without prejudice to that generality, for any of the purposes specified in Schedule 3 of the Act.[55]

The Noise at Work Regulations 1989[56] implement the provisions of E.E.C. Council Directive 86/188 on the protection of workers from the risks related to noise exposure at work and largely reflect the

---

[53] *Safety and Health at Work – Report of the Committee 1970–72,* July 1972, Cmnd. 5034, para. 345, page 110.

[54] s. 15.

[55] Schedule 3 includes purposes which relate to medical examinations and health surveys; monitoring of working conditions; matters affecting the conditions in which persons work, including in particular such matters as noise and vibration; requirements with respect to instruction, training and supervision of persons at work. These purposes could clearly include matters relating to occupational noise exposure.

[56] S.I. 1989 No.1790.

Robens Committee recommendations. The Regulations have, however, been the subject of criticism for failing to address fully the intentions of the Directive, particularly in relation to the control of noise at source.[57]

Occupational noise exposure problems – warning signs

It is clear from the evidence available that the effect of exposure to high noise levels may not become apparent for a considerable period, by which time it may be too late to correct hearing loss. There are a number of early warning signs that should be considered which may indicate a potential problem:

(a) workers find difficulty hearing each other speak whilst working in a noisy environment;

(b) head noises or ringing in the ears after being exposed to high noise levels;

(c) temporary loss of hearing, having the effect of muffling speech and certain other sounds which may occur after exposure to high noise levels for short periods;

(d) workers exposed to high noise levels for a longer period of time may complain that speech and certain other sounds have become muffled. They may have been told by their families they are becoming deaf;

(e) the turnover of labour in noisy work areas may be high;

(f) production in noisy areas may be relatively low.

If any of these indicators exist then investigation into the nature of the problem and its solution should be conducted.

---

[57] See "Noise at Work Regulations: UK and Europe", Bryson, Nigel, *Environmental Health*, August 1990, pp. 209–210. The Directive 86/188 is likely to be repealed following E.C. political agreement on a common position on the 11th June 2001. The Common Council position will reduce the first and second action levels by 5 dB(A).

The Noise at Work Regulations 1989

The Regulations apply to all workers in Great Britain[58] covered by the Health and Safety at Work etc. Act 1974, except employers, masters or crews of seagoing ships and the crew of any aircraft or hovercraft moving under its own power. Employers, and mine and quarry managers, are responsible for taking action in the workplace. Employees must co-operate with their employer's programme to prevent hearing damage. The Regulations only deal with the risks to hearing of employees. If noise produces risks other than hearing damage, action may be required to comply with other duties of the Act, for example:

(a) when background noise reduces the audibility of warning sounds,[59] an alternative warning or action to reduce the noise may be necessary;

(b) when non-employees are exposed to a noise risk, e.g. students[60] or visitors, the employer will need to take action to remove this risk. Every employer has to reduce the risk of damage to the hearing of his employees from exposure to noise to the lowest level that is reasonably practicable.[61]

Three "action levels"[62] are introduced by the Regulations:

the first action level – a daily personal continuous noise exposure of 85 dB(A);

---

[58] And outside in accordance with the Health and Safety at Work etc. Act 1974 (Application Outside Great Britain) Order 1995. See also *Reducing Noise at Work – Guidance on the Noise at Work Regulations 1989*, H.M.S.O., 1998.

[59] Such as fire alarms provided under the Fire Precautions Act 1971.

[60] Although certain trainees on schemes provided under section 2 of the Employment and Training Act 1973 have to be treated as employees by virtue of the Health and Safety (Training for Employment) Regulations 1990.

[61] Reg. 6.

[62] Reg. 2(1). All three action levels are likely to be reduced as a result of a European Parliament Council common position for adopting a Directive on the minimum health and safety requirements regarding the exposure of workers to the risks arising from physical agents (noise), contained in European Parliament session document Final A5–0038/2002, 21st February 2002.

the second action level – a daily personal continuous noise exposure of 90 dB(A);

the peak level (impulse noise) – a level of peak sound pressure of 200 pascals.

The daily personal noise exposure is defined as the value equivalent to the level of steady sound which would produce the same exposure in eight hours as the actual exposure over the working day.[63]

Every employer, when any of his employees are likely to be exposed to the first action level or above, or the peak action level or above, must ensure that a "competent person" carries out a noise assessment.[64] The assessment has to be reviewed when circumstances change and make it invalid.[65] As a rule of thumb, an assessment will usually be needed whenever it is necessary to shout to be understood by someone about two metres away or whenever it is difficult to talk to each other. There is no definition of "competent person". It may be that in straightforward cases noise can be measured by an experienced technician who can then recommend simple control measures. Other competent persons may include acoustic consultants, safety advisors and, in the case of enforcing authorities, Environmental Health Officers. The need for properly qualified and experienced people to carry out noise assessments is highlighted by a report of the Health and Safety Executive which said that "out of the first assessments ... examined by the H.S.E. the majority failed to meet the most basic requirement of enabling the employer to identify *whose job* involves exposure reaching the action levels".[66] If effective noise control programmes are to be introduced, adequate assessments are essential. Otherwise, time and money will be wasted. Inadequate assessments are mainly due to lack of appropriate skills and expertise on the part of the "competent person", failure to understand the purpose of assessments and confusion over their requirements. An assessment must:

---

[63] See the Schedule to the Regulations.
[64] Reg. 4(1).
[65] Reg. 4(2).
[66] *Sound Sense,* H.S.E. leaflet, February 1991. See also *Health Surveillance in Noisy Industries – advice for employers,* H.S.E., August 2000.

(a) identify those employees exposed to noise at or above the specified action levels; and

(b) provide the employer with sufficient information about the noise which will allow him to comply with the following duties:

(i) when any employee is likely to be exposed to the second action level or above, or to the peak action level or above, reduce, so far is reasonably practicable[67] (other than by the provision of personal ear protectors), the exposure to noise of that employee;[68]

(ii) to ensure, so far as practicable,[69] that any employee likely to be exposed to the first action level or above in circumstances where the daily personal noise exposure of that employee is likely to be less than 90 dB(A), is provided, *at his request,*[70] with suitable and efficient personal ear protectors; any employee likely to be exposed to the second action level or above, or to the peak action level or above, must be provided[71] with suitable personal ear protectors;

(iii) ensure, so far as is reasonably practicable,[72] that each ear

---

[67] Reg. 8. This term is not defined but for interpretation see *Halsbury's Laws of England,* fourth edition reissue, Volume 20, paragraph 550.

[68] Reg. 7. However, a conditional exemption certificate from this requirement may be granted by the Health and Safety Executive provided the daily personal noise exposure of the relevant employee, averaged over a week in accordance with Schedule 2, is below 90 dB(A) and there are adequate arrangements to ensure this is not exceeded.

[69] See footnote 67 above.

[70] This is an apparent anomaly, having regard for the employee's duty to take reasonable care for his own health and safety in accordance with section 7 of the Health and Safety at Work etc. Act 1974. This noise level is likely to be reduced to 85 dB(A) in accordance with a European Council common position of June 2001.

[71] See *Crouch v British Rail Engineering Ltd.* [1988] I.L.R.L. 404, C.A. It was held that the duty of care owed by an employer depended on the circumstances of each case. In this case the plaintiff was not working close to where protective equipment (in this case goggles) was stored and the employer was under a duty to provide the equipment into the plaintiff's hands. Storage of ear protection at the work station might, therefore, be necessary.

[72] See footnote 67 above.

protection zone[73] is identified as such and signs are provided advising of the need to wear personal ear protectors whilst in any such zone;[74]

(iv) provide adequate information, instruction and training to all employees likely to be exposed to noise at or above the first or peak action levels.[75]

A certificate of exemption[76] from the requirement to reduce the exposure of employees[77] can be issued by the Health and Safety Executive subject to specific conditions being met, provided that the health and safety of people likely to be affected by the exception will not be prejudiced.[78]

Undertaking a noise assessment

The Health and Safety Executive has published a number of noise guides dealing with the legal duties imposed by the Regulations and providing advice on noise assessment, information and control.[79] A proper assessment should provide an employer with guidance and recommendations sufficient to ensure that they know precisely what action to take to comply with the Regulations. This may require the provision of information additional to that contained in the noise guides. Considerable care is required if relevant and

---

[73] An area where any employee is likely to be exposed to the second or peak action levels or above.

[74] Reg. 9. At the second action level or above, warning signs are obligatory.

[75] Reg. 11.

[76] Reg. 13.

[77] Reg. 7.

[78] Reg. 13(2).

[79] Two booklets have been issued containing the following eight guides:
Noise Guide No. 1, *Legal duties of employers to prevent damage to hearing;*
Noise Guide No. 2, *Legal duties of designers, manufacturers, importers and suppliers to prevent damage to hearing;*
Noise Guide No. 3, *Equipment and procedures for noise surveys;*
Noise Guide No. 4, *Engineering control of noise;*
Noise Guide No. 5, *Types and selection of personal ear protectors;*
Noise Guide No. 6, *Training for competent persons;*
Noise Guide No. 7, *Procedures for noise testing machinery;*
Noise Guide No. 8, *Exemption from certain requirements of the Noise at Work Regulations 1989.*

accurate information is to be provided and duplication of effort avoided. The workplace organisation and activities should be reviewed to decide on the approach to be adopted. A noise assessment should consider certain important factors:

(a) the employees exposed to noise;

(b) the processes and equipment;

(c) ear protection;

(d) ear protection zones;

(e) information needs.

Employees exposed to noise
The assessment must identify employees likely to be exposed to noise at or above the first, second and peak action levels. It has to distinguish between these categories of exposure. Assessments which fail to quantify *daily personal noise exposures* will not meet the requirements of Regulation 4(1)(a). If noise exposure is below the first action level, the Regulations merely place a general duty on employers to reduce the risk of hearing damage.[80]

Processes and equipment
The assessment should note the machinery,[81] tools and processes likely to contribute to employee noise exposure. Exposure at or above the second or peak action level is particularly important with regard to the noise reduction requirements of Regulation 7. The noise measurement element of the assessment should include at least the following information:

(a) a sketch of the measurement site showing relevant dimensions, e.g. size of room, machinery dimensions, microphone location and object being measured;

(b) type and serial number of measuring instruments;

---

[80] Reg. 6.
[81] See also *Keep the noise down – advice for purchasers of workplace machinery*, H.S.E., November 1997.

(c) calibration method;

(d) weighting networks used;

(e) description of sound and background noise levels;

(f) information on machinery or processes being measured, e.g. machine type, load, speed;

(g) date and time(s) of investigation.

In considering any noise reduction programme which may follow from the assessment report, a noise map may be of value. This will show the relevant locations of the noise sources and enable the production of noise contours (lines connecting points of equal sound levels). This will show the areas where noise levels are too high and be a starting point for planning noise reduction measures. It will also provide an information base against which future measurements can be taken following the implementation of a noise reduction programme.[82] The Health and Safety Executive noise guides do not require this specific information but in complex situations a detailed approach is essential if an effective noise reduction programme is to be produced.

Ear protection
Where noise exposure above the first action level is likely, the assessment must include information to assist employers to select personal hearing protectors required by Regulation 8. Two cases arise depending on the level of noise exposure:

1. Employees likely to be exposed to daily personal noise exposure at or above the first action level, in circumstances where the daily personal noise exposure is likely to be less than 90 dB(A), need to be provided with personal ear protectors, at their request. The H.S.E. advise that the minimum hearing protection in such cases is 5 dB(A)[83] and employers should ensure that the chosen hearing protectors will achieve this.

---

[82] See Noise Guide No. 7 and also useful booklets by Bruel and Kjaer: *Measuring Sound/Machine Condition Monitoring/Vibration Testing.*
[83] Noise Guide No. 1, page 11.

2. Where employees are likely to be subjected to exposure at or above the second or peak action levels, the employer has to make available suitable ear protectors and ensure they are used. Frequency analysis of the noise may be an important factor in selecting suitable protection against exposure to very high noise levels,[84] as may the attenuation data of the protective devices.

Ear protection zones
The assessment must identify working areas where employees are likely to be exposed to noise at or above the second or peak action levels, and advise that these areas are to be designated "ear protection zones" for the purposes of Regulation 9.

Information needs
The noise assessment should produce enough information to enable the employer to decide what information, instruction and training is required to comply with his duties under Regulation 11. The "competent persons" observations of working practices may provide additional commonsense advice on action to minimise exposure, e.g. the correct use of existing noise enclosures, the proper use of ear protectors[85] and avoiding remaining in noisy areas during work breaks.[86]

HEARING CONSERVATION

Measurement of hearing

Whilst not a specific requirement of the Noise at Work Regulations 1989, in noisy environments, hearing measurement and conservation will assist an employer in meeting his duty of care under section 2 of the Health and Safety at Work etc. Act 1974, as well as allowing him to evaluate the success of any action taken by him to comply with his duty under the Regulations. An audiometric testing programme is the ultimate control on the effectiveness of the

---

[84] Any personal ear protectors provided must meet the requirements of any Community Directive listed in Sch. 1 to the Personal Protective Equipment at Work Regulations 1992 which is applicable to those ear protectors. See also *Noise at Work – a guide for employees*, H.S.E., 1991.

[85] See fn. 71, p. 419 and fn. 83, p. 422.

[86] See also *Noise at work – advice for employees,* H.S.E., March 1993.

conservation programme. The effectiveness of any steps taken to reduce noise exposure can only be accurately assessed in this way. Audiometric tests are valuable in a number of ways:

(a) pre-employment audiograms will reveal the presence of hearing loss that may respond to treatment;

(b) a pre-employment test may in part protect an employer from liability if the person examined has already suffered noise induced hearing loss.[87] It will allow an employer to place the employee in a relatively quiet environment if the audiometric test reveals hearing loss which needs to be protected from further deterioration;

(c) follow-up tests – most early noise induced hearing loss occurs around 4,000 Hz and frequently passes unnoticed, as loss in this frequency range does not affect speech communication. Some people are particularly susceptible to noise induced hearing loss and repeat tests are the only reliable way of detecting early hearing loss;

(d) examination at the end of a person's employment in a noisy environment may help to protect an employer against any future action in respect of alleged noise induced hearing loss.

Most audiometric tests can be carried out by a suitably trained person. However, diagnosis and treatment of hearing loss, the approval and validation of audiometric records, and assessments of hearing tests must remain a medical responsibility and employers should recognise that evidence of hearing loss, whether in respect of claims under the common law of negligence or for industrial injury benefit, will only be accepted if given by a person medically qualified to give that evidence.

Hearing conservation programme

Once a working environment is known to exist which exposes employees to the risk of hearing damage, there are certain basic

---

[87] It will not necessary protect him, however, if further hearing loss occurs as a result of additional exposure to high noise levels.

remedial steps which may be taken to reduce the exposure. These may be summarised as follows:

1. *Noisy machinery* – use a quieter process if possible, e.g. welding rather than riveting;

    – isolate machines on suitable resilient mounts (these must be properly designed to deal with the particular problem (see generally Chapter 1));

    – mufflers may be effective on machines discharging high velocity steam and air, such as gas turbines, air nozzles and steam safety values;

    – apply damping to resonating surfaces;

    – modification of machinery may be possible without significant additions to costs. Shearing, marking and punching are inherently noisy but in some instances it may, for example, be possible to alter the angle of cut so that a slicing action rather than punching is achieved.

2. *Maintenance* – good maintenance can reduce machine noise. Automatic feeds, bearings, clutches and gears should be regularly checked to ensure proper tolerances are maintained. Guards and similar parts should be kept secure to reduce vibration. Lubrication procedures should be strictly followed. Rubber wheels may replace metal ones. Metal bench tops may be covered with wood.

3. *Acoustic treatment* – this can often reduce the noise level of an entire plant or a limited area. Acoustic tiles, ceiling baffles or acoustic shields may alone or in combination reduce noise levels.

4. *Acoustic enclosure* – where practicable it may be possible to enclose offending machinery completely, or at least partition it off.

5. *Personal ear protection* – even where the above measures are adopted it may still be necessary (especially to comply with the Noise at Work Regulations 1989) or desirable to provide ear

protection for employees. Ear protection should not be used as a substitute for effective noise control. Employees require a type of hearing protection which is effective and acceptable to those people using it. There are four types of ear protection:

(i) ear plugs;

(ii) canal caps (or semi-inserts);

(iii) ear muffs;

(iv) special types of protector to deal with particular problems.

Advice on the correct type of protection is best left to the medical or safety adviser. Provided that adequate noise attenuation can be achieved it is usually best to allow personal choice to prevail; it is then more likely that the hearing protection will be used.

Noise Guide No. 5, *Types and selection of personal ear protectors,* gives detailed advice on the types of protection available. Manufacturers will be able to provide details of the attenuation provided by their products to enable the employer to assess whether they meet his particular requirements. It is desirable to issue hearing protection on a personal basis and it should be maintained in a clean state.

The following matters should be considered when selecting hearing protectors:

(a) ear muffs are rigid cups covering the external ear and are held against the head by a spring loaded, adjustable band. The seal against the head is provided by a soft cushioning ring. The space in the cup is fitted with absorbent material. The seal must remain unaffected by perspiration, hair oils and the skin, and must be of a non-toxic and non-irritant material. The degree of noise reduction will depend on:

    (i) the frequency, content and volume of noise to be attenuated. The ear protectors must be capable of providing the correct type of control;

(ii) maintenance of the cup seal – this will be reduced if they are worn over long hair or spectacles;

(iii) the pressure of the cups against the head – the correct pressure is important and bending the band to reduce the pressure will reduce the degree of noise attenuation;

(b) ear muffs provide the best hearing protection and are suitable for high noise environments;

(c) one size of ear muff fits the majority of people and they can be worn by people unable to wear ear-plugs because of ear infections;

(d) pre-formed ear plugs which fit into the ear should be available in a variety of sizes, must be smooth, airtight and fit comfortably. They must be easy to clean;

(e) the noise reduction of ear plugs depends on their being well fitting;

(f) disposable and re-usable ear plugs are made from various compressible materials such as plastic foam or fine mineral down. This type of plug may not be suitable for all noise environments and medical and manufacturers' advice should be sought on the most appropriate material;

(g) permanent rubber or plastic plugs are available but must be a correct fit in each ear to provide satisfactory performance;

6. *Re-allocation of duties* – to prevent further hearing loss or to reduce exposure to well below 90 dB(A) 8-hour L_{eq}, this approach may be adopted.

VIBRATION AT WORK

Occupational exposure to vibration occurs in a number of ways, with two transmission routes:

1. Whole body vibration.

2. Hand-arm vibration.

In whole body vibration, the energy is transmitted to the worker through contact with a vibratory surface and arises mainly from riding in vehicles, e.g. via vehicle seats or floors. It can also be transmitted from complete structures that are shaken by machinery, e.g. rock crushing plant. Employees most at risk from this type of vibration include vehicle drivers, machinery operators and ships' crews.

Hand-arm vibration is more frequently encountered. Employees in the construction, servicing and manufacturing industries who use portable hand-held vibrating power tools may be at risk from some types of vibration-induced injuries. Vibration from some tools can effect the lower back, shoulders, neck and head, but the majority of hand-held power tools transmit vibration to the hands and arms. Regular use can cause permanent injury. Such injuries are known as hand/arm vibration syndrome (H.A.V.S.), the most common example of which is vibration white finger. The main symptoms of vibration white finger are tingling/numbness in the fingers, loss of sensation and manual dexterity, finger blanching (white finger), and aching digits and limbs. Once H.A.V.S. symptoms are noticed, the damage is often irreversible.

Research conducted on behalf of the Health and Safety Executive[88] found that around 4.5 million people are regularly exposed to potentially harmful levels of hand-arm vibration at work. It also found that more than 1.2 million people are exposed to levels of hand-arm vibration in excess of the H.S.E.'s recommended action levels. Of 1.1 million workers with symptoms of H.A.V.S., 515,000 suffered disturbed sleep as a result of the discomfort and 335,000 found it difficult or impossible to fasten buttons. The greatest exposures were found in bricklayers, building contractors and masons, carpenters and joiners, electricians and gardeners.[89] The most common sources of vibration were percussion drills, hand-held grinders and jigsaws.

---

[88] Reported in *The Health and Safety Practitioner*, December 1998, p. 42.
[89] For a useful guide on the control of hand-arm vibration, see "The management of exposure to hand-arm vibration", Hill, K., *The Health and Safety Practitioner*, July 1999, pp. 28–32.

Vibration has not so far been the subject of specific statutory control in the workplace, although the various general provisions of the Health and Safety at Work etc. Act 1974 and its associated Regulations described elsewhere in this chapter apply equally to vibration as a health and safety matter. However, in 2001 the Council of Ministers of the European Parliament reached political agreement on a proposal for a European Directive specifying minimum standards for the health and safety of workers exposed to hand-arm and whole body vibration.[90] The Directive will, when there is likely to be a risk from exposure to vibration, require employers to:

(a) reduce exposure to a minimum;

(b) provide information and training;

(c) assess exposure levels;

(d) when exposure reaches the exposure action value, carry out a programme of measures to reduce exposure and provide appropriate health surveillance;

(e) keep exposure below the exposure limit value.

What is an acceptable level of vibration exposure?

This issue was one of several considered in the case of *Armstrong v British Coal Corporation*.[91] In this case, the Court of Appeal upheld an award of damages to seven employees of the British Coal Corporation (B.C.C.) who claimed damages for vibration white finger. All employers owe their employees the common law duty of care to provide safe plant and equipment. The standard is one of reasonable care and, for a claim in respect of vibration white finger to succeed, the employee must show that their exposure to vibration,

---

[90] Common Position (EC) No. 26/2001, adopted by the Council on 25th June 2001. However, in a progress report of 2nd November, it was reported that a number of amendments to the text of the draft Directive had been proposed. These were to be the subject of debate during the time period allowed for the Council second reading of the Directive.

[91] *Armstrong v British Coal Corporation*, Trans. Ref: QB ENF 97/1578/C, 31st July 1998.

and therefore the risk of developing vibration white finger, was greater than a prudent employer should have allowed.

The Court of Appeal decided that, after January 1976, B.C.C. should have implemented a range of precautions, including training, surveillance, job rotation and warnings where vibration exposure was significant. It also considered the question of to what degree, if any, employees can reasonably be exposed. The Court considered BS6842:1987 and the H.S.E. Guidance on Hand-Arm Vibration[92] which specifies the likely vibration levels from certain types of vibrating equipment and the recommended maximum daily usage times. The guidance refers to the vibration "dose" which is normalised over a standard reference eight hour working period to produce a time-weighted average or "A8". Exposure regularly exceeding an A8 of 2.8 m/s² would lead to a 10% risk of an employee developing vibration white finger. The Court of Appeal considered 2.8 m/s² to be an appropriate level of permissible exposure for prudent employers to apply (the plaintiffs had proposed a lower level). Exposure in excess of that level required job rotation in addition to warnings and health surveillance. The Court also suggested a form of words for a sensible warning.

The Court awarded damages for seven miners totalling £124,735 followed by a bulk settlement of £500 million for some 40,000 ex-miners affected by vibration white finger.

In the Court of Appeal, in the case of *Allen v British Rail Engineering Ltd.*,[93] it was ruled that compensation for vibration white finger may be reduced where employees were already injured by vibrating tools before employers knew of the danger of such tools. An employer's liability for negligence arose only after the date when it should have realised that the use of vibrating tools might involve some risk to employees.

The court must do the best that it can on the evidence to apportion compensation, and should not refuse to compensate an employee

---

92   HS(G) 88 1994.
93   (2001), reported in *Croner's Health and Safety Case Law Briefing*, Issue 51, 12th October 2001.

who cannot accurately prove what proportion of the injury is attributable to an employer's negligence.

SAFETY REPRESENTATIVES/SAFETY COMMITTEES

A specially trained member of the workforce has the daily job of ensuring safety in the workplace. He or she is not necessarily highly trained but is someone who is capable of recognising a hazard and advising those with the expertise and authority to take remedial action. A single safety officer in a large workplace may find it impossible to monitor all potentially hazardous conditions. Many companies have employed safety representatives for years. The Safety Representatives and Safety Committee Regulations 1977[94] entitle trade unions to appoint safety representatives in workplaces where one or more persons are employed by an employer by whom the trade union is recognised.

The Regulations do not however apply to non-union employees, although similar requirements in relation to non-union employees are contained in the Health and Safety (Consultation with Employees) Regulations 1996.[95]

Functions of safety representatives[96]

The Health and Safety Commission has published a code of practice on safety representatives and guidance notes on the 1977 Regulations which should be read by employers and employees.[97] The functions of safety representatives are stated in Regulation 4(1):

> "In addition to his function under section 2(4) of the 1974 Act to represent the employees in consultation with the employer under section 2(6) of the 1974 Act (which requires every employer to consult safety representatives with a view to the

---

[94] S.I. 1977 No. 500.
[95] S.I. 1996 No. 1513.
[96] The Safety Representatives and Safety Committees Regulations 1977, Reg. 4, S.I. 1977 No. 500.
[97] See *Safety Representatives and Safety Committees,* Health and Safety Commission, H.M.S.O., 1977.

making and maintenance of arrangements which will enable him and his employees to co-operate effectively in promoting and developing measures to ensure the health and safety at work of the employees and in checking the effectiveness of such measures), each safety representative shall have the following functions:

(a) to investigate potential hazards and dangerous occurrences at the workplace (whether or not they are drawn to his attention by the employees he represents) and to examine the causes of accidents at the workplace;

(b) to investigate complaints by any employee he represents relating to that employee's health, safety or welfare at work;

(c) to make representations to the employer on matters arising out of sub-paragraphs (a) and (b) above;

(d) to make representations to the employer on general matters affecting the health, safety or welfare at work of the employees at the workplace;

(e) to carry out inspections in accordance with Regulations 5, 6 and 7;[98]

(f) to represent the employees he was appointed to represent in consultations at the workplace with inspectors of the Health and Safety Executive and of any other enforcing authority;

(g) to receive information from inspectors in accordance with section 28(8) of the 1974 Act;[99] and

(h) to attend meetings of safety committees where he attends in

---

[98] Reg. 5 entitles the safety representative to carry out regular inspections. Reg. 6 allows for inspection following notifiable accidents, dangerous occurrences or occurrence of a notifiable disease. Reg. 7 entitles safety representatives to examine documents that the employer has a statutory duty to keep in connection with s. 53(1) of the 1974 Act.

[99] s. 28(8) requires inspectors to give certain types of information to employees and employers.

his capacity as a safety representative in connection with any of the above functions."

The Regulations also require the employer to consult safety representatives with regard to the introduction of measures which may substantially affect health and safety, arrangements for appointing competent persons under the Management of Health and Safety at Work Regulations 1999, health and safety information given to employees, safety training and the health and safety consequences of introducing new technologies. Every employer must provide such facilities and assistance as are reasonably required by the safety representatives to enable them to carry out their functions.

The code of practice[100] suggests that safety representatives keep themselves informed of the relevant law on health and safety at work, the particular hazards and control measures necessary to eliminate risk and the health and safety policy of their employer and his arrangements for fulfilling that policy. The code also recommends that the safety representative encourages co-operation on these matters with management and submits reports, both oral and written, to the employer on unsatisfactory conditions.

Occupational noise exposure is an important aspect of health and safety and is clearly a matter to be carefully considered by safety representatives and safety committees. The safety representative may be a shop steward, although this is not essential. Normally management and unions will negotiate the number of safety representatives and their location in the place of work.

Safety committees

Safety committees are required to be established for the purposes of section 2(7) of the 1974 Act if at least two safety representatives submit a written request to the employer.[101] The code of practice gives detailed guidance on how the safety committees should operate. Generally the safety committees will advise and direct

---

[100] In particular, clause 5.
[101] Reg. 9(1).

general policy, determine the matters that will be considered by the committees and make recommendations arising from particular incidents referred to them. It will normally be desirable to have the safety representatives sitting on the safety committee although there is no legal requirement to do so. This will assist the co-ordination of safety and welfare activities and the spread of information amongst employees. For this reason it is helpful if the safety representative is a member of the shop floor work force.

Education and training[102]

Union sponsored courses will often be used to train safety representatives but these are usually general in nature. They include legislation, policy statements, fire hazards, safety committees, accident prevention and record keeping. The safety representative is a vital link in the education of the workers he represents as he has direct contact. Good training is therefore essential. The general nature of union sponsored courses can be supplemented by some detailed and specialist "in-training" at the workplace, particularly in larger organisations.

Training on particular matters can be given by management, Health and Safety Executive representatives and experts on particular matters such as noise.[103] Such training needs to be related to the particular needs of the workplace and will help safety representatives and management to recognise the particular problems they have to deal with. It is important to ensure that supervisors and managers are equally aware of potential hazards as they may be required to implement day to day controls over the working environment. Where a high risk exists, e.g. in an area where noise levels exceed the recommendations of the code of practice for reducing the exposure of employed persons to noise, an operator training programme will help to ensure the maintenance of good safe working conditions.

---

[102] s. 2(2)(c) requires employers to provide such information, instruction, training and supervision as is necessary to ensure, so far as is reasonably practicable, the health and safety at work of their employees.

[103] In relation to training for "competent persons" for the purposes of the Noise at Work Regulations 1989, see H.S.E. Noise Guide No. 6.

A good working environment means that accidents and ill health are less likely to occur and therefore less time will be lost.

REPORTING OF WORK RELATED HEARING INJURY

The Reporting of Injuries, Diseases and Dangerous Occurrences Regulations 1995[104] (RIDDOR) require the enforcing authority to be notified forthwith of any work related accident causing death, injuries or conditions of a specified nature,[105] or where there is a specified dangerous occurrence.[106] If a person is incapacitated for more than three consecutive days as a result of a work related injury or accident, the enforcing authority also has to be notified.[107]

The Health and Safety Executive maintains statistics on these reports. In its latest report,[108] some of the main findings that were reported included:[109]

1. A 1995 survey gave a prevalence estimate of 170,000 cases of self-reported deafness, tinnitus or other ear conditions caused by work.

2. A Medical Research Council survey in 1997–98 gave a national prevalence estimate of 509,000 people in Great Britain suffering from hearing difficulties as a result of exposure to noise at work.

3. New cases of noise-induced deafness qualifying for disablement benefit have been falling steadily since the mid-1980s, from just under 1,500 in 1984 to 226 in 2000.

4. The industry groups with the highest average annual incidence

---

[104] S.I. 1995 No. 3163. Following a review, revised Regulations are anticipated in 2003; see *Croner's Health and Safety Briefing*, Issue 209.

[105] Reg. 3(1)(a)–(d).

[106] Reg. 3(1)(e). Hearing damage could be a reportable dangerous occurrence from an incident involving an explosion of blasting material in a mine – see clause 34, Sch. 2, pt. 2 of the Regulations or clause 74 of Part V in respect of off-shore installations.

[107] Reg. 3(3).

[108] *Health and Safety Statistics 2000/01*, Health and Safety Commission, H.M.S.O., 2001.

[109] *Ibid*, pp. 116 and 117.

rates of new cases qualifying for benefit (based on 1999 and 2000 figures) were extraction energy and water supply, manufacturing and construction.

5. The main occupational groups with the highest incidence rates were craft and related occupations, and plant and machine operatives. More specific occupations with high incidence rates included labourers in foundries, electrical/energy and related plant operatives, metal plate workers and labourers in engineering.

Noise damage is not an illness or injury specifically cited in RIDDOR; therefore there may well be many unreported cases of hearing injury.

MANAGING HEALTH AND SAFETY AT WORK

A number of regulations and approved codes of practice relating to the management of health and safety stemming from European Directives came into force in 1993 and have been amended or revoked in the intervening period. Failure to comply with any provision of the approved codes is not in itself an offence, although failure may be taken into account in criminal proceedings as proof that a person has contravened the regulation to which the provision relates.

The Management of Health and Safety at Work Regulations 1999[110] and their related approved Code of Practice[111] deal with, amongst other things, workplace risk assessment,[112] provision of information for employees[113] and training arrangements.[114] Where other regulations also contain requirements for risk assessment, but are addressed specifically to the hazards and risks covered by them, then those risk assessments will not be requirements of the

---

[110] S.I. 1999 No. 3242.

[111] *Management of Health and Safety at Work: approved code of practice,* H.S.E. L21, H.M.S.O.

[112] Reg. 3. For the general principles of risk assessment, see paragraph 3 of the Approved Code of Practice.

[113] Reg. 10.

[114] Reg. 13.

Management of Health and Safety Regulations as well. In relation
to workplace noise exposure, the assessment required for the
purposes of Regulation 4 of the Noise at Work Regulations 1989
will suffice. The advice of the Code in relation to the provision of
employee information and training will help employees comply
with the relevant requirements of both sets of regulations.

Regulation 5 of the Management of Health and Safety at Work
Regulations 1999 requires that "every employer shall ensure that
his employees are provided with such health surveillance as is
appropriate having regard to the risks to their health and safety
which are identified by the (risk) assessment". Accordingly, this
imposes a requirement to monitor the effects on hearing of an
employee's exposure to high noise levels at work identified by the
requirements of the Noise at Work Regulations. Additionally,
employers are required to appoint one or more competent persons
to help in applying the provisions of health and safety legislation.[115]

Employees themselves also have personal health and safety
responsibilities. In particular, they have a duty under section 7 of
the Health and Safety at Work etc. Act 1974 to take reasonable care
for their own health and safety. This duty includes using correctly
work items provided by their employer, in accordance with their
training and the instructions they receive to enable them to use the
items safely. This duty is supplemented by a requirement in the
Management of Health and Safety at Work Regulations 1999
which states that:

> "Every employee shall use any ... safety device provided to him
> by his employer in accordance both with any training in the use
> of the equipment concerned which has been received by him,
> and the instructions respecting that use which have been
> provided to him by the said employer in compliance with the
> requirements and prohibitions imposed on that employer by or
> under the relevant statutory provisions."[116]

Employees are also required to inform their employer of any

---

[115] Reg. 7.
[116] Reg. 14(1).

situation which could reasonably be considered to represent a serious and immediate danger to health and safety[117] and any matter which could reasonably be considered to represent a shortcoming in the employer's protection arrangements for health and safety.[118]

To meet these requirements it is clearly necessary for employees to use any ear protectors provided, to advise of any deterioration in machinery performance which increases noise levels and to notify any shortcomings such as defective ear protectors, missing signs in ear protection zones and the presence of unprotected or untrained people in noisy work areas. The duties of employees do not negate the responsibility of the employer to comply with his duties under the law. In particular, employers need to ensure that employees receive adequate instruction and training to enable them to comply with their own duties under the Regulations.

The Regulations require an employer to have regard, in entrusting tasks, to an employee's capabilities as regards health and safety; to ensure they receive adequate health and safety training at the time of recruitment and on being exposed to new and increased risks associated with a transfer or change of responsibilities, introduction of new work equipment or a change involving such equipment, the introduction of new technology or new systems of work. Training has to be repeated periodically where appropriate.[119]

The Provision and Use of Work Equipment Regulations 1998[120] and the accompanying guidance[121] deal with the implementation of European Directive 89/655/EEC requiring similar basic laws throughout the E.C. on the use of work equipment. The Regulations deal generally with the duties of employers, the selection of suitable equipment, maintenance, information and instructions, and training. They also deal with the need for equipment to be able to control selected hazards. In relation to noise, the Regulations require that,

---

[117] Reg. 14(2)(a).
[118] Reg. 14(2)(b).
[119] Reg. 12(3).
[120] S.I. 1998 No. 2306.
[121] *Safe Use of Work Equipment: Provision and Use at Work Regulations 1998: Approved Code of Practice and Guidance on Regulations,* H.S.E. L22, H.M.S.O.

in respect of items of work equipment provided for use in the employer's premises or activities, the employer must ensure the equipment complies with any enactment which implements in Great Britain any of the listed Community Directives.[122]

The Personal Protective Equipment at Work Regulations 1992[123] require employers to provide suitable personal protective equipment to employees who may be exposed to a risk to their health and safety. The Regulations do not apply to ear protectors. These are specifically excluded because they are covered by the Noise at Work Regulations 1989. However, in selecting suitable head protection in cases where an employee is also likely to be exposed to high noise levels, e.g. on some construction sites, safety helmets with integral hearing protection may be considered.

OBLIGATIONS OF DESIGNERS, ETC.

Designers, manufacturers, importers and suppliers of plant and machinery for use at work are legally required to provide noise information and control the noise emission of machinery. Section 6 of the Health and Safety at Work etc. Act 1974[124] imposes general duties on suppliers, etc. to provide articles that are safe and without risks to health, and to provide information needed for their safe use. Manufacturers of machinery must keep abreast of legal requirements and guidance on noise testing and limiting noise emissions from their products. If a machine is likely to produce noise capable of harming health, it will be necessary to reduce the risk as far as reasonably practicable. This will require an engineering assessment of the feasibility of control and the application of effective noise

---

[122] Schedule 1 of the Regulations specifies the Statutory Instruments giving effect to Community Directives relating to noise. The Directives relate to the determination of the noise emission of construction plant and equipment, the permissible sound power level of compressors, the permissible sound level of tower cranes, welding generators, power generators, powered hand-held concrete breaks and picks, lawnmowers, compressors, and limitation of noise emitted by hydraulic excavators, rope-operated excavators, dozers, loudspeakers and excavator loaders.

[123] S.I. 1992 No. 2966.

[124] As amended by the Consumer Protection Act 1987, Sched. 3, para. 1. See also H.S.E. Noise Guide No. 2, H.M.S.O.

control techniques. Information will also be needed on any noise control measures required when the machine is used. Regulation 12 of the Noise at Work Regulations 1989 also amends section 6 of the Health and Safety at Work etc. Act 1974 to require that, where an article for use at work or articles of fairground equipment are likely to cause any employee to be exposed to the first action level or above, or to the peak action level or above, adequate information is provided concerning the noise likely to be generated.

The Supply of Machinery (Safety) Regulations 1992[125] apply essential health and safety requirements to the supply of relevant machinery.[126] The Regulations implement Council Directive 89/392/EEC as amended by Council Directive 91/368/EEC (the Machinery Directive). The Regulations do not apply to specified types of machinery,[127] to machinery first supplied or put into service in the Community before 1st January 1993, or machinery first supplied or put into service in the Community on or before the 31st December 1994 if it complies with the health and safety provisions in force in the relevant member state at 31st December 1992. The Regulations do not apply before 1st July 1995 to certain specified machinery covered by other Directives.[128] They do not apply to machinery where the health and safety risks covered by the Machinery Directive are wholly covered by other applicable Directives nor to electrical equipment where the safety risks are mainly of electrical origin.[129]

Relevant machinery cannot be supplied unless it satisfies the relevant essential health and safety requirements[130] and the appropriate conformity assessment procedure has been carried out.[131] The essential health and safety requirements relating to the design and construction of machinery are contained in Schedule 3. The requirements in respect of noise and vibration are that machinery must be so designed and constructed that risks resulting from the

---

[125] S.I. 1992 No. 3073.
[126] Defined in Reg. 3.
[127] Reg. 5 and Sched. 5.
[128] Reg. 9.
[129] Reg. 10.
[130] Regs. 11 and 12.
[131] As described in Regs. 13–15.

emission of airborne noise and vibration are reduced to the lowest level, taking account of technical progress and the availability of means of reducing noise and vibration, in particular at source. All relevant machinery must be supplied with specified instructions including information about airborne noise emissions where these exceed certain specified criteria.[132]

Subject to a defence of due diligence,[133] the maximum penalties under the Regulations are imprisonment for up to 3 months, and/or a fine in Great Britain not exceeding level 5 on the standard scale or in Northern Ireland £2,000.

---

[132] Specified in Sched. 3, para. 1.7.4(f).
[133] Reg. 31.

BIBLIOGRAPHY

General

100 practical applications of noise reduction methods, 1983, H.M.S.O.

"Acoustic monitoring: an alternative approach", Hinton, J. and Jellyman, A., *Environmental Health Vol. 95 No. 12*, December 1987.

Acoustics, Beraneck, L.L., 1954, McGraw Hill Book Co.

A.C.U. Motorcycling G.B. 2002 Handbook, The Auto-Cycle Union.

Air Pollution and Noise Bulletin, an information service for Local Government published monthly by Birmingham Central Libraries.

"A review of the influence of meteorological conditions on sound propagation", Ingard, H., *Journal of the Acoustical Society of America Vol. 75*, May 1953.

British Standard 4142:1997 – Method of Rating Industrial Noise affecting mixed residential and industrial areas, British Standards Institution.

Code of Practice for the assessment, specification, maintenance and operation of sound systems for emergency purposes at sports grounds and stadia in pursuit of approval by licensing authorities, Sound and Communications Industries Federation, March 1992.

Code of Practice for Water Skiing and Noise, October 1999, British Water Ski Federation.

Code of Practice on Environmental Noise Control at Concerts, 1995, The Noise Council.

Code of Practice on Noise from Clay Target Shooting, Midlands Joint Advisory Council for Environmental Protection, Third Revision, March 1993.

Code of Practice on Noise from Ice-cream Van Chimes etc., Department of the Environment, 1982, H.M.S.O.

Code of Practice on Noise from Model Aircraft, Department of the Environment, 1982, H.M.S.O.

Control of Noisy Parties, Joint Guidance Note produced by the Department of the Environment and the Home Office, September 1992.

Crime and Disorder Act 1998: Anti-social behaviour orders – guidance, March 1998, Home Office.

444 *Bibliography*

Damage to hearing arising from leisure noise: a review of the literature, M.R.C. Institute of Hearing Research, 1985, H.M.S.O.

Domestic Noise Complaints, Grimwood, C. and Ling, M., B.R.E. Report No. 204732, December 1999.

Draft code of practice on environmental noise at concerts, The Noise Council.

Draft code of practice on the control of noise from pubs and clubs, November 1999, Institute of Acoustics.

Effects of environmental noise on people at home, Grimwood, C.J., B.R.E. Information Paper IP 22/93, December 1993.

"Effects of Noise on Man", Cohen, A., *Journal of Boston Society of Civil Engineers 52.1*, January1965, pp. 83–84.

Effects of Noise on Physiological State, Noise as a Public Health Hazard, ASHA Report 4, 1969, pp. 89–98.

Environmental Health Vol. 102, September 1994, The Journal of the Institution of Environmental Health Officers.

Environmental Health Annual Report 1992/93, The Institution of Environmental Health Officers.

Environmental Health Criteria 12 – Noise, 1980, World Health Organisation.

Environmental Noise Measurement, Bruel and Kjaer.

Environment Programme 1977–1981. Draft resolution on the continuation and implementation of a European Community policy and action programme on the environment, Commission of the European Communities, 1976.

Extended liquor licensing hours on Sundays, Home Office Circular 2/ 2001.

Future Noise Policy, Commission of the European Communities, Com (96) 540 Final, 4.11.1996, Brussels.

Garner's Environmental Law Vols. 1–3, Butterworth and Co. (Publishers) Ltd.

Good Practice for Police and Local Authority Co-operation, 1997, Chartered Institute of Environmental Health.

Guide to health, safety and welfare at pop concerts and similar events,

Health and Safety Commission/Home Office/The Scottish Office, 1993, H.M.S.O.

Hearing Hazards and Recreation, Noise Advisory Council, 1977, H.M.S.O.

Machine Condition Monitoring, November 1989, Bruel and Kjaer.

Manual of Environmental Policy: the E.C. and Britain, Haigh, N., 1991, Longman Group U.K. Ltd.

Measuring Sound, September 1984, Bruel and Kjaer.

Measuring Vibration, September 1982, Bruel and Kjaer.

Mechanical Vibration and Shock Measurements, Bruel and Kjaer.

Motor Sports Association Competitors' Yearbook 2002, The R.A.C. Motor Sports Association Ltd.

Neighbourhood Noise, Noise Advisory Council, 1971, H.M.S.O.

Noise, Taylor, Rupert, 1970, Pelican Books.

Noise, Final Report of the Committee on the Problem of Noise, Cmnd. 2056, 1963, H.M.S.O.

Noise Abatement: A Public Health Problem, 1965, p. 12.

Noise Climate: A Review of National and European Practices, 1st June 1999, D.E.T.R.

Noise Climate Assessment – Review of National and European Practices, Report for the D.E.T.R. by Environmental Resources Management, November 1997.

Noise from neighbours and the sound insulation of party walls in houses, Langdon, F.J., Buller, I.B. and Scholes, W.E., B.R.E. Information Paper IP 13/82, August 1982.

Noise in Public Places, Noise Advisory Council, 1974, H.M.S.O.

Noise in the Next Ten Years, Noise Advisory Council, 1974, H.M.S.O.

Noise Management Guide, 1997, Chartered Institute of Environmental Health.

"Noise, Stress and Human Behaviour", Jones, Dr. Dylan M., *Environmental Health*, August 1990.

N.S.C.A. National Noise Survey 2001, June 2001, N.S.C.A.

N.S.C.A. Pollution Handbook 2001, National Society for Clean Air & Environmental Protection.

"Objective method of assessing nuisance caused by amplified music: results of field trial", Fothergill, L.C., Building Research Establishment, *Clean Air Vol. 22*, No. 1, 1992, pp. 40–41.

Our Countryside: the future – a fair deal for rural England, Cmnd. 4909, November 2000, H.M.S.O.

"Public Health Aspects of Housing in the U.S.S.R.", *W.H.O. Chronicle 20.10*, October 1966, p. 357.

Report of the Noise Review Working Party 1990, H.M.S.O.

Statutory Nuisance: Law & Practice, Malcom, R., Pointing, J., 2002, Oxford University Press.

The Future for Mediation, Holder, P., February 1994, N.S.C.A.

The U.K. National Noise Attitude Survey 1999/2000, Grimwood, C.J., Skinner, C.J., Raw, G.J., B.R.E. Report to C.I.E.H. Noise Forum Conference, May 2002.

The U.K. National Noise Incidence Study 2000/2001, Skinner, C.J., Grimwood, C.J., B.R.E. Report to C.I.E.H. Noise Forum Conference, May 2002.

This Common Inheritance – Britain's Environmental Strategy, Cmnd. 1200, September 1990, H.M.S.O.

Time for reform: proposals for the modernisation of our licensing laws, Cmnd. 4696, April 2000, H.M.S.O.

Towards a National Ambient Noise Strategy: A consultation paper from the Air and Environmental Quality Division, November 2001, D.E.F.R.A.

Vibration Testing, 1983, Bruel and Kjaer.

Woods Practical Guide to Noise Control, Sharland, I., 1972, Woods of Colchester Ltd.

Noise Abatement Zones

"Noise Abatement Zones – A little more theory – more practice", Penn, C.N., *Environmental Health*, September 1975.

"Noise Abatement Zones – One way to deal with the new provisions", Penn, C.N., *Environmental Health*, January 1976.

"Noise Abatement Zones: Part 1", *Building Research Establishment Digest No. 203*, July 1977.

"Noise Abatement Zones: Part 2", *Building Research Establishment Digest No. 204*, August 1977.

Noise levels at the boundaries of factories and commercial premises, Jenkins, M.P., Salvidge, A.C. and Utley, W.A., Building Research Station, June 1976.

Construction site noise

British Standard 5228: 1984 – Code of Practice for Noise Control on Construction and Open Sites.

Part 1 "Code of Practice for basic information and procedures for noise control".

Part 2 "Guide to noise control legislation for construction and demolition, including road construction and maintenance".

Part 3 "Code of Practice for noise control applicable to surface coal extraction by open cast methods".

1992 Part 4 "Code of Practice for noise and vibration control applicable to piling operations".

Road traffic and railway noise

"Acoustic performance of the M6 noise barriers", Nelson, P.M. and Abbott, P.G. (Transport and Road Research Laboratory) and Salvidge, A.C. (Building Research Establishment), *T.R.R.L. Digest LR 731,* 1976.

A model to calculate traffic noise levels from complex highway cross-sections, Tobutt, D.C. and Nelson, P.M., T.R.R.L. Digest of Research Report 245, 1990.

A New Deal for Transport: Better for Everyone, Cmnd. 3950, July 1998, H.M.S.O.

An examination of the relationship between noise measures and perceived noisiness, Watts, G.R. and Nelson, P., T.R.R.L. Digest of Research Report 318, 1991.

An examination of the relationship between tyre noise and safety performance, Nelson, P.M., Harris, G.J. and Robinson, B.J., Transport Research Laboratory Project Report 1993.

An outline guide to criteria for the limitation of urban noise, Robinson, D.W., 1969, National Physical Laboratory.

A preliminary investigation into lorry tyre noise, Underwood, M.C.P., Transport and Road Research Laboratory Report LR 601, 1973.

"A quiet heavy lorry", Watkins, L.H., *Commercial Motor*, March 1974.

A survey of traffic-induced vibrations, Transport and Road Research Laboratory Report LR 418, 1971.

Code of Practice on noise from organised off-road motor-cycle sport, 1994, The Noise Council.

"Community Noise – Surface Transportation", Thiessen, G.J. and Olsen, N., *Sound and Vibration Vol. 2*, 1968.

"Community response to neighbourhood noise", Utley, W.A. and Keighley E.C., *Clean Air Vol. 18*, 1988.

Designing against Road Traffic Noise, Scholes, W.E. and Sargent, J.W., Building Research Current Paper CP 20/71, May 1971.

Design Manual for Roads and Bridges, Vol. 11 Environmental Assessment, Department of Transport, June 1993, H.M.S.O.

Designs of silencers for internal combustion engine exhaust systems, Davies, D.O.A.L. and Alredson, R.J., Symposium on Vibration and Noise in Motor Vehicles, 1971.

Development and Compensation – Putting People First, 1972, H.M.S.O.

Effects of noise from passing trucks on sleep, Paper QI, 77th meeting of the Acoustical Society of America, 1969; also reported in *Urban traffic noise – strategy for an improved environment*, 1971, O.E.C.D.

"External Traffic Noise", *Proceedings of Institute of Acoustics, Vol. 15 Part 2*, 1993.

"Highway Noise and Acoustical Buffer Zones", Zulfacor, A. and Scott Clarke, C., *Transportation Engineering Journal*, May 1974, pp. 389–401.

Improving the performance of traffic noise barriers, Watts, G., T.R.L. Published Article, 1995.

London Noise Survey, 1968, H.M.S.O.

Lorry tyre noise, Underwood, M.C.P., T.R.R.L. Digest of Report LR 974, 1981.

National Road Traffic Forecasts (G.B.), 1997, H.M.S.O.

New Roads in Towns, July 1972, H.M.S.O.

Noise and road traffic outside homes in England, Harland, D.G. and Abbott, P.G., T.R.R.L. Digest of Report LR 770, 1977.

Noise and vibration from traffic (1991-1993), Current topics in Transport No. 21, April 1993, Transport Research Laboratory.

Noise from vehicles running on open textured road surfaces, Nelson, P.M. and Ross, N.F., T.R.R.L. Digest of Report SR 696, 1981.

Noise reduction exercise on a medium sized goods vehicle, Tyler, J.W., T.R.R.L. Digest of Contractor Report 213, 1990.

"On the Right Tracks", *Environmental Health Journal*, September 2001.

"Performance of a Motorway Noise Barrier – Heston", Scholes, W.E., Mackie, A.M., Vulcan, G.H. and Horland, D.G., *Applied Acoustics (7)*, 1974.

"Possible methods of reducing external tyre noise", Nilso, N.A., *Proceedings of the International Tyre Noise Conference*, Sweden, 1979.

QHV 90 Project: Leyland DAF goods vehicle noise reduction, Parkess, A.M., T.R.L. Digest of Contractor Report 318, 1992.

QHV Project: Reduction of noise from lorry exhausts and air intakes, Peat, K.S. and Callow, G.D., T.R.L. Digest of Contractor Report 226, 1993.

R.A.C. Motor Sports Association Yearbook 1994, The R.A.C. Motor Sports Association Ltd.

Railway Operations and the Environment – Environmental Guidelines, Office of the Rail Regulator, 1996.

Report of the Urban Motorways Project Team to the Urban Motorways Committee, 1973, H.M.S.O.

Roads and the Environment, Transport and Road Research Laboratory Report LR 441, 1972.

Road Surfaces and Traffic Noise, Franklin, R.E., Harland, D.G. and Nelson, P.M., T.R.R.L. Digest of Report LR 896, 1979.

"Road vehicle legislation – past, present and future", Dunn, E. and Gillingham, S.G., *Institute of Mechanical Engineering Conference Proceedings*, 1990.

Some aspects of motor-cycle noise emission, Nelson, P.M. and Ross, N.F., T.R.R.L. Digest of Report SR 795, 1983.

Some notes on the noise disturbance caused by motor-cycles, Nelson, P.M., T.R.R.L. Digest of Report SR 569, 1980.

Subjective response to road traffic noise, Griffiths, I.D. and Langdon, F.J., Building Research Station Current Paper 37/68, 1968.

"The effects of traffic calming measures on vehicle and traffic noise", Abbott, P.G., Taylor, M., Layfield, R.E., *Traffic Engineering & Control*, September 1997.

"The effects of vegetation on the perception of traffic noise", Watts, G., Chinn. L., Godfrey, N., *Applied Acoustics* 1999, Vol. 56, pp. 39–56.

The Environmental Foresight Project, Volume 3: The Future Road Transport Noise Agenda in the U.K., Mason, K.D., Centre for Exploitation of Science and Technology, 1993, H.M.S.O.

The use of vegetation for traffic noise screening, Huddart, L., T.R.R.L. Digest of Research Report 238, 1990.

Traffic induced ground-borne vibrations in dwellings, Watts, G.R., T.R.R.L. Digest of Research Report 102, 1987.

Traffic induced vibrations in buildings, Watts, G.R., T.R.R.L. Digest of Research Report 246, 1990.

"Traffic Noise Barriers", Watts, G., *T.R.L. Annual Review 1995.*

Traffic Noise: the Vehicle Regulations and their Enforcement, Noise Advisory Council, 1972, H.M.S.O.

Traffic vibration and building damage, T.R.R.L. papers presented at Acoustics '87, Ed. Watts, G.R., T.R.R.L. Digest of Research Report 146, 1988.

Transport and the Environment: Developments since 1994, Cmnd. 3752, September 1997, H.M.S.O.

Transportation Noise Reference Book, Ed. Nelson, P., 1987, Butterworth and Co. (Publishers) Ltd.

Transport Statistics, Great Britain, Department of Transport, 1991, H.M.S.O.

Transport: the Way Forward, Cmnd. 3234, April 1996, H.M.S.O.

Urban Traffic Noise – Strategy for an improved environment, O.E.C.D., 1971.

Vehicle and traffic noise surveys alongside speed control cushions in York, Abbott, P.G., Phillips, S.M. and Layfield, R.E., Project Report 103, 1993, Transport Research Laboratory.

Vibration damage to occupied buildings, Muskett, Dr. C.J. and Hood, Dr. R.A., T.R.R.L. Digest of Contractor Report 144, 1990.

Vibration nuisance from road traffic at fourteen residential sites, Baughan, C.J. and Martin, D.J., T.R.R.L. Digest of Report LR 1020, 1981.

Vibration nuisance from road traffic – results of a 50 site survey, Watts, G.R., T.R.R.L. Digest of Report LR119, 1984.

Aircraft noise

1982 Helicopter Disturbance Study: main report, Atkins, C.L.R., Brooker, P. and Critchley, J.B., DR Report 8304, September 1983, Civil Aviation Authority.

Adverse effects of night-time aircraft noise, Porter, N.D., Kershaw, A.D., Ollerhead, J.B., R. & D. Report 9964, prepared by D.O.R.A. on behalf of D.E.T.R., March 2000.

Aircraft Noise and Sleep Disturbance: Final Report, D.O.R.A. Report 8008, August 1980, Civil Aviation Authority.

Aircraft Noise as a form of Pollution, Hill, R.J., paper presented to National Society for Clean Air, 1977.

Aircraft Noise: Review of Aircraft Departure Routeing Policy, Noise Advisory Council, 1974, H.M.S.O.

Air Traffic Forecasts 2000, May 2000, D.E.T.R.

Assessment of revised Heathrow early mornings approach procedures trial, Cadoux, R.E., White, S., Critchley, J.B., National Air Traffic Services Ltd., 1998, D.E.T.R.

A study of community disturbance caused by general and business aviation operations – final report, University of Southampton Institute of Sound and Vibration Research, July 1998.

Birmingham International Airport Environment and Community Report 2000/2001, Birmingham International Airport.

B.S. 5727:1979 – Method for describing aircraft noise heard on the ground, British Standards Institution.

CEC Joint Study of Community Response to Aircraft Noise 1984: Main Report, Diamond, I.D., Walker, J.G., Critchley, J.B. and Richmond, G.C., DR Report 8601, July 1986, Civil Aviation Authority.

Control of Aircraft Noise, Consultation Paper, August 1991, Department of Transport.

Control of Noise from Civil Aircraft, July 2000, D.E.T.R.

Current Market Outlook 2000: Into the New Century, Boeing Commercial Airlines Group, August 2000.

"Effects of noise on sleep of babies", Ando, Y. and Hattori, H., *Journal of Acoustical Society of America Vol. 62 No. 1*, July 1977.

Guidance to the Civil Aviation Authority on environmental objectives relating to the exercise of its air navigation functions, January 2002, D.T.L.R.

Helicopter Noise in the London Area, Noise Advisory Council, 1977, H.M.S.O.

"Helicopters in London", Southwood, R.M., Hill, C. and Stanbury, C., *Environmental Health*, May 1991.

Human Rights and aircraft noise, Macrory, R., ENDS Report 321, pp. 53/54, October 2001.

"Mental Hospital Admissions and Aircraft Noise", Abey-Wickrama, I., a'Brook, M.E., Gattoni, F.E.C. and Herridge, C.F., *The Lancet*, 13th December 1969.

Night Flights at Heathrow, Gatwick and Stansted Airports. Proposals for revised restrictions (a) for summer 1994 (b) winter 1994–95 to summer 1998, Consultation Paper, November 1993, Department of Transport.

Night-time ground noise, Jopson, I., Jones, C., Porter, N., White, S., August 1998, National Air Traffic Services Ltd., London.

Noise and Sleep, C.A.A. Paper 78011, June 1978, Civil Aviation Authority.

"Noise Control at London City Airport – a new approach", Simpson, R. and Freeborn, P., *Environmental Health*, July 1991.

Noise Controls at U.K. Airports, SASIG Technical Note, January 2001.

Noise from arriving aircraft: final report of the ANMAC technical working group, 13th March 2000, D.E.T.R.

Proposal for a Directive of the European Parliament and of the Council on the establishment of a community framework for noise classification of civil subsonic aircraft for the purposes of calculating noise charges, Com (2001) 74 final, 20th December 2001, Brussels.

Reaction to aircraft noise near general aviation airfields, D.O.R.A. Report 8203, May 1982, Civil Aviation Authority.

Recommended measures to help reduce the noise related nuisance from light aeroplanes, Civil Aviation Authority.

Report of a field study of aircraft noise and sleep disturbance, December 1992, Department of Transport.

Report of the Public Inquiry into the causes and circumstances of the accident near Staines on 18th June 1972, Aircraft Accident Report No. 4/73, United Kingdom Air Investigation Branch.

Review of aircraft noise legislation: announcement of conclusions, March 1993, Department of Transport.

Social Survey 1992 – report of the local authority noise monitoring group, December 1992.

Summary of responses to control of noise from civil aircraft, March 2002, D.T.L.R.

"The effects of aircraft noise in schools around London airport", Crook, M.A. and Langdon, F.J., *Journal of Sound and Vibration 34*, 1974, p.221.

The noise benefits associated with use of continuous descent approach and low power/low drag approach procedures at Heathrow Airport, Paper 78006, April 1978, Civil Aviation Authority.

The Use of L_{eq} as an Aircraft Noise Index, Critchley, J.B. and Ollerhead, J.B., D.O.R.A. Report 9023, September 1990, Civil Aviation Authority.

United Kingdom Aircraft Noise Index Study, D.O.R.A. Report 8402, 1985, Civil Aviation Authority.

Integrated Pollution Prevention and Control

Environment Agency Noise Guidance – internal guidance for the regulation of noise at waste management facilities under waste management licensing regulations, version 2.0, draft for external consultation, May 2000.

Environmental Assessment and Appraisal of B.A.T., I.P.P.C. Guidance Note H1, 2001, Environment Agency.

Integrated Pollution Prevention and Control: A practical guide, Edition 1, August 2000, D.E.T.R.

Integrated Pollution Prevention and Control (IPPC), Horizontal Guidance for Noise: Part 1 – Regulating and Permitting, Final draft version 1, I.P.P.C. Guidance Note H3, December 2001, Environment Agency.

Integrated Pollution Prevention and Control (IPPC), Horizontal Guidance for Noise: Part 2 – Noise Assessment and Control, Draft version 1, I.P.P.C. Guidance Note H3, October 2001, Environment Agency.

Integrated Pollution Prevention and Control (IPPC), Part A(1) Installations: Guide for Applicants, Version 2, December 2000, Environment Agency.

Protocol agreed by Local Government Association and the Agency on arrangements to implement the requirements of the IPPC Directive, November 2001, Environment Agency.

Planning and development

A report on the production of noise maps of the City of Birmingham Environmental Services Department, Birmingham City Council, February 2000, D.E.T.R.

British Standard B.S. 5821:1980 – Ratings of the sound insulation of floating party floors, Sewell, A.C. and Aphey, R.S., B.R.E. Information Paper IP 10/83, June 1983, Building Research Establishment.

"Double glazing for heat and sound insulation", *B.R.E. Digest 379*, February 1993, Building Research Establishment.

Effects of environmental noise on people at home, B.R.E. Information Paper IP 28 22/93, December 1993.

Environmental Appraisal of Development Plans: A Good Practice Guide, 1993, D.O.E.

Environmental Assessment, Lichfield, N., J.P.E.L. Occasional Paper 16, November 1989, Journal of Planning and Environmental Law.

Environmental Assessment: a guide to the procedures, DoE, 1989, H.M.S.O.

Improving sound insulation in your home, B.R.E. Leaflet, November 1992, Building Research Establishment.

"Improving the sound insulation of separating walls and floors", *B.R.E. Digest 293*, January 1985, Building Research Establishment.

Intermediate timber floors in converted dwellings – sound insulation, Defect Action Sheet DAS 45, February 1984, Building Research Establishment.

Local Plans and Unitary Development Plans: A Guide to Procedures (2000) and *Structure Plans: A Guide to Procedures (2000)*, Circ. 07/99, D.E.T.R.

Masonry separating walls: airborne sound insulation in new-build housing, Defect Action Sheet DAS 104, July 1987, Building Research Establishment.

Masonry separating walls: improving airborne sound insulation between existing dwellings, Defect Action Sheet DAS 105, July 1987, Building Research Establishment.

Measurement in Building Acoustics, January 1988, Bruel and Kjaer.

"Mediation in the Planning System", *Journal of Planning Law,* September 2000, pp. 904–907.

Methods for improving the sound insulation between converted flats, Fothergill, L.C. and Nielson, O.S., B.R.E. Information Paper IP 6/88, June 1988, Building Research Establishment.

Methods for reducing impact sounds in buildings, Fothergill, L.C. and Savage, J.E., B.R.E. Information Paper IP 9/88, July 1988, Building Research Establishment.

Minerals Planning Guidance: Coal Mining and Colliery Spoil Disposal, M.P.G. 3, July 1994, DoE.

Planning and Noise, Circular 10/73, Department of Environment, 1973.

Planning Controls and their Enforcement, 7th edition, Little, A.J., 2001, Shaw & Sons Ltd.

Planning: delivering a fundamental change, December 2001, D.E.T.R.

Planning Policy Guidance: Development Plans and Regional Guidance, P.P.G. 12, February 1992, DoE.

Planning Policy Guidance: General Policy and Principles, P.P.G. 1, March 1992, DoE.

Planning Policy Guidance: Industrial and Commercial Development and Small Firms, P.P.G. 4, November 1992, DoE.

Planning Policy Guidance: Planning and Noise, P.P.G. 24, September 1994, DoE.

Planning Policy Guidance: Planning and Pollution Control, P.P.G. 23, 1994, DoE.

Reforming Planning Obligations: a consultation paper, December 2001, D.T.L.R.

Sound control for homes, BR 238, CIRIA Report 127, 1993, Building Research Establishment.

Sound insulation and the 1992 edition of approved document E, Fothergill, L.C., B.R.E. Information Paper IP 18/92, October 1992, Building Research Establishment.

"Sound insulation: basic principles", *B.R.E. Digest 337*, Revised 1994, Building Research Establishment.

"Sound insulation of lightweight dwellings", *B.R.E. Digest 347,* September 1989, Building Research Establishment.

"Sound insulation of separating walls and floors Part 1: Walls", *B.R.E. Digest 333*, June 1988, Building Research Establishment.

"Sound insulation of separating walls and floors Part 2: Floors", *B.R.E. Digest 334*, Revised 1993, Building Research Establishment.

The Building Act 1984. The Building Regulations 2000. Proposals for amending Part E – Resistance to the Passage of Sound, January 2001, D.E.T.R.

The Building Regulations 1991: Resistance to the Passage of Sound – approved document E, 1992 edition, H.M.S.O.

"The role of the E.H.O. in environmental assessment", Ryall, C. and Wood, C., *Environmental Health*, April 1991.

The role of the Environmental Health Officer in the control of noise through planning, Horrocks, D., presented to Institute of Acoustics 1992.

Town and Country Planning, Cmnd. 3333, 1966/67, H.M.S.O.

Occupational noise

Control of Noise in Quarries, HS(G)109, 1993, Health and Safety Executive.

"Defence against deafness", Cairns, J., *The Safety and Health Practitioner*, February 1992.

Essential elements of noise at work assessments, Kyriakides, K. and Galbraith, R.N., June 1991, Sandy Brown Associates.

Health and Safety Statistics 2000/01, Health and Safety Commission, 2001, H.M.S.O.

Hearing and Noise in Industry, Burns, W. and Robinson, D.W., 1970, H.M.S.O.

"How to design an effective health and safety audit", Read, J.A. and Law, G.A., *The Health and Safety Practitioner*, October 1992.

If you think your job has made you deaf, NI 207, April 1991, Department of Social Security.

Indecent Exposure, Croners Health & Safety Case Law Briefing, Issue 21, 12th April 1999.

Industrial injuries disablement benefit, NI 6, April 1992, Department of Social Security.

Industrial noise and its effects on hearing, Cmnd. 4145, 1969, H.M.S.O.

Industrial noise control and hearing testing, Bruel and Kjaer.

Keep the noise down – advice for purchasers of workplace machinery, November 1997, H.S.E.

Management of Health and Safety at Work, Approved Code of Practice, H.S.E. L21, 1992, H.M.S.O.

Noise and Glass Container Manufacture, Bednall, A.W., 1988, Health and Safety Executive.

Noise and Noise Control in the British Rubber Industry, Bednall, A.W., 1987, Health and Safety Executive.

Noise and the Worker, Health and Safety Booklet No. 25, 1971, H.M.S.O.

Noise at work – advice for employees, March 1993, H.S.E.

"Noise at Work Regulations: UK and Europe", Bryson, N., *Environmental Health*, August 1990.

Noise Guide No. 1: Legal duties of employers to prevent damage to hearing, 1989, H.M.S.O.

Noise Guide No. 2: Legal duties of designers, manufacturers, importers and suppliers to prevent damage to hearing, 1989, H.M.S.O.

Noise Guides Nos. 3 to 8: Noise assessment, information and control, 1990, H.M.S.O.

Noise in the workplace – a select bibliography, 1990, Health and Safety Executive.

Occupational Deafness, Cmnd. 5461, 1973, H.M.S.O.

Occupational Deafness, Leaflet NI 207, 1991, D.S.S.

"Risk assessment – a practical guide", Kazer, B.M., *The Safety Practitioner*, May 1993.

Safety and Health at Work, Report of the Committee 1970–72, Cmnd. 5034, Para. 345, p. 110, July 1972, H.M.S.O.

Safety Committees: Guidance to employers whose employees are not members of recognised independent trade unions, Health and Safety Commission H.S.C. 8, 1976.

Safety Representatives and Safety Committees, Health and Safety Commission, 1977, H.M.S.O.

Selecting a Health and Safety Consultancy, March 1993, Health and Safety Executive.

The Effects of Occupational Noise on Hearing: Recent Developments, Review SHE, 4th April 1991, The Loss Prevention Council.

"The management of exposure to hand-arm vibration", Hill, K., *The Health & Safety Practitioner*, July 1999, pp. 28–32.

"The need for routine hearing checks", Frost, G.P., *The Safety and Health Practitioner*, February 1992.

The Noise at Work Regulations and their insurance implications, Circular SHE 4, April 1991, The Loss Prevention Council.

Work Equipment: Provision and Use at Work Regulations 1992, Guidance on Regulations, H.S.E. L22, H.M.S.O.

APPENDIX

Forms and Records Relating to Noise Control
published by and available from SHAW & SONS LIMITED
Shaway House, 21 Bourne Park, Bourne Road, Crayford, Kent DA1 4BZ.
Tel: 01322 621100; Fax: 01322 550553.

Cat. No.	Description	Statutory Ref.*

Summary Proceedings to Deal with Noise

PA 70	Abatement notice in respect of noise nuisance	s. 80, 1990 Act
PA 70X	Abatement notice in respect of noise nuisance – to be affixed to unattended vehicle or equipment	s. 80A(2)(b), 1990 Act
EPA 31	Information – contravention/failure to comply with nuisance abatement notice	s.80(4), 1990 Act
EPA 32	Summons – contravention/failure to comply with nuisance abatement notice	s. 80(4), 1990 Act
EPA 34	Complaint for order in respect of statutory nuisance	s. 82(1), 1990 Act
EPA 35	Summons in respect of statutory nuisance	s. 82(1), 1990 Act
EPA 36	Abatement/prohibition order in respect of statutory nuisance	s. 82(1), 1990 Act
EPA 37	Information – contravention of abatement/ prohibition order	s. 82(8), 1990 Act
EPA 38	Summons – contravention of abatement/ prohibition order	s. 82(8), 1990 Act
EPA 81	Notice as to recovery of expenses	ss. 81(4), 81A, 1990 Act
PA 110	Application for consent to operation of loudspeaker	Sch. 2, 1993 Act
PA 111	Notice of [refusal of] consent [with conditions]	Sch. 2, 1993 Act

Construction Sites

PA 77	Control of noise on construction sites – notice imposing requirements	s. 60(2), 1974 Act
PA 80	Application for prior consent in respect of works	s. 61(1), 1974 Act
PA 81	Prior consent in respect of works on construction sites	s. 61(4)(5)(6), 1974 Act
PA 82	Notice of refusal of prior consent	s. 61(6), 1974 Act

* The Acts referred to above are:
   1974 Act — Control of Pollution Act 1974
   1990 Act — Environmental Protection Act 1990
   1993 Act — Noise and Statutory Nuisance Act 1993

INDEX

A

C

I

J

K

L

M

N

O

S